Francie

by

Joe Robinson

Printed and published by TUPS BOOKS
30 Lime St, Newcastle upon Tyne, NE1 2PQ
Tel: 0191 2330990   Fax: 0191 2330578
ISBN 1-901237-04-4

for all those unacquainted with privilege,
not blessed with talent,
and overlooked by fortune,
but who nevertheless refuse defeat

Acknowledgements

My thanks are due principally to my Grandma Francie O'Callaghan, née Nichol, for a story which she told with astonishing verve, animating descriptions of her contemporaries - the characters of this book - with humour, pathos, affection, and sometimes with anger.

I also wish to thank those members of her family who gave me so much help, and in particular, her daughter Francie.

I wish to thank Alex Glasgow and Sid Chaplin who first brought the story to the attention of John Bright-Holmes of George Allen & Unwin, whose skill and confidence turned the manuscript into a book.

I would like to thank Bill Slater, Eric Davidson and Doug Mawson of the BBC for helping to garner further information from my grandmother after the publication of the first edition.

For help with photographs and information, I wish to thank Evelyn Robinson, Edmund O'Callaghan, Nellie O'Callaghan, Joan Meeks, and the staff of South Tyneside Libraries.

For help with proof-reading I am grateful to Hannah Robinson, and for help with editing and virtually every stage of the book, I wish to thank Judy Robinson.

For his constant support, enthusiasm and production skills, I must thank Dave Temple of TUPS BOOKS.

JOE ROBINSON was born in South Shields, became a scientist in the field of medical and veterinary microbiology and worked in Britain and abroad in hospitals, universities and industry. Eventually he gave up his career in science to concentrate on writing about life on Tyneside.

He has previously published **The life and Times of Francie Nichol of South Shields** (George Allen & Unwin, 1975), (Futura, 1977), **Claret & Cross-buttock** (George Allen & Unwin, 1976), the biography of his forbears who were famous Tyneside pugilists in the Nineteenth Century, and **Tommy Turnbull - a miner's life** (TUPS BOOKS, 1997).

Joe's play, **Pineapple Grill-time**, a humorously dramatic event in his own family, is to première on Tyneside in the near future.

Foreword

So many people have written to me over the years since I first published my grandmother's story in 1975, asking if the book was going to be reprinted, and if it was, whether there would be any pictures of her this time, that in 1996, using the thirty hours of tape recordings made twenty-three years ago after the first edition of the book with a view to adapting her story for BBC television, and using photographs that I have collected, I decided to re-write the book using all the additional material, and here it is.

Prologue

James Nichol, a bricklayer, was a hard-working man when sober. He was honest and he probably loved his wife and children, but he was a very hard drinker and when he drank he was brutal.

Elizabeth Billclough was short and well built, pleasant of face and gentle of countenance. She was honest as well, and even harder-working than her husband, but she could never afford the luxury of an alcoholic drink. Together they made fourteen children...seven boys and seven girls; six of the boys came as twins but out of them all, only six girls survived: JaneAnne, who was usually known as 'Jinny', Alice, Nelly, Lily, Lizzie, and Francie.

On a Saturday in the year 1891, JaneAnne, the eldest daughter, was married to Jim Kilcaddy, a Scot by descent and a Geordie by birth. The following day Sunday dinner was being served in the Nichol house which was in Heron Street...

In those days the man, the husband, the father, was the undisputed lord, no matter how small the manor, no matter how frugal the fare. Ritualistic discipline was the order, the man of the house at all times presiding, with the woman giving at least a show of support. No backchat was tolerated, no other opinions entertained; not from the woman, and certainly not from the children because their father wouldn't be challenged with even so much as a defiant glance. The wife took her frustration out on the washing as she possed it with her wooden oar, or out of the stone floor as she scrubbed and scrubbed and the tears disappeared into the dirty water that swilled around her knees. Both Jimmy Nichol's and Bessie Billclough's fathers and grandfathers had been the same, and had any of their sons survived, they would have expected them to grow up into men who acted in exactly the same fashion. It was the law of nature. Women couldn't reproach or reason with their men, or they'd likely get a touch of the old leather; because when all was said and done, women were for the convenience of the men, and children were just the by-products. Cleaning, washing, shopping, cooking, rearing, nursing, and being thankful for it, was their lot. It was better than being in the work-house. And that, too often, was the only alternative...

Dinner was now on the table.

'What the bloody hell does she think she's doin'?'

Lizzie had put her finger in the rabbit pie and stuck it in her mouth before the roaring, drunken father had gathered up his knife and fork.

Father threw over the table, picked up a chair and threw it at Mother who was sent crashing against the wall where she lost consciousness and slithered to the floor.

'I'll teach ye to bring them up the proper way!' he shouted when she came around and staggered to her feet. But she was too soft to stand up for herself.

'Please, Jim... She's just a bairn... She doesn't have any sense yet.'

'I'll murder the little bastard for doin' that to me!'

Mother had tried to restrain Father but it was no good, she'd all ready gone too far. The furniture was over, the food spilled on the floor, and the bigger children had scattered and ran out the door. Mother now had the carving knife held to her throat; Father had dragged her over to the window, opened the front of her dress, and was pointing to the clock.

'As for you, ye interferin' bitch... When that big pointer gets to twelve, I'm ganna cut ya bloody throat for ye!'

Father had knocked her about a fair bit from time to time, but nothing like this, this time he was really angry, this time he'd had about as much as he was going to take. Normally Mother never raised her voice in protest or her hand in defence, but this time she was very frightened.

'It won't ever happen again, Jimmy. I promise ye... Please, Jimmy.'

'It'll not happen again, all right. I'll see to that..! I'll fettle ye this time, ye stupid bloody bitch!'

'Jimmy, Jimmy! I'm sorry... Ye'll regret it afterwards... She's only four. Ye know she's not very bright.'

'Shut your mouth, woman! Or I'll do you in right now..! If she's backward, it's because of the way you're bringin' her up!'

By now, all but Francie who was too young to realise what was going on, had fled to the landing outside and Alice had run to seek JaneAnne and Jim Kilcaddy who were just living a few doors down the street. Jim and JaneAnne came running back with her and Jim flung the door open, rushed over to his father-in-law and wrested the gully from his father-in-law's hand. In the ensuing scuffle, he knocked his father-in-law to the floor and kicked him again and again, he would probably have killed him had it not been for his mother-in-law's pleas.

'No! No! Leave him be! Leave him be! He didn't really mean it. He was just upset. Our Lizzie had been naughty and he just lost his temper. They've all been told before. They know he doesn't - '

'Come on, Ma. You're comin' with us. You get little Francie, and I'll get your stuff. What d'ye want..? These chairs..? Here, Jinny. Put those over there in a box or somethin'. I'll bring the rest... And if he makes one move to stop we, I'll break his bloody arm!'

'No, no! You mustn't take it. Make him put it down, Jinny. I want nothin'... Leave them... I'll go with ye but ye can't do any more to him. They belong to him. He worked for them, so they're his.' By now Mother had been ushered out and on to the landing where her daughter JaneAnne was holding her to prevent her from interfering with what her son-in-law was doing.

'I'm takin' the whole bloody lot!'

'No, Jimmy! Don't! Please! Ye've got to leave him somethin'. He's got little enough as it is.'

'Don't worry, Ma. He won't hurt you. The sod's lucky to be left in one piece.'

'Bugger off, the lot o' ye!' Father shouted from where he lay in the corner, as his son-in-law carried the last armful out. 'Gan on! Get out of my house! The whole bloody lot of ye!'

The son-in-law, who by the way had also had his Sunday morning skinful, started angrily towards the glowering, threatening father who had now got to his feet, and he clenched his big ham of a fist. Jim Kilcaddy was a big fellow, much bigger than Jimmy Nichol. Mother then yelled 'If you harm him or lay another finger on him, I'll brain ye, Kilcaddy..! I'll come with ye, but ye've got to leave him alone now.'

'Ye must be daft, Ma. That's all I can say. I could break his neck for him right now and all your troubles would be over...'

Big Jim and little Jim stood there, several feet apart, snarling at each other.

'Howay then,' said big Jim. 'If that's what ye want... Leave the bugger to stew in his own juice... He'll never get another one like you... And that's for bloody sure!' he shouted in his father-in-law's face.

Francie Nichol, born on the 18th April 1889 in Heron Street, South Shields, was now two years old. Her mother had finally decamped with her remaining five children. Bessie Nichol had often thought about leaving her husband and had even gone so far as to threaten it, but it had finally happened, and for the time being she had few qualms.

1

For the next few nights we all had to sleep on the floor in our clothes. There were no blankets because they were all at my father's and my mother dare not go back for them. If she'd gone back and asked, he'd have chased her and either used her, given her a good hiding, or both.

But we couldn't stay at Jim and JaneAnne's for long, they'd have been put out by their landlord if we had; there was only one room and everything had to be done in it...the cooking, washing, sleeping and everything else. There was no privacy for anybody and it must have been hard luck for Jim and JaneAnne just starting their marriage. Fortunately my mother wasn't one for just sitting down and crying, and before three weeks had passed she'd got us a little place in Foster Street for one shilling and sixpence a week. It was on a very steep bank and it was nothing like our own home, which hadn't been great either, but at least it was better than living with Jim and JaneAnne. There was nothing in it, it was just a single bare room, but it was our own place, so it was a start. There was a little alley at the back with one cold water tap and two middens that we shared with ten other families, but we were used to that so that was no hardship.

For the first two weeks we just slept on the bare boards, but straw was cheap so Mam and the older girls sewed sacking around it and made comfy little beds for us all; mind, the bugs loved them so we'd have to change them fairly often. With bricks and planks Mam and the girls collected from houses that were being pulled down, we built a table which my mother varnished to keep down the spelks, and when it had a bit of oilcloth on it, it didn't look any different to a proper table with short legs. Then Mam got somebody to knock a few planks together to make two wooden forms, like long crackets, and we put one at each side of the table so we could all sit up.

All the while Mam was working packing herring in the kipper house at Woodhouses where she'd worked all her life, and that's where the money for the rent and food came from. When she finished at the end of the day, she'd ask the foreman if she could have any broken ones; Woodhouses would never sell any fish unless they were perfect, so they'd nearly always have some for her. She would then fetch them home and pour them out on the table and patch them up so they looked all right, and then she'd go around the streets selling them to folks in houses. That way she brought in a few valuable extra coppers.

Because we had no proper cups or plates, we made do with whatever we could find. Milk tins made good mugs because they had no sharp edges, and milk was practically as cheap as water; it wasn't Nestlés or anything like that, just the ordinary stuff you could buy at the market. We didn't have gas, just an oil lamp; Mam didn't like candles, she thought they were expensive and dangerous. But the oil light was all right and whenever we could afford a penn'orth of fuel for it, we filled it and it brightened the place up on nights when there was no fire in the grate.

My mother never stopped working; whether or not she went out with the broken herring, she still took in all the washing she could get and charged tuppence or thruppence a load, depending on what it was. Not only did she do mangling with an old mangle she'd picked up, she also did hand-wringing; hand-wringing was much harder work, much harder on the wrists, but it took less out of the clothes and it paid an extra penny. In no time she built up quite a canny little laundry business and the house would always smell and be damp with it.

When the fishing season finished she worked in the potato fields picking 'tateys'. She never had time for anything other than work, except if somebody was needing help, and that always meant even more work. She never went to the variety hall or anything, she never even went for a walk in the park; going to the market for the few bits and pieces she got for us was her delight, her only break. I've seen her work all day in the fish factory or in the tatey fields, come home at night, and before she's even had a cup of tea, start washing and laying out some neighbour who'd died during the day. And then she'd more than likely sit up all night with them as well if they had nobody else. Somebody might have been waiting all day with their husband or their wife lying there, not knowing what to do and unable to help themselves, waiting for my mother to come home from work so she could come and do the necessary. She was what people called a 'handywoman'...she would deliver babies and wash them, and she would treat people's little injuries and illnesses; they'd have to be on their last legs before anybody would call the doctor.

It was from my mother, when I got older, that I learnt how to do laying out myself. She would know for instance that if they hadn't been dead very long, or if they'd died quickly, that something might have to come away from them yet and they might need to be padded or stuffed with cotton wool, bits of rag or even newspaper if they had nothing else. In some cases, depending on whether they were a man or a woman and what they'd died of, she might have to make them a little nappy. If it was a woman, she'd put a nightie on them; if it was a man, she'd give him a clean shirt. Then she'd comb their hair and put their false teeth in if they had any, to make them look presentable and at peace.

If they were going on a trestle, she'd put a white sheet down first and then a little pillow. Then she would drape the windows, the fanlight and the walls, with white sheets and a little bit of helio ribbon. After that, they were ready for their visitors. Then their old friends and relatives would come in and have a look at them and pay their last respects. There'd be a clean hankie over the face and some would lift it up and kiss whoever it was; it didn't make any difference whether they were a man or a woman; some did it and some didn't according to their own lights. Then the visitor would be asked if they wanted to follow the coffin when it went to the cemetery, and again some would say yes and some would say no.

I never kissed anybody when they were laid out except one very old man who Mam said was my granda, although I don't know which one it was. She lifted the hankie and told me to kiss him and I did but I was petrified. It was a very long time before I could get the feeling of those cold stiff lips off my mouth, and she never made me do it again. When my grandmother died I saw her laid out on the table but I didn't have to do anything except look and say a little prayer; they must have been fairly well off because there were three rolls of bacon hanging above her head.

After a while we were getting along champion without my father. The older girls were getting work in the factory or going into service, so we were able to get a few bits and pieces to make the place a bit more comfortable. You could put stuff in your window and sell it at that time, it was called a 'parlour shop', and Mam used to make ginger beer, cinder toffee, vinegar and buns, and put it in ours, and that would bring in a few more shillings. Now we got cups to drink out of; the biggest girls had the cups with the handles, and as they got a better one, they'd pass their old one down till eventually we all got one; same with plates, spoons, knives, forks and everything. My mother really did her best to make things nice for us and folks roundabout always spoke well of her because she worked so hard for us kids and because she was so clean and willing to help anybody. It was a good job they did think highly of her, because washing was the only all-year-round work she had. Picking tateys only lasted about six weeks, if that, and even the herrings were only seasonal, so even at the times we were doing canny, she never let up.

I can never remember seeing my mother with her sleeves down. Same with the bit of print women had at the bottom of their skirts that they used to let down at their leisure; my mother's was always pinned up for work. She was nice to look at, she always had a gentle expression on her face, but her hands were terrible and her hair was as white as snow. I can never remember her looking any different. Her hands were full of keens that never healed and they bled all the time in winter; no sooner would one close up, than another opened up. She could hardly bear to dry them after she'd washed them, they were so sore, she just had to dab at them with a cloth. The keens were caused by the kind of jobs my mother had, her hands were always cold and wet. All day her hands were either in cold wet soil that was sometimes covered in frost and used to get into the cuts, or they were in barrels of water with ice in it. She had to split the herrings with the ice still on them and pull the bones out, then she'd be lifting the blocks of ice, breaking them up and sprinkling the pieces on the fish. Or she'd have to put them in boxes with coarse salt and sprinkle that on them; all with bare hands, none of the gloves they had then would have lasted five minutes.

Sometimes she used to rub on this ointment called Snowfire, all the fish-lasses and fishwives used it, but it washed off in no time. Sometimes when it was a really cold day her hands would seize up like a claw, but the fingers had become so twisted through time that she could never straighten them out properly anyway. We should have had a fire burning in the grate for when my mother came home, to warm her poor hands and bones, but we couldn't afford the coal to have a fire every day. Those of us girls still at home were always down at the beach when the tide came in, looking for wood that had been washed up. It didn't burn very well after it had been in the sea, but it was better than nowt; the problem was there were always plenty other people down there doing the same thing. We used to go to the cinder heaps and the same thing happened there. Most of the life was already burnt out of the cinders but if you got the fire going with something else, they would redden up like coke and keep it going for a while. But if you weren't there when the wagons came in, it was like not being at the beach when the tide came in...there'd be nowt left by the time you got there.

My mother often worked through the night as well as during the day, especially with the washing or when she was making her stuff for the window, and she never got so much as a penny out of my father. Even on a Sunday, which was supposed to be the Sabbath and it was supposed to be a sin, she'd do washing if she could get it. Two stones of weekend washing might fetch in half a crown, but that's a lot of washing, especially if a lot of it was hand-wrung. No wonder sometimes even her face was blue.

The Woodhouse kipper factory job usually lasted from June to August when they were bringing in loads of good big herring, and this was the only time she'd have sufficient money to get her stock in for the winter. She'd buy a big drum of flour, sugar, tea and such like, and a pair of shoes for each of us if she could manage it, because she knew every winter would be a hard one with only the washing to rely on.

As soon as I was old enough I was sent to St Stephen's School near Mile End Road and the only reason I went was to avoid trouble with the School Board Man. My mother needed me more than the school did and I would stay off as much as I could to help her. This meant that even when I went it was a waste of time because I was worse than useless at lessons. But the man who used to come was understanding; they weren't as tough as the Catholic ones and we didn't have a priest at the door every fortnight telling us we were all going to Hell, the way some folks did. The School Board Man must have known it was no good insisting you went to school if you were hungry and hadn't clothes and shoes enough, and maybe your mother was sick at home and couldn't get out of bed. He would listen to what my mother had to say and then he would sigh and say 'Well...try to get her to school as much as you can, Mrs Nichol.'

The teachers were different though, because they never visited the kids' homes and didn't know how they were living, and I had one who used to cane me for being off too much. They always called you 'lazy', when the truth was just the opposite. There were no lazy people lying abed in our house and not many roundabouts either.

When we had no shoes Mam was too proud to send us in bare feet, and when the School Board Man came she'd have to tell him and he would give her a police ticket and this used to get you shoes and stockings. The shoes were heavy and black but strong, and little holes had been punched in in a special pattern, and the stockings were black with a white band; this was to stop you pledging them. Sometimes we were so desperate we had to go to the Workhouse Guardians and they would give vouchers for essentials. Plenty kids had 'police' shoes and stockings but everybody hated the Guardians. Like many other people, my mother would rather have starved than went, she only ever went because of us kids.

School was more of a nuisance than anything else for my mother, and it was nothing but a trial for me because I was always being punished for not knowing my lessons. You couldn't come home to our house and start doing homework; there was broken herring to be sorted all over the table, driftwood to be collected, cinder heaps to go to, piles of washing to be hung up and ironed. The law allowed you to leave in Standard Two when you were twelve, and I wouldn't be going a single day longer. Working and making money was far more important than being a scholar.

Even though he caused her so much trouble, my mother would never say anything bad about my father, not to anybody. It took my mother all her time to say 'damn', yet if anybody had a right to be a sinner it should have been her, because she had an awful life. We changed places umpteen times to try and get away from my father because he would keep bursting in and causing trouble; but he was crafty, he would go around all the schools and look in the playground at playtime to see if we were there, and then follow us home after school that night. Mam couldn't keep us off altogether or she would have been in trouble with the law, so sooner or later he always found out where we were. We would sometimes just be sitting down to tea, when he would suddenly fling the door open and come crashing in, drunk as hell. My mother was always terrified of him and she never once got the better of him that I can remember. He would knock her into a corner and have her up against the wall making sounds just like a frightened animal, and she would just stay there not knowing what to do. Our Alice was a big strapping girl and she was the only one who ever dare put up a fight, but eventually she would give up under his blows, he had very hard hands and strong arms. Alice would give him a load off her tongue while she was having a go, but he wouldn't put up with any 'lip', as he called it, from my mother, she had to take her hammers in silence.

I could never understand how after he'd come in like this and spoiled our tea and our home and everything, and bashed several people, that my mother would end up loving him...by that I mean letting him 'use' her...it was only one room, so everybody knew. He would stay for a few days and she would treat him like a husband, and then he would come in badly drunk on payday, give her a thrashing and disappear again. After it had happened a couple more times, my mother would say she'd had enough and we'd pack everything up and go somewhere else; and then she'd have to start all over again, making a home out of a single room, finding new customers to get washing off, and making a new window shop. It was a very wearying business for all of us, but not like it was for my mother who had all the worrying of finding a new place far enough away, shifting all the stuff on a handcart, and keeping on with her work at the same time. One night when I was about four or five, he came in and started his antics...upsetting the table with all the food on, smashing up the furniture and bashing my mother all over the place... Then when there was nothing left to smash or turn over, he came over all quiet and said to her, 'Come here and give's a kiss... Ye think I don't love ye, but I do, ye know...as surely as the shore dashes on the waves.' He was so drunk he could hardly speak and yet he could come out with something like that.

Because he carried bricks all day and was a short stocky feller, my father was very solid on his feet, but one day he was so drunk Alice knocked him arse over tip. It was really by accident and it happened so fast everybody got a surprise. He had been cursing Mam and calling her worse than muck, and had then turned his attentions on Alice, saying she was even worse, when she suddenly rushed at him and gave him a great big shove. There was a bath of water on the floor behind him that we'd all just had a bath in, and he fell backwards into it.

There was murder on! He couldn't have yelled more if he'd been pushed into the fire. The angle he went in, he'd got his behind jammed, and he was so drunk he couldn't get out. The bath wasn't a proper tin one, it was just an old rain barrel that had been cut in half...what we called a 'kit'...and the sides were very steep and the wood very slippy. His clothes were drenched and he was yelling and cursing and splashing and there was water all over the place. Mam and the rest of us ran out and hid in the alley until we saw him leave; you couldn't see Alice for dust, I don't know which way she went. He must have felt a bit of a fool because he didn't come around for quite a long time after that.

When I got bigger, about eight or nine, I started working in the tatey fields picking potatoes with my mother and sisters; I'd go after school and at weekends and sometimes instead of going to school. It was hard work and when my mother could see we younger ones were getting tired, she'd say 'When we get back tonight, we'll have a bit of luxury.'

'What's that, Mam?' we'd say.

'Never mind. Wait and see.'

When we got back she'd maybe send for a penn'orth of fresh butter and bake some fresh bread, and that would be a luxury and very much appreciated; or she might send out for two white puddings and fry them in the pan with gravy, and that was even better. Other times she'd buy a three ha'penny tripe bag and stuff it with sage and anything else she could find, and boil the whole lot; it never amounted to a great deal of nourishment but the smell of it would nearly drive you mad with delight.

If we were well enough off at any time she'd make 'panhagilty', which was bacon stewed with vegetables, and you'd feel good for days after that. We never had regular meals like breakfast, dinner, tea and supper. We'd just have a slice of bread or a lump of porridge before we went off to school or work, no dinner, and then when we came back from school or work, something cooked...maybe tatey pot or a bit of fried fish my mother had scrounged from the factory; it would be mainly fish if she was working at the factory, tateys if we were working in the fields, otherwise it would be bread and syrup. We never had supper.

My mother made pastries, sherbet drinks and various sweetmeats to sell from the window or from her little stall that she set up at the fish quay if she had enough stuff, but we wouldn't get to eat any of it. That money was for our keep. And when she was on the quay she used to mind the fish-lasses' oil petticoats as well as her stall. Fish-lasses that could afford it would have these very heavy oil-petticoats for when it was snowing or pouring with rain, but when it faired up they'd never want to be seen in them. Most of them really fancied themselves and strutted along the quay like peacocks in front of all the men, and oil-petticoats did nothing for anybody except keep the wet out. So as soon as the sun came out they would take them off and give them to my mother to watch until they came back, and she would charge a ha'penny or a penny, depending on how long she had to look after them for; she did the same with their baskets. Some of them would go on the boats for an hour or more, but not to sell fish.

Mam was always very tidily and properly dressed but she could never have afforded the fancy petticoats with all the tucks, or the earrings and things, that the young and swanky fish-lasses wore, she couldn't even afford a waterproof. If she got soaked or got her clothes full of fish scales, she just had to wait until she got home and wash and dry them. She washed her own clothes every day and made us wash ours. 'Mebbes ye cannot help bein' poor, but ye can help bein' dirty,' she'd say.

In the winter, when the herring season was long over and the tateys had all been picked, and regular work was hard to come by, we had some really cold days in our house. It wasn't so much the cold as the damp that used to get into your bones. It didn't bother me so much because I was a growing girl and I was very hardy, but it must have got into my poor mother's and I don't think it ever properly got out, not even during whatever summer we got. I was always trying to find anything that might burn to try and keep the place warm for her and to help dry the clothes, and sometimes I'd bring something in and light it and it would fill the place with black smoke because there was rubber or tar or something in it, and then we'd have to try and put it out and open the windows and doors to let the smoke out, and the whole place would be colder than ever.

If we had nothing at all to make a fire with and we couldn't wash our clothes because they wouldn't have dried by morning, my mother was so ashamed. She'd have this awful sad look and you could almost see the cold coming out of her face and hands; her hands especially were always blue, you never saw them any other colour. We girls always had a bit of pink in our skins but Mam's never did; any red would be trickles of blood, either from the fish or from her keens. Sometimes her skin all over was a horrible colour...even her neck and chest and her back and the tops of her legs.

The Gas Board used to dump their slag in a yard off King Street and if you poked around long enough, you'd usually find something in the way of a few cinders, sometimes even a bit of coal. I used to take my tatey bags down. There were stacks of people there, all doing the same thing...bending over picking and chucking, and calling things out now and again to try and make you laugh. Your hands would sometimes be cut to ribbons because there'd be splinters of metal in it, but it was well worth it if you could get a sackful. When you saw the cart coming, if you had enough energy left you would run up and follow it in and sometimes get the pick. Coal carts were even better and people would follow them all over the streets. When they jerked along the cobbles, little bits of coal would be dropping off; and if it didn't, it was up to you to help it. I suppose it was dishonest but you'd tell yourself it would only have dropped off anyway and somebody else would have got it. And everybody did it. It was all dishonest, if that's the way you wanted to look at it, and you could be put in prison even for taking the cinders if you were caught, but nobody took any notice.

Sometimes there was nothing to be had in the yard except slag. But then on a good day there'd be plenty of cinders and you'd fill your sacks or barrow or whatever you had, and pile them against the wall while you carried home what you could. If you found somebody keeping an eye on somebody's, you'd ask them if they'd keep an eye on yours as well while you raced home and back. Sometimes they would, and you'd give them a few cinders for their trouble; other times you'd come back and they'd be gone and so would all the cinders; they might have thought 'Look at that greedy little bitch! Look how much she's got! And then she has the nerve to ask me to keep toot for her! Huh!'

After a shipwreck I used to go down to the long beach at South Shields, but it wasn't every day you had a shipwreck, and practically the whole town would get themselves down there. But nearly every day at low tide there'd be lumps of driftwood and sometimes small coal washed up as well, and if you were prepared to wade out, you could get the biggest bits. It was a long way from where we were living, but Mam stopped it in the finish, the tide comes in quickly and there was always somebody being drowned or washed away and never heard of again.

Over the years since we left my father, through being careful with her money and keeping her eyes and ears open for a bargain, my mother had gradually collected a canny bit of furniture; we now had a proper table and a few chairs, a rocking chair, a wardrobe and even a chest of drawers. We had also got rid of the wooden tub and now had an iron bath in front of the fire. In our house the youngest got washed first, the oldest last...the opposite way to the way it was with clothes and everything else; I think it was because my mother felt that the dirt that came off grown-ups' bodies was dirtier in some way than what came off children's. Even though it wasn't easy to be proud with so little room for privacy, the older girls were very particular and would never show themselves with nothing on, not even to their own sisters; only Mam was allowed to see everybody. Because there was only one room, we littler ones would go to bed as soon as we'd been bathed, and when it came to the big'uns', they would get in one at a time and nobody would look.

2

When I was eleven I told my mother I wanted to have a go at selling the fish, I felt I had a flair for it and was certain I could do well and be a great help to her if only I was given the chance.

'No, you're far too young, pet. It's not nice for little girls to do. You stick in at school till ye get a bit older.'

But I was no scholar so what was the point, I could just about read the Gazette and that was the only reading that mattered.

'Please, Mam. Just give's a try. I can help bring the money in. I know I can.'

'No. Only I do that... None of your sisters have ever done it and I'm not havin' you doin' it... I'm not havin' ye goin' out in hail and snow and ruinin' yourself the way I've done.'

'But, Mam. Our Lily's a fish girl.'

'Not in that way, she's not. She has a proper job, packin' and cleanin' and makin' kippers. She doesn't go out sellin', and she never has. She never would, even if she got the chance. She's got too much sense.'

But my mother couldn't stand up to anybody for long, and although I was still little, I was persistent and I nagged on and nagged on until eventually she gave in.

'Maybe just a few fry herrin', then. Just to try... But mind, if I think it's too much for ye...'

My mother started at six o'clock in the fish factory filleting fish and rolling herrings, and she'd been doing it for twenty-five years for the same man. At the end of the day when they finished up, he'd give her some of the leftover cheap fish like blackjack and cod, plus some broken herrings. She would then fetch them home, clean them and set everything out all nice on a board, get changed, and go out around the streets with it on her head to sell it to people at their own doors. The board was made of heavy wood about three feet long, and the fish was big fat stuff which she would slice up with her mallet and gully, however the customers wanted...they could have it as big or as little as they liked, no order was too small. On her fingers she carried strings of herring threaded through the gills, ones that had been broken by the fishing hooks or torn in the nets; they were perfectly good fish, lovely eating, they'd just be a bit bashed up and she would have straightened them out best she could.

The night she brought a few for me, she also brought me a sixpence ha'penny basket...something I kept for years and years after...and I sold the whole lot. One and thruppence I got for them, and I sold them in no time. I was as proud as a peacock. The next day I asked her to fetch a few more, and she did, and I sold them as well. And that's how I got started. I'd say to her, 'Look, you go straight home and clean up and make the tea. I'll go round with the whole lot and have them sold before ye've got the kettle boiled.'

Some of the herring my mother got for next to nothing was beautiful and packed with roe, and the foreigners down by the docks loved it like that. They wouldn't know enough of the language to be able to chat to you, and you didn't know theirs either, but both of you understood figures, and that was all that mattered. There were lots of them down there and I could sell any amount of it. I was even selling herring for salting to the shops because they couldn't get it any cheaper than what my mother could get it for.

The way I'd find out what anything was worth, was to offer it for sale at a certain price. If they let me walk out the shop with it, I'd know my price was too high. If they took it straight away, I'd know it was too low, and I'd know better for the next shop; kids can be every bit as cute as grown-ups, and I wouldn't be made a fool of even though I was only eleven.

Because my mother didn't work in the factory all year round, I couldn't sell herring when she stopped. I was dying to do something else but work was hard to get. If you were a girl, or even a woman, you could only get the lowest jobs and the pay was always lousy. The going rate for a live-in maid was £12 a year and £4 of that was deducted towards the upkeep of a pew in a local church, and too bad if it wasn't the same church as yours. Eight pounds might sound a lot of money but when you stretched it out over fifty-two weeks, it came to little more than three bob a week.

Anyway I much preferred to work outside, I loved having a crack on with customers and fish-lasses alike, but you had to take whatever you got and be thankful. The first house job I was able to get was at Captain Davidson's, he was captain of a big ship and away most of the time. His wife was what you would call a 'lady', but she was a kind one. I got one and six a week and that was good money, because I wasn't 'in service' which is a different thing altogether. Mind you, things had to be very clean, she was very particular. Every morning before school I had to go and scrub the steps and edge them white with rubbing-stone, then I had to polish all the woodwork in the hall, clean the kitchen and scullery and wash the dishes. And then after school I'd go back to see if there was anything else. Alice, Nellie and Lily had all worked there, first one and then the other; when one left, she would speak for the next one, and that one would get the first one's place and so on. Alice was in service there right up until she got married, she got three and six a week for it and considered herself very lucky; even a live-in maid's job was by no means easy to get.

When the Master was home from his ship he would leave all his boots out and I would give them a good blacking and polishing, and before he went back he'd leave a tanner inside his big boots, sometimes even a shilling if there'd been an extra few pairs. He was a polite and generous man and she was a good woman especially to my mother. She would let my mother do her washing and every now and again she'd say 'I've got some old clothes for the children, Mrs Nichol. Send someone around for them.' Things like that.

As soon as the herring season started and my mother got her job back at the factory, I would start again with the selling and I got to be so good at it that I wanted to sell other things as well. I loved going around the streets with my basket and shawl, meeting all the different people and traders with all their different wares and street cries. Everybody had their own call and no sooner would one move on than you'd hear another coming along, and sometimes two or three of them would all be calling together...fish-lasses, rag-and-bone men, somebody sharpening scissors and knives, or any of half a dozen others. Between one Sunday and the next, the streets were never empty, never quiet, especially in the morning time.

Mam didn't mind me going out now, she knew she could trust me and she couldn't deny that I was helping by the money I was bringing in, even though it wasn't all that much. So I told her I wanted to have a go at selling small vegetables, which we called 'greens'. I wouldn't be down the quays so much with them; the quayside always had a bad reputation because of all the foreign sailors...not that the English ones were any better from what I heard. With the greens I'd have something to do when the herring season was finished, and this meant I could keep on with my customers.

On Thursdays and Fridays I would take the afternoon off school, rent a big barrow for a shilling in the market...you got sixpence back when you returned it...wheel it down to the river and get the ferry across to North Shields. You could always buy the greens cheaper on that side, especially in places like Preston, and I would buy anything green...vegetables or flowers; whatever they had for sale, I would sell. I found that not only was stuff cheaper across the Tyne, but it was also better quality and the variety was greater.

If it was a good day, sometimes all the barrows would be out and I'd run back for my fish basket; it was round and deep and nearly three feet long, so I could get a fair load of stuff in it.

There was a ha'penny ferry and a penny one, a ha'penny or a penny each way. I'd get the ha'penny one, it made little difference to me if it took an extra five minutes. You paid your money at a little paybox and then they let you on. There'd always be plenty of lasses like me going to get their baskets or their barrows filled with this or that, and all kinds of tradesmen taking their stuff across, some of them with ponies and carts. They were always exciting trips, even though they were just from one side of the river to the other. For me it was like going to another world, with all the shipyards with their huge cranes, big ships, all the great bridges along the river, and the city of Newcastle just beyond.

My back would be bent nearly double on the way back to the ferry from the nurseries, and then all the way back home, because whether I had a barrow or my basket it would be full to the brim. If I had the barrow, I'd have so much in it that I'd have to tie a clothesline over the top and underneath and round and around again and again; I wouldn't lose so much as a single brussel sprout. If I had the basket, it would take two fellers to lift it onto my head. They'd say 'I don't know how you're ganna manage with this, hinny.' And I'd say 'Once it's up, ye hardly know it's there.' But it pressed down so much that at times I thought I'd lose my neck, and I'd clamp my hands tight around my throat so it wouldn't sink down too far.

As soon as I got home I'd empty the barrow if I had one, and run back with it, it had to be in by a certain time or you'd lose your deposit. Once I got back home I got everything cleaned and sorted out and all the bad leaves pulled off, and if Mam wasn't out working she'd help me. We'd tie the flowers and scallions and things into neat little bundles and then divide everything into three lots...morning round, afternoon round and evening. Then we'd arrange a lovely display with all the vegetables in neat rows, best side out. It makes all the difference in the world if you're clean and well turned out yourself, with your hair all combed and a pretty frock, and your display bright and inviting with a lovely smell coming off it.

Big things like rhubarb and cabbage would be sold first thing Saturday morning for their dinner. Scallions radishes and lettuce went out on the afternoon load, those would be what they'd want for their tea. Straight after tea I'd go out with my small stuff...mint, sage, wallflowers, thyme and other seasonings; nobody would dream of buying that sort of thing before tea, they never bought any further ahead than the next meal. In most of the streets I went around, nobody could afford to save anything, they all lived from hand to mouth, and one of the reasons they liked coming to me was because I'd sell them as small a quantity as they wanted. If they wanted one flower or one scallion, that's what they could have; I'd nearly split a radish to please somebody.

When I went out with the small stuff I used to try to get my tick in. I always had the same route for both the fish and the greens, and going back three or four times a day down the same back lanes, I knew every one of my customers. I knew who the good payers were, the ones who would always come out with their purse the minute they heard me, and I knew the ones who'd take a deaf fit or pretend they were out. They were all valuable customers, it was just that you had to work a bit harder on some than others.

Any night my mother came in with a few strings of broken herring I would go straight out and sell them so folks could have them for their tea, and I was so keen that she had started buying shellfish from the quay and I was selling that as well. This meant that during the week I might have sold fish and greens every day, and that I might have a good lot of tick out by the weekend. Some people would never buy anything unless they could pay for it there and then, others never until the weekend because that's when their wages came in. So by the time the weekend came, I couldn't let any more tick go out. Things might have been tight for them during the week, but like as not they'd have been tight for me as well, and I often had to pawn my shawl to buy my stocks with, and then get it back after I'd done my rounds.

Really poor people rarely had the money to pay you straight away, yet if you were kind to them, they were nearly always your most regular customers. Mind, you had to insist on lodging house people paying cash because they were always coming and going. They would mainly buy fish because it was easy to cook; the crabs, prawns, winkles and mussels that I'd boiled and dressed myself, usually went to the hotels like the Royal Grill and the Criterion. Shellfish were regarded as luxuries and you wouldn't let things like that go out on tick; if they didn't have the money to pay for them now, they wouldn't have it later either. Mint, sage and flowers were treated the same way, so if you had somebody who'd gone on tick for their blackjack or their cabbage for instance, you couldn't let them have sage and wallflowers as well...especially not on a Saturday when you had to try and get all your money in to start off the new week with a clean slate.

When I went to get my tick in, which would usually be last thing on a Saturday when I knew the men would have got paid, I'd get especially nicely dressed up because this was more formal business. I never wrote down what people owed because I couldn't write very well, but I had a very good memory for figures. I'd say to myself, 'Let's see, so-and-so four doors up owes seven pence for cod from Tuesday... Mrs Green Door had a shilling's worth of broccoli... Her with a limp, in the broken window, still owes sixpence for cabbage.'

I never asked for money though. I would just shout up the stairs.

'Are ye in, upstairs..? Are ye there, hinny..? I've got somethin' I think you'd like... Lovely white celery down here! Beautiful crisp radishes! All they want is a pinch of salt!'

They would know what I meant. Sometimes the husbands would come down and say 'How much does she owe you, pet..? I'll pay ye... Here.' Then they'd more than likely go in an play war with them.

'Oh, no. It's all right, mister. It's not much. I'll come back later when she's in.'

Some men would go mad if they found out how much their wife had run up, even though it was for their teas. Other times, if the woman came out and genuinely seemed to forget she owed you, you could say 'Have ye still enough onions left? Or d'ye need a few more?' Then they would cotton on and say 'Eeeh, that reminds me... I haven't paid ye for the last lot... Here y'are, pet... What was it again..?' And then you'd be right.

If I'd finished in good time and it was a fine night, I might go back to the market with my money and buy a few herbs like marjoram, peppermint, spearmint or thyme, and a yard of nice twine. I'd then go somewhere by myself, like up on the steps of the Customs House where I wouldn't be disturbed, and sort them all out into tiny bundles so I could tempt poor people with a little bit of luxury that they might be able to afford. And then I'd go around my streets yet again to see if I could wring a few last coppers out of them before the weekend. And if it was the season for oranges, I could never resist filling my basket and taking them to the Empire and the other theatres and variety halls. People would be standing in long queues with nothing else to do except wait for it to open, and they'd always be in a good mood and have money in their pockets. I was a bonny girl in a healthy sort of a way and I'd go up to the fellers with a smile on my face, and they'd hardly ever refuse.

'Penny a gaff, mister,' I'd say.

If you went up to the feller, he wouldn't want to appear mean in front of his lass, especially if you said 'Lovely ripe orange for your lady-friend, sir..? I'll pick a nice one for you or you can do it yourself... Ooh! Look! There's a beauty!' you'd say, pulling one out and holding it out to her. If one of their hands was open and you could manage to put an orange in it, or you got hold of their hand and opened it yourself and put one in it, they'd very rarely put it back in your basket. And if they were still a bit hesitant, you might say in a jokey way, 'Just in case you don't like the show.' They would usually laugh then and put their hand in their pocket. They weren't supposed to chuck peel at acts they didn't like, and there'd be notices up telling them not to; but if the comedian wasn't up to much, or the singing was a bit flat, they'd have the ready to do something about it if they wanted to. Even on a good night the place would have orange peel all over, and all the seats stained with the juice by the time they came out.

Although I liked the greens and they were less messy and didn't stink your clothes like the fish, there was much more glamour in selling fish; I don't know why, there just was. So because I was good at it, I began to sell whatever fish I could get; not only what my mother fetched home from the fish factory or the quay, but what I bought myself from the fish market at North Shields. I was getting to be a big lass now, strong and very fresh coloured, with long, nut-brown hair, and I was brimming over with confidence.

I loved being one of the Shields fish-lasses. We didn't carry a backcreel like the Cullercoats girls, and we weren't as famous, but people said we were every bit as bonny...at least the Shields people did. The backcreels were raffia bags with straps that they put their arms through and everybody knew the Cullercoats girls by them. They had their way of dressing, and we had ours; they carried creels on their backs whereas we carried baskets on our heads. And they also sold different fish; sometimes you'd see theirs jumping on their back, but ours were bigger ones that came from deeper waters and had had all the life knocked out of them.

Every day I'd put on a clean shawl, clean apron and clean petticoats. The shawl was necessary to keep the fish scales out of your hair, and not only did it stink by the end of the day, it got lousy from the fish. Directly under the basket was a 'weeze', which was a ring of straw wrapped with cloth, and it went around your head like a crown to cushion the weight of the basket; they never lasted very long but they made a big difference, so you were always making them up.

I was so proud with my shawl and my print apron and my fish-lass's petticoat with the folds right down to the feet, the shawl would be loose at the sides to show your big earrings...and I'd saved up for ages for a pair. Once I was given a pair of long boots with buttonholes that laced all the way up, but scrubbed clogs were all right and they were much more serviceable, they'd send you clicking and clocking along the cobbles and everybody liked the sound. Cobbles used to bring the sound out of so many things, the way a road never could...horses' hooves, cart wheels, men's working boots... I was proper swanky walking along with my basket on my head, never holding it with my hand or anything, just walking along as though it was a big fancy hat. Seeing a proud young woman walking like that, very erect, is something that never fails to catch the eye.

We never had toothbrushes or hair brushes or anything like that at home, just a big thin-toothed comb that did for the nits, and we all shared it. I'd never heard of talcum powder and we certainly couldn't afford what you might call 'make-up'. What we used to do if we wanted to change the colouring on our cheeks, was to wet our fingers with spittle and rub it on the flowery designs on the wallpaper; the colours used to come off and would last all day as long as it didn't rain. I never needed to use red because I had such a healthy complexion but I'd sometimes hear one of the fish-lasses say to another, 'Mind, she's got plenty on, hasn't she?' And I'd say 'Is that so..? Well, why not come over here and see if ye can rub if off!'

I was always on the lookout for a bit of old lace or any nice bit of material to sew on to my dress to make it look as though I was wearing something new, and if ever I got a hole in my stocking I'd draw it together very carefully and then put a bit of wallpaper colouring on the thread to make it match. Some of them used to stuff plumped-up newspaper inside the front of their clothes but I never needed to do that.

My mother knew I loved to dress up but all of us girls had to be very proper, she would never allow us to show bare necks or any part of our legs. 'A lady shows no skin except on her hands and face,' was what she used to say; so we had these steel spines in our collars to keep them right up to our chins, and our dresses were so long they would trail along the ground rather than show any ankle...even though it meant more washing and they always wore away that much quicker.

I was never much of a singer but by now my voice was really strong and I used to shout all kinds of things at different times. I would wait till somebody else had shouted...maybe the coalman...and when he'd caught their attention but before he'd got all his words out, I'd come in with mine. Your words would run into each other and even you yourself would forget what you were supposed to be shouting; but people knew what you meant all the same, they soon recognised your particular call.

'Byalabsta! Byalasta! Bylasta! Byasta..!' That was supposed to mean 'Come and buy my lobster,' though we hardly ever sold them because they were too dear. We called prawns 'little lobsters'. And if they wanted big ones, they got crabs. I'd get the crabs from a feller at the beach and my mother and I used to boil them in the boiler we used for the washing. Her and I would have great fun setting them out in such a way they looked as though they were coming out at you; they were all dead of course by this time, but you could tease customers a bit and it never did any harm.

When the herring season was finished Mam would go down to the quays and the fish market and buy loads for both of us to sell in the afternoons, but if I wasn't out with the greens, or if she had a lot of washing on, I'd sell the lot myself. The fish was auctioned very early in the morning as soon as the boats came in; the merchants would buy a hundred barrels or more and then set the price, and the fishwives and lasses would be waiting by till all the dealing was over and then buy a barrel themselves.

I was now selling in places my mother would never go to and wouldn't even have known about. She'd be afraid of the foreigners, but I wasn't. They were all the same to me; they paid their money and they got their fish, and if they gave a bit of lip, they got a bit back.

On a good day when we were both at it, Mam and I would sometimes go back and forth across to North Shields on the ferry as many as four or five times, and get rid of it all. The fishermen were a bit on the rough side but they were mostly kind-hearted and usually never gave you any trouble unless you asked for it. Mam would never let me go on to a ship to sell, and told me that if she ever heard tell of me going on board any ship, I was finished as far as selling fish was concerned. Some of the fish-lasses did, and some of them used to stay on a very long time; you'd see them going down the rope ladders, with the sailors shouting and putting their hands up their skirts and everything, and they laughing and shrieking and not caring if the whole world should see them. But I didn't like that sort of thing; I went down to sell fish, nothing else. Not that I didn't like a nice young feller if I met him; occasionally you'd meet one who was a real gentlemen and he might take you to the Empire and buy you chocolates. Not all seamen were as bad as some would have you believe.

25

Sometimes when the fishing boats were late in, we fish-lasses would be waiting for them on the quay and we'd have fetched our knitting with us so we wouldn't be wasting our time, and we'd have a great bit carry-on, especially if my mother wasn't there, laughing at each other's jokes and tales about this one and that. Some of the girls were really clever with a couple of needles and could get a canny bit for it, but I wasn't a fancy knitter myself...socks and scarves were about my limit.

When at last the boats came in, it was a wonderful sight. They'd come over the horizon and up the river, each one different in its own way; some gaily coloured, others more dour; some with flags, some with religious things; each one saying something about its own skipper. Once they tied up, they wasted no time getting their catches off and on to the quay. They would unload their boxes and set them out all along the stones of the quay, packed with quivering fish, and it was a lovely sight. If the sun was shining and coming off the river as well as the fish, you couldn't imagine anything more beautiful. Sometimes the sun wouldn't be shining and everybody wouldn't be laughing and jolly, and you just had to get on with it all the same; it might be quite dark and very cold and wet, and if you got soaked you just had to keep moving till you dried off.

Although I loved selling fish, I still continued with the greens; I had to, nobody lived off fish alone and some would never touch it. I could sell things like herbs and flowers which some of the girls hated because they just didn't have the knack, and after I'd sold mine I'd sometimes take their baskets and sell theirs for them. 'Give's tuppence for every shillingsworth I sell, and ye can come with is and I'll show ye how it's done,' I'd say; and I think it was a fair offer. I trained a good few of them that way; I'd show them how to watch for a good pitch, how to follow the ladies with a sprig of mint under their noses...nobody can resist that but you need a bit of neck to do it...and how to arrange their stuff to look its very best. I'd tell them to keep arranging their baskets all the time, putting their brightest flowers or vegetables at the front so as not to let their last few customers think they're just getting the dregs; and if it was flowers they were selling, to always go for the men when there was a man and a woman together. 'Always keep a couple of your best smellers in your hand,' I'd tell them. 'And don't be frightened to follow them down the street, wavin' them in their faces. Ye won't need to keep that up very long before they cave in.'

All the girls fixed their prices, they were very fair like that; but if they got the first ferry and you missed it, some of them would go tappy-lappy down your lanes and tell your customers you mustn't be coming today, that you were poorly or something. For all that, if it ever happened to me I still went round and I still sold my stuff.

I liked hawking and I never saw anything wrong in it, my mother did it and she would never do anything that wasn't right. The only thing that ever bothered me was that I might meet up with Johnny Robinson or any of his brothers...Johnny and I weren't courting or anything, but I fancied him and I think he fancied me. When I was a kid, if ever I was passing his place he'd often run up and pinch my hat and run away with it so that I'd run after him, then I'd do the same to him. But his family were well off and now that I was bigger I didn't want him seeing me hawking. Lots of people went around the streets selling all sorts of things, or offering their services for this, that or the other, it was honest trading just like anything else, yet people with businesses of their own would put notices up outside their houses saying 'No hawkers allowed'. I hadn't any airs or graces and wasn't entitled to any, but my business was honest.

I knew I was too young for courting and I didn't have the clothes for it anyway, my best clothes were my working clothes, and my main concern was helping my mother to make ends meet. All the same...

3

Our Nellie was very sort of genteel and would rather get a situation like Captain Davidson's for three and six a week, than earn five bob hawking. She was too polite to sell anything and she was so particular she'd take off her knickers...old-fashioned bloomers they were...every single night, and wash them ready for the next day. Where the rest of us might make ours last two or three days at a time when the weather was bad and we had no fire to dry them, Nellie would rather wear damp ones than ones that weren't completely fresh. Yet for all that, she still got in the family way with the help of Septimus Johnson. At first Sep's mother wouldn't allow them to get married; she reckoned her son could never have done a dreadful thing like that, even if there'd been no other man on earth, Sep wouldn't have been the father...although Sep himself had already owned up to it.

Mam was now fifty and the burden of life was really beginning to tell. She'd been deeply upset enough herself when she found out about Nellie, but was shamed nearly to distraction by what Sep's mother was going around saying. So with the others all away working or married, Nellie, Mam and me moved to Bird Street in North Shields; this way at least we'd get away from all the talk. But I think the business with Sep's mother was the last straw for her, and we were only there a matter of weeks before she became very poorly. She had to give up the selling because she couldn't walk very far without getting tired and she was now only able to manage the odd load of washing.

Our moving had at last pushed Sep into doing something, and he and our Nellie got married just before a very weak bairn was born premature. Sep was a decent hardworking man but got very little as a blacksmith's apprentice, he couldn't afford to get a house for the two or them, or rather the three of them...and there was no room for him at our house so he had to go on living with his mother for the time being. Poor Nellie now had to forget about trying to be posh, and take any kind of work that was going, whether in the fish factory or anywhere else, because it was obvious Mam was beyond going out to work any more. So Nellie went out to work and I stayed at home to nurse both Mam and the bairn while she was away; it was a seven months baby and so sickly it spent the whole of its short life wrapped in cotton wool in a cardboard box in the fireplace.

Even though she hadn't the energy to work in the fishhouse or the tatey fields any more, my mother was still taking in washing and hand-wringing whenever she could get it, you just couldn't stop her. One morning she got up to light the fire for the washhouse and I heard an awful noise on the landing, like a dog choking. Sep was living with us now and he and Nellie slept in the other bed to Mam and me, but he'd gone off early to look for work. Nellie was getting her clothes on beside their bed.

'What's that funny noise outside?' I says to her.

'I don't know. We'd better have a look.'

She only had her skirt half on, so I jumped out of bed and opened the door.

It was Mam...she was crawling along the passage with one of her legs dragging behind her and her face all twisted and a terrible look in her eyes.

'Mam..! What's the matter? What are ye doin'?'

She couldn't speak, she didn't even look like herself any more.

'Nellie!'

Nellie came rushing out but we couldn't get Mam up, she was just making this awful noise and trailing an arm and a leg as though all the life had gone out of them. I went to get a coat to cover her because she was still just in her nightie, and Nellie ran downstairs into the street to get help. A couple of minutes later she came back up with two men who got hold of Mam and carried her up into the room and laid her down on the bed. She had now become very quiet and very still. The men said we'd better fetch the doctor, so Nellie went while I stayed.

The doctor was what we called the 'cheap doctor' and he'd come to practically anybody but he wouldn't waste much time. You got two visits and a bottle of medicine for one and six from him and you never sent for him unless you thought somebody was dying. The ordinary doctor would have cost you five shillings...maybe even seven and six...and that just for the two visits and a bottle. I don't know whether one was any better than the other, we'd never had any experience of the other one. Anyway, as soon as he came, he took one look at Mam and said she'd had a stroke, and on the quiet he told Nellie she had no more than twenty-four hours to live and that in all probability she'd be gone by midnight.

When midnight came, nobody could sleep. Sep was still away, and I was terrified of my mother, I'm ashamed to say; she had this wild look in her eyes and her face seemed to be even more twisted up than it had been in the morning.

'I'm frightened,' I whispered to Nellie. 'What's happenin' to her? Why can't she speak? Why can't she move? Will she get better, d'ye think?'

'Hush, will ye. I'm stoppin' up to watch her and you'll have to stop as well. She cannot move, so she cannot do ye any harm.'

The following morning Mam seemed to be a little better and we thought everything might be all right after all, we were too young and too daft to realise what was really happening

For the next six weeks Mam seemed to get a bit better and brighter every day, but I was still having to stay at home and look after her and I couldn't go out to work at all. Sep still hadn't managed to find work and the little Nellie brought in wasn't enough to do much more than pay the rent. In the finish we had to go to the Guardians and plead for a ticket; that got you a jug of soup and a bread bun each at Saville Street on a Tuesday and Thursday, but Mam would never take her share and ate hardly anything at all. She could speak a bit by now and she'd say 'Ye must take it for yourselves. It's yous two that need it. It's a waste givin' it to me.'

Poor Nellie... She'd always tried to be so proper, though never in a smug way, she only ever wanted a little bit of dignity after the life we'd had with my father. She was the nicest and the best of all my sisters, and now she had a dying bairn in the hearth, a mother sick in her bed, a husband away looking for work, a young sister she was now responsible for, and she was having to take any work she could get, even working as a labourer in the brick yard.

I had started taking over some of Mam's old washing customers because I found I could do that and keep an eye on her at the same time, and I was beginning to make a few shillings. One day I bought some rice and made a pudding to see if I could tempt her to eat something. It was a lovely sunny day and I'd got the place nice and clean and tidy, and the smell from the rice was beautiful. I opened the street door to let the sunshine up the stairs and was pummelling the pillow and propping her up ready. She smiled a lovely smile at me.

'Eeeh, you're comin' on champion now, aren't ye?' I said to her.

'Yes, pet. I am. If only I can get over this, I'm goin' to take in a couple of extra washin's and get you a nice frock and a nice pair of shoes. And then I'm goin' to buy ye a nice coat to go out in. For when ye see Johnny Robinson.'

'Really..? Ooh, thanks, Mam! That'll be smashin'!'

Just then the doctor came in.

'Look at that, doctor... She's right as rain nearly. Isn't she? She's been sittin' up all by herself and chattin' away like a good'un.'

'Doctor,' my mother says to him. 'I was just thinkin'... As it's such a fine day, maybe I could go downstairs and sit at the doorstep for a while. It might just put me right, I think.'

'I don't see why not, Mrs Nichol.'

Just then, Mam gave a little gurgle and fell back on her pillow.

'Oh... She's in a faint again, doctor. She often does it... I'll go and get some water.'

But when I came in with it, he knocked the cup out of my hand and it spilled all over the floor.

'Quick!' he said. 'Put a mustard plaster on the back of her neck! Don't give her anything to drink! I'm going to get something from the surgery. I'll be back shortly.'

I made up the poultice as quickly as I could and was just putting it on the back of my mother's neck when she says 'Oh dear... Oh, me bairn...ye've lost your mam.' She sighed a long sigh and it was the last breath she ever took. When the doctor came back, they tell me I was just staring at her lovely face.

'Francie,' he says to me... 'Francie!'

'She stopped talkin' all of a sudden. And now I don't know what's the matter with her.'

He turned to somebody else who was standing there...I cannot remember who...and said quite matter-of-factly, 'You know, I've seen children die like this many a time. But never an adult. She was talking so well not quarter of an hour ago... Send that girl along to my surgery. I'll give her something. She's had an awful shock.' And he went out.

'Mam, can ye hear is?' I put my hand on her heart, the way I'd see people do. It wasn't going any more, her whole body was very still. A big feller who was a neighbour came in just then and picked me up in his arms. 'Howay, lass. Come wi' me. The doctor'll gi' ye somethin' to make the pain go away.' And he carried me down the stairs and all the way to the doctor's house. My poor mother was only fifty-two years old. My father would live nearly twice that long.

From then on things were very hard. It was 1904 and I was fifteen and all of my sisters were married, some to good men and others to not so good. JaneAnne was the only one of us who never went out to work. My father was still at home and working when she was growing up, and so was my mother, so JaneAnne had been a maid-of-all-work and her main job had been to look after us little'uns. JaneAnne wasn't much to look at and I'd have to say she wasn't very bright either; and although she was very house-proud, she had little else going for her. Her man, Jim Kilcaddy, had been in the navy and he was one of those clever-dicks who think they know everything when in fact they know bugger-all about anything. He was pretty stupid as well...and tight, like our JaneAnne...but at least he had a good sense of humour and he was always playing jokes on somebody, more often than not on poor JaneAnne. Neither of them amounted to much but at least they always stuck together, I'll say that. He was hard on her, the way all men were in those days, but he was always canny enough with me.

Alice, on the other hand, was both pretty and bright, and the tallest of all of us. She went into service from the time she was twelve and stayed there until she got married to Bob Charlton, a big handsome bloke who worked in a chemicals factory in Jarrow; he was a good worker but a terrible, lustful man and I hated him all my life for the disgusting things he did to me.

Lizzie was the only one I would call 'beautiful'. She was smaller than the rest of us but still very well made, and very clean in her habits when she was young, very like our Nellie. Unfortunately, when she was about fourteen somebody hit her over the head with a tin can and it affected her brain, and all she did for a long time after that was sing hymns all day long. Eventually she got better and she never sang another hymn for the rest of her life, in fact she turned right the other way, but whether it was the tin can or not, nobody ever seemed to know. When she was seventeen she was going with two boys at the same time, one a teetotaller called John Noble, the other a wild feller called Bob Elsdon who could never get enough to drink...he used to come to the window at yon time of night, shouting about how much he loved our Lizzie. Mam used to say he and our Lizzie gave her grey hairs. Lizzie would ask her over and over again, 'Mam, which one d'ye think I should marry?' And Mam always answered the same way: 'It's not my place to make your mind up for ye. Ye'll have to pick your own. You're the one who has to live with him. God knows, I'm no judge.'

Like many girls would have done, Lizzie went for 'Wild Bob' and it wasn't very long before she realised she'd made a mistake. The other feller mightn't have been the right one either, but Bob Elsdon certainly wasn't, and if he was bad before he got married, he was a whole lot worse afterwards and he gave Lizzie one hell of a time. She went to pieces and lost interest in herself, lost interest in keeping the place clean, and lost interest in their three bairns. Bob died of drink when he was little more than twenty and Lizzie then completely lost her head. She wouldn't accept help from anybody and eventually her bairns were taken off her and put in a home...which was probably just as well, because the littlest lad used to take these awful fits. Lizzie was sent to the workhouse where they made her work and look after herself, and after a while she got in with one of the inmates, and the next thing we heard she was back out and living with him. We all thought this was a terrible thing and my mother once went around and broke a cup over his head...a thing nobody ever thought she could do to anybody... After that I think the family more or less cut Lizzie off, although she wasn't much older than me.

When Mam died, the rest of us went to see Lizzie to tell her about the funeral, and we had an awful job finding her. We knew she wouldn't have any decent clothes to wear, so we took some borrowed ones for her. But she never came.

Nellie was the cleverest of all of us, and though she was the least well-built, she was still nice-looking; and she was the one who was most like Mam...always above board, never tell a lie and never hurt anybody if you can help it. She had followed Alice into service but there wasn't enough money in it, you couldn't get married and stay in service. She got the best man of the lot when she got Sep; he was good to her, he was good to Mam, and he was good to me as well.

Lily was bright as well, and canny enough looking...not startling, but more than just passable. Lily went straight into the herring business as soon as she was old enough and she stayed in fish-factory work all her life. She married a feller called Jack Bee and the two of them worked very hard on shift work at a factory in Shields to try and get enough money to make a decent home for themselves; from six o'clock at night till six o'clock in the morning, they worked, year in, year out. But although Jack was a hard worker and quite a generous chap, he drank too much. I used to mind their bairns when she was out working, but then she was having them so quickly, one after the other, that she could hardly work at all. I was working very hard myself at the time, hawking the fish and greens, besides looking after her bairns, and she wasn't very kind to me. Eventually they went to work in Hull and made it their home.

4

My father had called a few times to see my mother near the last; and afterwards, and even before she had taken ill, she had often talked to Nellie and me about having him back and giving him another chance. As it was, she didn't get around to it and I think it was probably just as well; people who knew the way he had treated her said he was rotten, nothing but a waster and would never make anything of himself. I loved my mother and I hated my father for what he'd done to her, but when all was said and done he was still my father, I had always called him 'Dad', and when I saw him on the corner of the street just standing there looking, I could never pass him by and pretend he meant nothing at all; I wouldn't know if he had anywhere to stay or anything to eat, and it was just like a knife in me when I gave him a little nod or a bit of smile and then carried on until I'd gone out of sight. I would feel his eyes on my back and know he'd be watching me until I'd gone, wondering if I was going to go back and say something to him.

My father used to do little bits of jobs here and there when he could get it, maybe a bit of bricklaying for somebody who wanted a wall built or something, or chopping a few sticks and selling them for firewood. He always had his hodman's cap on but you could still see his hair was going white here and there. My mother always felt guilty about leaving him and talked about him all the time, and whenever we hadn't seen him for a while she'd get herself really worried. Then when she found where he was, she'd send one of us round with a bit of pie or some little thing for him, to try and make his life a bit more comfortable. She wouldn't go herself because she was afraid of what he might do to her if she caught him in one of his moods. So when she heard he'd got this place in Thames Street, and knowing he'd have nobody to do for him, she told me to go around, tidy it up and give it a bit of a clean; I was about nine years old at the time.

'Watch till he goes out and then go in and get everythin' spick and

35

span for him comin' back.'

So I took around a pail and some cleaning stuff and waited around the corner till I saw him go out, then I hurried in. Mam had said I'd to have everything sparkling white, so after I'd washed his dishes and swept the floor, I found a packet of whitening powder, poured it into the pail and washed everything with it...stairs, table, chairs, pepper-pot, everything I could lay my hands on, and then right the way along the passage as well. Nobody had ever seen anything like it, it was so white. When I was done I was so pleased with myself I fetched old Mrs Hewison from next door to show her.

'Look, Mrs Hewison,' I says. 'I've got me Da's house all bonny and white. Come and see.'

As soon as Mrs Hewison clapped eyes on it, she says 'Oh my godfathers! Oh my godfathers! Francie! What've ye done..? Quick! Ye better come with me!'

She went straight for her hat and coat and put them on and said 'Howay, lass! We'll gan and see your mother afore it's too late.'

When we got home, she went running in the door. 'Eeeh, Bessie! Ye'll never believe it! There'll be murder on when he comes back and sees his house! He'll come and kick your entrance out!' She told my mother what I'd done, and my mother sent two of the other girls around to try and get rid of all the white; but it was impossible to get rid of it all. When my father came in, he nearly went mad. He sent word to my mother that I was never to go anywhere near his house again as long as I lived.

My father was always getting into trouble with his drinking and not being able to pay the rent and was always being put out of one place or another, and off and on, our JaneAnne and Jim would take him in. My mother was always happier when he was over there because she knew he was being looked after and she knew Jim wouldn't put up with him messing JaneAnne around too much. Jim loved my mother the way only a son would and I'm sure he took my father more for her sake than anything else.

My mother never asked my father for anything except once when she was ill and we were really scraping the bottom of the barrel. She told him she wanted nothing for herself or the other girls, who could then fend for themselves, as long as he'd give her a few shillings a week for me. She said if he didn't, she'd have to take him to court;

but it was just a threat, she'd never have taken anybody to court, she wouldn't have had the faintest idea how to go about it. He told her he was only able to earn a few bob for himself because work was so hard to get and bricklayers were carrying their own bricks. Nobody could ever have found out how much my father was really getting because he always subbed his wages, and by the time pay day came he had nothing to come. My mother never bothered again after that, if he didn't want to give it to her, she wouldn't make him.

Whether it was because he couldn't or whether it was because he wouldn't, I don't know, but he didn't help to bury Mam either. Those of the girls who were working had been putting so much aside for her when she was ill, just in case there was a funeral, but in the end we'd had to use it for medicine, food and rent. For years an insurance man had come and my mother would leave tuppence a week on the mantlepiece for him, but after she died we found he hadn't been putting it down in his book, and we never saw him again. My sisters all had to go into debt to give her a decent funeral.

I think Mam must have known she was going to die, because one day she said to me, 'Ye know, Francie, I think your dad might mend his ways now that he's gettin' older. If I wasn't here, he could look after you and you could look after him. There'd be just the two of you and I think ye'd get on together. Nellie and Sep will be away soon and it means I wouldn't have to worry about the two of you any more.'

I was nearly fifteen years old now and old enough to do what was right, so I made up my mind to do what my poor mother had wanted me to do, and I really thought in my own heart that my father deserved another chance. Sep wouldn't have put up with him so I told Nellie what I was intending to do, and she and I found a little room for the two of us back in South Shields. Then I found my father. 'Look, Dad,' I said. 'Why don't we pull together and see if we can make a really happy home of it. I've started back with the greens and fish again and I can make a canny bit out of it. And you must be gettin' a few bob from your odd jobs. The rent's only two bob a week. We can easy pay that between us. I'm not a bad cook now and I'll do me best to make your meals the way ye want them, and I'll keep the place spankin' clean for ye. And mebbes we can even manage to put a bit away for a rainy day... What d'ye say?'

By the look of him he wasn't doing too well on his own so I didn't think I was asking too much of him, and he agreed to my plan. It wasn't much of a place and it was wick with beetles and mice, but I was determined to make a go of it. I cleaned it from top to bottom and got a few things to make it homely and comfy, I went out every day hawking, came back every night and made the dinner, washed his clothes for him and whatnot, and I put all my earnings into the kitty. But it wasn't enough... A bottle of stout and half an ounce of baccy had to be laid on for him every day whether he was working or not, and he expected them even when he didn't come home till yon time of night, so drunk he could hardly walk. I was doing the housework and making him his breakfast before I went to work, and then hurrying back every night to make him a nice meal in the hope he'd come back for it. Things were tighter now and people don't eat so much when times are hard...especially not greens...and I was having to pawn my nice hawking clothes two and three times a week to get starting money for the next day, and having to go round the streets like a ragbag.

One Sunday I made up my mind that I'd had enough of me paying all my money into the house and him spending all his in the pub, and I decided to have it out with him. But first I'd have to get him into a good mood, so I made him a lovely breakfast of fried sausages, black pudding and tatey slices, and beside it I put an extra bottle of stout with his baccy. While he was eating I was trying to think of the best way of tackling him, and now he was nearly finished and still I hadn't decided, so I just came straight out with it. 'Dad,' I says. 'I'm ganna need some money to get the shoppin' in. D'ye think ye can give is a few shillin's?'

He looked up at me with one eye and then he slowly put his hand in his pocket, brought out a florin and put it on the table, pressing it down as though he was forcing it into the wood. When he took his hand away I picked up the florin and went out to get a loaf of bread and some milk and things. When I came back he asked for the change. I said there wasn't any. And he went mad.

'What! Ye mean to say ye spent the lot?'

'Well it wasn't very much.'

'I only lent ye it! And now I want it back.'

'I haven't got anythin'. That's why I asked you for it.'

'Pawn your bloody petticoat, then!'

'I can't. It's Sunday. It's shut. Anyway I need it to be able to get me stock in tomorrow.'

'Ye managed to find some place open!'

'That was for wor food... What did ye think it was for..? To spend on mesel'? Like you do..! I'm keepin' you, instead of you keepin' me...the way it should be!'

I know I was cheeky but I was just about past myself with him, and now I was about to find out what my mother had to take all those years. He jumped up and grabbed hold of my hair and bashed me from one end of the room to the other, and though I was strong and sturdy I couldn't defend myself against him. He gave me a hiding I would never forget, just as he said it would be. Eventually the neighbours must have heard the shouting and screaming, and several of them ran in, dragged him off, and threw him into the street. But you could still hear him shouting at me.

'I'll murder ye when I get in, ye little whoor!'

'Keep the door bolted after we go out, Francie,' big Mr Johnson from two doors up, said to me. 'Get the rent book and hide it. Don't let him get his hands on it, and the police won't be able to put ye out.'

I did as they told me but I never slept a wink at all that night and I was too frightened to go into the yard for water or to the lavatory in case he was out there waiting for me. The next morning the neighbours came back again and asked me if I'd had any breakfast.

'No... I daren't go out in case he gets in. He's probably hidin' in the coalhouse waitin' his chance.'

'We'll have a look for ye, pet,' Mrs Johnson says, 'and let ye know if it's safe. He won't dare touch ye when we're here.'

Mr Johnson and another woman went to check the yard. 'It's all right,' they said when they came back. 'He's not there. I've been right around the back. He's nowhere to be seen. Out ye go and do what ye want. An' get your kettle filled up... We'll wait till ye come back.'

They helped me then but they couldn't stay with me all day, so I sent for a friend called Liza Green and she stayed for two days and nights. After that she had to get on home; in any case she was too terrified to stay any longer, my father had kept coming back and shouting through the shutters, it was enough to give you a heart attack.

'I can see the two of ye movin' in there, ye little buggers!' his voice would come when you least expected, and the two of us would grab hold of each other. 'Get out of my house, you, or I'll fetch the police! You're trespassin' on my property..! As for you, Francie, ye bloody little bitch... I can hear ye breathin'... I know what your breath sounds like... I'm comin' in and I'm ganna teach ye to lock me out of me own house..! I'm ganna strangle ye and throw ye in the river!'

I didn't like having to send for Jim Kilcaddy, no more than my mother had ever wanted to, because there was always a right carry-on when he came. But I had no choice; I was a prisoner here, and if I didn't go out and work I'd get put out anyway. And there was nothing left to eat. So before Liza went, I made her promise to go for him.

Half an hour after she went, Jim and JaneAnne came. They brought my father in with them but he was quiet as a lamb now, I think somebody must have given him a good hiding; they said they were taking him to live with them and he had come to pack his things.

'Go on, then,' I says, getting a bit of my courage back. 'Get all your lousy old togs out of my house!'

He went and got his gear that he used for work, which was all he really had, plus a few clothes and bits and pieces, and left without saying a word; but as he was going out the door he gave me a funny look. Jim was right behind him and gave him a shove in the back. 'Howay, wi' ye. Out ye get and gi' the lass some peace.'

I wasn't going to stay there by myself, not with all those beetles, and a couple of weeks later the landlord came and said I wasn't allowed to keep it anyway. I then went to JaneAnne's, Alice's and Nellie's in turn, and told them they could have whatever they wanted from the house, anything I'd got for Dad and me, and anything left of my mother's. I wanted shot of everything so I could go. My father had already fallen out with Jim and JaneAnne so JaneAnne said I had to go and live with them until I got somewhere else.

I stayed with Jim and JaneAnne in their house in Commercial Road for six months, and hawked greens and fish harder than I'd ever done before, until the time came I couldn't stand our JaneAnne's silly spiteful ways any more. Both of them were as mean as sin and took every penny I earned. But what galled me more than anything, was having to watch Kilcaddy and my father coming back every night, drinking it all away. None of the other sisters or their husbands would have had my father, even if he'd wanted it, but he and Kilcaddy got on like the best of pals when they were in drink together, and all would be forgotten. So I left and went to live with Alice, who was living in Jarrow. But Alice wouldn't have the fish and all the mess that goes with it at her house, and I couldn't very well go back to JaneAnne's...and Nellie and Sep only had a tiny room and they were really hard up...so I had to give it up and do tatey picking, cleaning work and anything else I could get.

Our Alice, I'm sorry to say, turned out to be every bit as mean as JaneAnne, and much less considerate. Sometimes I'd be working in the tatey fields crying all day and wouldn't be able to stop myself because I was so unhappy. My mother had gone, my father was no good, and the sister who'd taken my mother's place was as mean as cat's muck. Not only did Alice want everything I worked for, she pawned the only frock I had to go out in. As it was, I went to work in rags because you can't pick tateys in anything else, but when I came back at the end of the day I wanted to have something else to put on, I didn't want to have to wait till the end of the week to redeem my clothes so I could feel better than a tramp. If you went to work in rags and came back in rags and were mucky from head to foot, especially if it had been a wet day, people used to see you coming up the street and think you were no better than muck yourself, just like they did with the pitmen. But if I'd managed to save up enough to get my clothes back on a Saturday, Alice would have them back in first thing on the Monday without fail.

One night I was so upset I was crying bitterly in the lane outside Alice's backyard, I'd come back from work and was still all mucky and in my rags, but couldn't bear to go in the house and face our Alice and her horrible husband. An old woman from across the road must have heard me and come out.

'What's the matter, love?' she says. 'By, the skies must have fallen in for ye to be cryin' like that.' She put her skinny arm around me. 'Howay, tell is what's wrong.'

I told her how unhappy I was and how I wished I was dead.

'Eeeh, a young lass like you's no call to say things like that! That's a sin..! May God forgive ye for sayin' such a thing!'

I told her I was fed up with the way my sister was treating me and that it was her who was doing the sinning. 'She's as mean as sin.'

'Oh, come on. She can't be that bad. I'm sure she's doin' the best she can for ye.'

'Ye won't say anythin' to her, will ye..? She'll go mad if she knows I've been talkin' about her.'

'Course I won't... You get yourself in and get your tea. Ye'll feel different tomorrow. You'll see.'

But she did tell Alice, and after a big row Alice put me out. So I went to Nellie's. Three days later Alice came for me and told Nellie I'd got things all out of proportion, and Nellie persuaded me to go back to save causing any trouble between her and Alice. I knew why Alice wanted me back, and it didn't have anything to do with being 'worried about me' and 'wanting to take care of me', like she'd said it was. But I knew Nellie was hard put with me there, so I went back with Alice.

Nine shillings a week I brought in, which was a lot of money, and I never got a penny back; no pocket money and nothing for clothes. Yet I was always kept hungry. I was growing and I was strong and I worked like a man and had an appetite like one, but the men always got twice as much to eat as the women, plus all the meat and the best of whatever was going. If you were a woman, it didn't matter how big or small you were, or how hard you worked, and it was the same at our Alice's. I know some men did very hard physical labour. But day after day, bent double with your apron bag full of cold wet hard tateys that felt just like stones, in the freezing wind or drizzling rain, was no pushover either.

But neither that nor our greedy Alice stopped me, I was always grateful for work when I could get it, be it in the tatey fields or anywhere else; after watching my mother grinding away all those years, for me there was no disgrace like the disgrace of being out of work, no vice like laziness; what was the point of being proud if it meant you starved to death? So I'd put on my rags and my big coarse bag apron, and off I'd go; I'd meet up with a few of my pals and away we'd go around the various farms. There were no buses and we had no money for fares anyway, so we'd walk from one farm to the other looking for work. If the farm was a long way away, sometimes they'd send a great big cart for you to pile on to, and sometimes it would be snowing on you and you'd look like a snowman by the time you got there.

We would go into the yard and find the foreman and say 'Can ye give's a day's work?' And he would look you over and say 'Right. You, you and you. In the big field over there. Six of you in that one yonder... And see yous get all the soil off..! Ye don't get paid for soil... The rest of you follow me.'

Then away we'd go, at maybe half past seven in the morning, off after the plough. Four or five of us would be following it along the furrows, picking and wiping the tateys and putting them into our aprons. The ground would sometimes be hard and frozen and your apron and clothes would soon get wet, and after a while your fingers would be swollen and stiff and your hands would have no feeling in them, they'd be just like two red scoops at the ends of your arms. All we had to eat was maybe a crust of bread we'd brought with us and a raw carrot or turnip if we came across one in the fields. Gilroys were as well known for their hard labour as for the quality of their potatoes.

The pay was one and six a day, so you didn't complain; if you didn't like it there were plenty others willing to take your place and you were never allowed to forget that. It was no use coming home and expecting a bit of sympathy from Alice, like you'd have got from our mother that would have made all the difference, because neither she nor her man cared how hard you had to work to earn your keep so long as you handed it over. I'd now given up the greens as well as the fish because you can't do something like hawking occasionally, just when it suits you, you lose your round.

Right through the tatey picking season I'd be up, dressed and out, by six in the morning. By 'dressed', I mean the tough sackcloth that would still hang together long after your fingernails had worn away or broken off and been lost among the tateys. My feet would be in a worse state than my hands by the time I got back at night; once you were in the loose heavy soil the clogs wouldn't stay on your feet, and if you didn't take them and put them to one side you'd lose them altogether. When it became too dark to pull any more, they would cart us back to the dropping-off place and we'd walk back home. When you did work like this there was no time for dreaming about being a lady, it was a luxury just to get home, washed and go to bed.

One night when they dropped us off and I had parted from my

friends and was heading home on my own, I nearly did something I can never forgive myself for... You were starving after a day in the tatey fields, especially when it was cold and the wind had been blowing up your skirt and nearly blowing you flat on your face; and when you knew there'd be next to nothing on the table when you got home, it made you feel worse than the lowest animal. Even dogs can scratch around bins and nobody says anything, but it's different if you're a human being, no matter how hungry you are; they said if Gilroys caught you pinching a tatey, you could end up in jail...

I was so hungry this particular night I hardly knew what I was doing, and when everybody had gone out of sight, I went up to a big house up a private path I'd never been along before, intending to ask for a slice of bread to eat. I knew you weren't supposed to beg and that you could be locked up it, but I was so numb I didn't care. Just as I was about to knock on the door, a great big dog on a chain came running out of its kennel and started barking and baring its teeth; great strings of slaver were coming out of its mouth and I knew if it got off it would tear me to shreds. That brought me to my senses all right, and I ran away. And by God I'm glad I did, that big dog saved my soul.

When the tatey-picking was finished I went to Hood Haggies ropery in Howdon to see if they had any jobs going. I knew it would be rough work pulling rope around all day, and I knew the women who worked there had a reputation for being rough as guts. But the work was regular, it was honest, and at least you'd have a roof over your head most of the time.

Mr Blyth was the manager there, a stout man and very strict-looking. I stood in the queue.

'Age?'

'Fifteen.'

'Too young.'

'But I've got to have work.'

He looked up.

'This is no place for you. You should still be at school. Come back when you're sixteen... Next one!'

The very next day I went back and joined the queue again. I'd put my hair up in a bun, was standing straight up, and had a frown on my face, all to make me look a bit older.

'Age?'

'Sixteen.'

'Name..?'

'Francie - '

'Wait a minute... Weren't you here the other day..?'

'Yes, sir.'

'I told you you were too young, didn't I?'

'Yes, but I'm sixteen today.'

'Hmmh. I thought as much.'

'Look, mister. If ye'll only give is one chance to show ye what I could do, that's all I'm askin'... I'll do anythin'... I'll make a good job of whatever ye give is to do. I can scrub and clean and do all sorts of things. I've put - '

'All right, all right... You seem game enough. I'll start you and see how you get on. If you're no good by the end of the week, you're out on your ear. Understand?'

'Right, sir. Thank you. That's fair enough by me. Thank you kindly.'

We started at six in the morning and finished at half past five at night, and my first job was collecting the rope that was made in the factory, and coiling it into big drums. There was rope of every description, from stuff as thin as thread all the way up to stuff thick enough to tow a battleship. It was made from hemp which was rough hairy stuff that came in huge bales from somewhere like India or China, and it played havoc with your hands. My hands were like cobs after the tatey fields and I thought they'd be fine for handling the rope, but they were red raw by the end of the first day. The women said they'd toughen up after a week or two and that I shouldn't expect to be able to do this job no bother, not after 'a soft job like pullin' tateys'.

After a month I was put on rolling the drums to the loading bay; it was one of those jobs that look dead easy when you see somebody else doing it, yet it was one of the hardest jobs in the place. It wasn't physically hard but it was so exasperating it would make you swear. The feller who showed me had obviously been doing the job for a while, either that or he was a good footballer, because he just gave the drums a kick in the right direction and away they'd go right up to where they were supposed to, and then stop. But it wasn't as simple as that, not when I tried to do it. None of the rims were perfectly round, they all had little dints, and they all tried to go where they wanted to go instead of where I wanted them to go. No two would ever go in the same direction, and some would keep stopping and then when you got them started again, they would roll away like steamrollers and make a terrible din. They could have killed somebody and people were always getting their fingers or toes crushed under them; not by me though, thank God, I only hurt myself with them. After a bit, I learned how to control them by kneeing them into place, and after two or three days although my legs were badly bruised and swollen, and my hands cut from the metal spelks off the rims, they were going roughly where they were supposed to. All the time I was careful never to let on to Mr Blyth, and I'd always smile when he came by even though I might have just got a steel spelk three-quarters of an inch long in my hand. He was a fair man but he was hard enough. I suppose he had to be with all the women he had to deal with; they were a far rougher lot to handle than any amount of men would have been, and I pitied some of the young lads they got hold of, they did some awful things to the poor little buggers.

When I'd been on the drums for a while Mr Blyth took me off and put me on the machines, I don't think anybody could have done drum-rolling for very long without going mad. My new job would be more interesting and would put an extra shilling on to my wages if I could work it fast enough, so it was a kind of promotion. I had to feed the raw stuff into a machine and it would come out the other end as rope. It was just like rough wool, and whether it was something they put on it, or whether it was just the way it came, I don't know, but clouds of white powder would come off it and you would be covered in it; it got into your hair and up your nose and made you cough, and you had to work with your mouth shut and learn when to breathe and when not.

The hardest part of this job was sorting out the tangles. Every now and then the fibres would have knots in them and sometimes they'd get all ravelled up in the rollers and I'd have to lift the rollers up with a big jemmy to free them. If this didn't work, I'd have to climb up on the machine and pull the tangles apart with my hands, and chuck the rubbish stuff into these big cans by the side. If you weren't quick enough and the machines were still going, the fibre would wind itself round and round and make a hell of a mess and the machine would be labouring and making a funny noise until eventually it stopped altogether. Then there'd be hell on because somebody further down the line couldn't get on with their work, and somebody further up the line couldn't get on with theirs, and you'd have to send for the fitter to take the cover off and separate the rollers to get everything out.

Naturally you always tried to unravel the knots without switching the machine off, because if you did you'd have Mr Blyth and half a dozen others shouting and cursing. Some of the skilled men would be paid by the length or weight of the rope they turned out, so if you slowed them down even for five minutes, there'd be the devil to pay. Everybody was thinking about getting on with the job and producing piles and piles of ropes for Haggies, nobody was thinking about having an accident. Rope was what mattered, not safety, and there were so many ways you could happen an accident if you didn't watch out. Even the raw fibres when they were stretched would be so hard and tight and sharp like wire, that you could very easily lose your fingers; it moved so fast you'd only need to look away for a moment.

I was no good at machines; I didn't know what to pull and what to push, whether to screw this knob in or that one out, which lever you had to twist up and which one you had to twist down, and one day I got myself into a terrible mess with a huge tangle up on top. The machine jammed and came to a halt and I was first of all trying to get it started again so I wouldn't have everybody coming down on me like a ton of bricks. I was pulling this and pressing that and all of a sudden this big iron handle came down and split my hand nearly in two. There was blood everywhere...on the machine, on the rope stuff...and dripping down on to the floor. I was scared stiff I'd get the sack, so I bound my hand round with some rope strands to make a bandage, mopped up the blood on the machine and on the floor with some more, and chucked it away out of sight. This canny feller who'd seen what had happened, left his own machine which he wasn't supposed to do, and came over and put my machine right. By this time Mr Blyth had arrived to see what had caused the stoppage and I told him everything was all right now and I tried to keep my hand behind my back. But when he said 'Go on, then. Get on with it. Let's see you,' I had to bring my hand to the front and he saw the blood.

'What on earth have you done?'.

'Nothin', Mr Blyth. It's all right now. It was just a little cut. It's stopped now.'

'Give it here.' He took my hand and had a look at it, by now it had swollen to nearly twice its normal size.

'Away you go to the cabin. Somebody'll have a look at it and put a dressing on for you.'

'It's grand now. It's not even hurtin'.' It was though, it was hurting like hell.

'Never mind. Go on, off you get. I'll see you when you get back.'

I thought 'That's it. I've had it now.'

I went to the first aid cabin and they put some iodine on and bandaged it up properly.

'Will I have had it now?' I asked the one who was writing it down in the book.

'It's got nowt to do with us, pet. Mr Blyth's the one to see about that... I don't see why though. It's not as though you've lost your whole hand or anythin'... I'd say you'll probably be all right.'

'Oh, thanks, mister. Thanks very much. It feels fine now... Ye can write that down in your book if ye want.'

When I went back to my place on the machine I made sure Mr Blyth wasn't around, and quickly got on with what I was doing before, hoping if he came by he'd just think 'She seems to be managing all right. I'll just leave her to get on with it.'

Mr Blyth must have been busy with something else because he didn't come back, but I saw the foreman watching me very carefully for a long while. Luckily for me the machine behaved itself so I was able to do what I had to do nearly with one hand, and nobody said anything more either that day or after, but I was never able to make the shilling bonus. I was a hard worker but it was all I could do to keep the damned machine running at all, let alone get it to go any faster.

One day Mr Blyth came up and said 'I don't know what's the matter with you, Nichol. You're too slow to catch cold. Goodness only knows what kind of mother you've got. You - '

'Don't you dare talk about my mother, mister! I haven't got one anymore. So don't ever say anythin' about her. I mean it, mind ye! I'm warnin' ye!'

He just ups and away without a word and I thought I'd had my chips for certain; but he didn't come back or anything so I just got on with my work. I was catching up this flaming hemp wool stuff and wafting away the clouds of powder, and the tears were streaming down my face. 'Here I am,' I thought, 'workin' in this awful place all day and havin' to go home to another one.'

A couple of hours later Mr Blyth did come back, I knew it was him but I just carried on and didn't look around or say a word.

'I'm sorry for what I said before,' he says after a while. 'But I have to chivvy people up. That's my job.'

'Ye should be sorry an' all!' I blurted out.

'There you are... You cannot help yourself. You're too damned cheeky.'

'Ye can sack me if ye want,' I said. 'But I'm tellin' ye this... When I had a mother, I had a good'un...one every bit as good as yours. She never had much, but she wasn't lazy. And she never brought me up to be, either.'

I think he was sorry then because he went away. A few days later he came up again and said he'd only been trying to spur me on because he knew I needed the bonus, and that he was going to shift me to another job now. This one was shoving the hemp through a kind of mangle where it came out of the other side like thread...very strong thread, you couldn't have broken it with your teeth and it was sharper than a razor. It was an easier job than the last and I even managed to get an extra two shillings a week out of it, but the thread came through at a hell of a rate, much faster than the rope, and you had to keep your eyes on it all the time to make sure it was exactly the right thickness; by the time I went home at night, wherever I looked I could see this purplish red line going across everything.

After I hurt my hand I'd had a bit of a do with Alice, and although she was still taking my basic wage of seven shillings a week off me, if I earned a bonus I was allowed to keep it. It left me with very little, sometimes with nothing, and I wouldn't waste any of it on tram fares. I'd rather walk miles and miles every week, and spend it on a skirt or a blouse.

I had a boyfriend who used to come and meet me off the ferry every night, a very respectable lad, and I liked him, but I was never allowed out after nine at night, so we could never catch the second half of the pictures no matter what was on or how much we'd been dying to see it. There was never any point in going to see mysteries unless we knew somebody else who was going to see it who'd be able to tell us what happened in the end. The picture place we went to was called the 'Penny Gaff', it was just a big shop and there were no seats or anything. He must have been fed up with never getting his money's worth but he never complained. One night we were going to go to Sunderland to see a show and I brought him back with me from work and he was waiting outside for me to get washed and ready, when Alice comes up and says 'Where d'ye think you're goin'?'

'I'm goin' to the variety show at the Empire.'

'You're not doin' any such thing!'

'Why not?'

'Because ye've got no clothes. That's why not.'

'What d'ye mean?'

'They're all at the pawnshop.'

'How did they get there..? They're my clothes. I paid for them out of my bonus money. Ye've no right to do that!'

'You surely don't think the little you bring in keeps ye, do ye?'

There was no point arguing. I went out and told the lad I had toothache, there was no way I could go to the Sunderland Empire with the clothes I worked in at Haggies.

So many times did Alice do things like that, stopping me going out for one reason or another, and never letting me out more than twice a week, that the lad dropped me in the end, and who could blame him. It wasn't that she had anything against having a good time, because she liked a singsong and didn't mind a bit of carry-on herself, and she was very friendly with people; I think it was because she could never get out herself because of having so many kids and being so hard up, and couldn't stand the thought of me doing so.

I could have had plenty of lads when I worked at the ropery, they were always asking me out, and I could hardly say they weren't good enough for me because they worked at Haggies when I worked there myself; but what was the point. Mam had been strict with me, and she'd been just as strict with my sisters, but it's different coming from a sister than coming from your own mother. Lizzie might have brought shame on the whole family, but that didn't mean I was just waiting my chance to do the same thing. But because I was the youngest, they all stuck their neb in. In any case, I was safer out of the house than in it, with a husband like hers.

From what I saw, everybody who worked at Haggies earned every penny they got, and yet they were always trying to get overtime or get put on this job or that where they thought they might be able to get an extra shilling to put in their pocket. There were some tough people worked in the ropery, and if they thought somebody had been shown any favours, their life wouldn't be worth living. They did some rotten things to each other and I wouldn't like to speak about the things a gang of women can do when there's no men about...you could see why people classed you as 'low' if you worked at Haggies. They had their own ideas of what was right and what was wrong and dealt out their own kind of justice, and if you were on the receiving end you might have every reason to feel sorry for yourself. Every one of them came from the poorest parts and they thought and acted the way they were brought up, so you couldn't really blame them for their terrible cursing and swearing. They used to pass their dinner time kicking an old tin or playing some game squabbling over ha'pennies because they had nothing better to do. But when you got to know them, most of them were canny people and as good as you'd find anywhere else, men and women alike. One of them saved my life one day...

I used to wear my shawl to try to keep the fibres and dirt out of my hair, hemp is filthy stuff, and also to stop my hair getting caught in the machine and ending up as rope, and I was bending over the machine checking something when somebody came by carrying a bale of hemp and bumped against me. My head went right over towards what they called the 'gob', and my shawl got caught up in it. The shawl was always tied in a knot around my neck so that it wouldn't come off, and now it was being sucked in and I was slowly being strangled. By the time I realised what had happened, it was so tight around my neck that I couldn't speak. I couldn't yell or scream or anything. My face felt as though it was ready to burst and my whole head was going closer and closer into the machine and I was pulling back as hard as I could with my hands; but it was no good, the more I pulled back, the tighter it got. Suddenly this old feller who was working up above, saw what was going on and quick as a flash jumped straight down on to the machine, even though they were all going and he could easily have had both his legs broken. He pressed the button to stop the machine, but even with it stopped I was still choked tight.

'Stay where ye are, hinny!' he shouts. 'Don't move an inch. I'll soon have ye free.' He then got a knife from somewhere and cut the shawl off my neck. 'Ye'll be all right now,' he said. 'Say nowt to nobody.' And away he went back up to his own job.

Although Alice's meanness got under my skin, I could put up with it because I'd never been used to having very much anyway, and it wasn't as though it was being spent on drink or on herself; I knew it all went into the house one way or another. But my brother-in-law Bob Charlton was a different kettle of fish altogether, and he caused me some terrible embarrassment. Everybody except our Alice, his own wife, knew how randy he was, and I think she must have just closed her eyes to it at times, because she wasn't stupid. I'm not saying she knew what he did to me but I can't be certain she didn't either... I'd wake up in the middle of the night with the bedclothes pulled down and see this big feller standing at the bottom of me bed, grasping the rail and staring at me with a horrible look in his eyes. He did some awful things to me and I'd be terrified in case our Alice found out and thought I was leading him on; I knew she'd have taken his word against mine, whatever he said. In the finish I couldn't stand it any more and went and told Nellie. Nellie said she'd ask Sep if I could stay with them, when he came home from work. She didn't say she believed me and she didn't say she didn't, but I'm sure she did.

'Please yoursel', Nellie,' Sep said when she asked him. 'If you think we can manage, it's all right wi' me.'

So I moved in and shared their room in Nixon Street, and six months later I was still with them when they shifted to Aberdeen Terrace which was still just one room but a bigger one. Nellie was strict enough but they were both very kind to me; Nellie treated me like a daughter, and Sep treated me as though I was his little sister. I had to give up the ropery when I went to live with them because Nellie wouldn't have it, she'd rather me go into service, or at least do cleaning work of some kind. When I went to Mr Blyth to give my notice in, I asked him for a reference, Nellie had said at least it would be better than nothing.

'A reference? Why should I give you a reference..? What do you think it is? We don't give references here. This is a rope-works, not a hotel.'

I was frank with him and told him what Nellie had said about working there, and that if I continued at the ropery she'd put me out. I thought he wouldn't like that one bit, but to my surprise he said 'Maybe she's right... In any case, she's your sister. And if she's responsible for you, you'll have to do what she tells you. But I won't give you a reference from here. A reference from this place would condemn you... But I could give you one from my home address...a character reference if that would suit you.'

'Thank you! It would! That's just what I wanted. I'm much obliged.'

'Look, Nichol... "Francie", isn't it..? My wife and I have no children of our own. We'll take you in and look after you. You can do the housework. And if you still wanted a character reference, either my wife or myself could give you one.'

But I thought to myself, 'This man's practically a stranger... I've already had trouble with the man at one place... I've got a nice place with our Nellie. I don't want to be jumpin' into the fire again.' So I said 'No thanks... Thankin' you all the same, but it might upset my sister if I left her.'

He looked at me for a while and then he said 'All right... If you change your mind, you can let me know.'

When I left at the end of the week he gave me a fortnight's money to buy myself a maid's clothes, and a character reference on top, and afterwards I thought he'd probably meant no harm, it was probably just me; but I wasn't prepared to take the chance, not after Bob Charlton.

After I left Haggies I couldn't get any work for a while and felt very guilty living off Nellie and Sep, so when a place in service came up in Wallsend, I took it.

The Master of the house wasn't really the master, he was just a nervous little watchmaker, but he was kind to me when he dared, and I appreciated it. The real boss was the lady of the house, who had burst a vein or something in her leg and couldn't walk, and she was a right bitch. She was one of those people who could walk when they wanted to, and be absolutely helpless when it suited them, somebody who would never have got burnt if the house had caught fire. They had a guest house, a fine big house it was, and they took in guests and did fancy meals.

He was quite an old man, much older than her, and she kept him and me right under her thumb. I'd worked in tatey fields, I'd worked in a ropery and done other hard work as well, and although I'd often been hungry, I'd never fainted either from that or from working too hard; yet more than once it happened after I started at this place. At least wherever else I'd worked I'd always been able to get to my bed at night, and I'd nearly always be there by ten o'clock; here I was never in it before one o'clock in the morning, and I was never still in it after half past five.

One morning the old man had jammed the venetian blinds trying to get them open, and they were all cock-eyed, the cord was in a big tangle, and neither of us could get them up or down. Then Madam came in... As soon as she saw the blinds she gave such a screech you'd think he'd pulled half the house down.

'Who did that..! Who made that dreadful mess of my expensive blinds?'

He was shaking like a leaf and stammering and stuttering so I said it was me.

Without a word she ran straight over to her sewing box, pulled out a great big pair of draper's scissors, and instead of cutting the cord, which was what I thought she was going to do, she grabbed hold of my neck. She was in a terrible rage as though she was out of her mind, and I realised why the old feller had been so slow in owning up.

'I'm going to cut your stupid clumsy fingers off! They're no use to anybody! And I'm going to feed them to the dogs..! And then, thank God, she said '...if it ever happens again!' She then let go and rushed out. He looked at me and I looked at him, and I didn't know whether to strangle him or feel sorry for him. It's a wonder she hadn't burst a blood vessel in her head, let alone her leg.

When I was taken on, the job was supposed to be housework only...sweeping, dusting, cleaning, polishing the brasses and things like that; no laundering or cooking. But one day she set me on washing these socks, nineteen of them there were, all men's and all thick wool. I don't know where they all came from, whether they were the old man's and she'd been saving them all up, or what, but the feet were caked hard with sweat. It took me so long, with all the steam in my face while I was bending over this big sink and the bloody awful smell up my nose all the time, that I came over all funny and must have passed out. When I came to, she was standing there looking at me and she was in a right tizzy.

'I'm sorry, madam,' I said, 'but I'm afraid this job's too heavy for me. All them socks...'

Now that she saw I was all right, all her hoity-toitiness came back.

'All those beautiful stockings are ruined! They're boiled dry...every last one of them!'

I thought to myself, 'That's no great loss.'

'You'll have to pay for them out of your wages.'

I'd had enough of this, she was stark raving mad. 'I want to give in my notice,' I said.

'I refuse to accept it! You're an ungrateful, worthless little upstart! I knew that from the moment I set eyes on you. I could see from your cheeky face that you'd be nothing but trouble. But out of the goodness of my heart I thought I would give you a chance. Obviously I made a very big mistake!'

So I carried on, and every few days I was fainting with the overwork. But it didn't bother her now, and I just had to put up with it and with every kind of insult she could sling at me, because I didn't want to go and be a burden on our Nellie. One night, because I hadn't been able to get over to Nellie's for several weeks, Nellie had come to see if there was anything the matter. But the woman wouldn't let her in, she said I was asleep in bed. The truth was I'd had to lie down for a while because I'd fainted again and she just didn't want anybody to know.

But the time came when I couldn't stick it any more. I was only getting every other Sunday off, and that wasn't until after tea, and even then I had to be back by nine. It wasn't worth it for three shillings a week. I made up my mind to go back to Nellie's and look harder than ever for work, I'd do anything rather than spend another day in this awful woman's house. One day she sent me out for a message and I put on as many clothes as I could without rousing her suspicions, and went straight to Nellie's.

When I got there I said 'Oh, Nellie. I can't bear to stay in that house a minute longer. The work's killin' is. Ye've no idea what that woman's like.'

Nellie gave me a hug and made me a cup of tea and then she said 'You know you'll have to go back, pet, don't you? You have to do the honourable thing and give proper notice.'

'Oh, no, Nellie... I've tried but she won't take it.'

'Then do it just this once more. Make it to begin as soon as you get back, and that'll have to do her.'

When I went back and gave in my notice, the woman got really nasty. 'And when do you think you're going, may I ask?'

'At the end of the week. I can't stay any longer than that.'

'Then you get nothing!' she said. 'And you shall have none of your clothes or belongings. You'll leave here with nothing!'

And that's what happened. I worked the week and came away with nothing; my wages had gone on the socks, and all my personal belongings were kept to pay for other things I was supposed to have done or not done. Nellie took me back and told me she'd go and see the lady of the house herself and explain that I couldn't work there any more, and ask for all my things. But Nellie was no match for that tartar, she was too meek and mild, just like my mother was. She went, but she couldn't get any of my wages that were owing or any of my bits and pieces and my mementoes of my mam. I never saw her or any of my belongings again, she probably chucked them all in the bin.

I'd always been a very chirpy sort of a body, I had to be or I couldn't have done so well at the hawking or held my own at the ropery; but that woman took my confidence away for a long time. She wore me down with all the work and hardly any sleep, and she ground me down with all her insults and her spite; and because I was living in her house, surrounded by all her things and not able to see any of my own people, she nearly got the better of me.

I hadn't been back at Nellie's very long before I got several cleaning jobs and was making about four shillings a week, all of which I gave to her. She took it but she never spent a penny of it, it all went into a ticket at the C.W.S. for clothes for me. I knew things were very hard for them and I said 'Look, Nellie. I can't have Sep workin' for me as well as you.' But neither of them took any notice; Nellie was more concerned that I got myself dressed up and got a decent lad more than anything else, she wanted me to take up with Johnny

Robinson again, and Sep went along with whatever Nellie wanted.

But things got harder and harder for them and in the end Sep decided to go and look for a job in Canada, they were always advertising for men to go there, it was supposed to be a 'land of opportunity'; and when he got something he would send for Nellie, and if I wanted to come as well, I'd be welcome.

5

I must have only been ten when I first met Johnny Robinson, when we were kids playing in the street. He was good looking and all the girls liked him, so when he ran after you to grab you and give you a kiss, you made sure you never ran too fast.

They used to say the Robinsons owned half of South Shields, certainly they had property all over and some very large lodging houses. They were hard and they were tough and they had made their money from prize-fighting; in Shields, the very name 'Robinson' meant boxing and property. Johnny's father, Henry Robinson, had been heavyweight champion of the North, and his Uncle Johnny had been lightweight champion of the whole of England. They fought in the 1870's, the 80's and the 90's; prizefighters fought nearly all their lives in those days, from the time they were lads till the time they were fifty or more years old. According to Johnny, his grandfather, Peter, the biggest and the hardest of the lot of them, was the one who brought the Robinsons to Shields; he'd made his money in travelling boxing booths at fairgrounds offering to fight any man in the world.

Young Johnny, now that he was a young man, was quiet and shy. He was tall and slim and very healthy looking, dark-haired and had lovely grey eyes. When I was younger I used to knock about with a lad called Dickie Jennings. One day Johnny had come up and said 'I'm taking you off him.'

I said to him, 'You're kiddin' yoursel' though, aren't ye?'

He says 'I bet I do.' He just walked up to Dickie and told him to beat it, and if that's all Dickie was made of, maybe that was the best place for him. From then I was Johnny's girl, but only because I wanted to be all along.

When I used to do the hawking I'd always steered clear of the Robinsons' places if I could, especially the big house where they lived, but I was once going past Mrs Robinson's lodging house when she was coming out; it would be about three years ago when my mother was still alive...

'Is that you, Francie Nichol?' she says in this big strong voice that she had.

'Yes, Mrs Robinson.'

'What have you got there?'

'Oh, just some prawns and - '

'Let's have a look,' she says, coming up and looking in my basket. 'I'll have some of those. I'm going over home. Walk along with me and you can come in for a sup of tea.'

'I'm very grateful to you, Mrs Robinson. But I cannot stop till me basket's empty.'

'Well, all right. I'll take the whole lot. My gang'll soon make short work of them.' She took another look. 'Hmmh, there's scarcely enough to cover a plate. I'll chuck them in the pot.'

I knew she made broths and stews and sold it to the lodgers.

'Righto, thank ye,' I said. And I followed her home.

'Look who I've brought!' she says as she went in. 'Little Francie... You know...Bessie Nichol's youngest girl.'

Mr Robinson was sitting by the fire with his paper. 'Hello, Francie,' he says. 'Come and sit yoursel' down by the fire and show us what ye've got in your basket.' He was a very big and powerful looking man, but he was friendly. 'My, them look good... Still for sale are they?'

I looked at Mrs Robinson.

'Not now they're not,' she says.

'Pity. I could've done with those for me tea. Go down well with a glass of stout, they would... Why don't ye come around and play with our Lily and Mary Ellen sometime, Francie?'

'When like?'

'Come round tonight, if ye want. Ye can play 'shows' together.'

So I said yes; I might see Johnny and it was great to be in a house like this. I hurried back home and when I got there my mother had already set my small greens out, so I practically ran around the streets with them, got back, got washed, and went back to the Robinsons'. Mr Robinson made us some soup and gave us some bread, and we had a great time. When it came time to go Mrs Robinson said 'See you come to the lodging houses when you're down this way in future. It'll be a good bit of business for you.'

And I did and it was well worth the trouble. And over the next year or two Johnny and me became good friends although I never thought anything could come of it, what with me being a poor Protestant and him being a Catholic from a wealthy and respected family; and our Lizzie didn't help any. I'd got her work in one of their lodging houses, cleaning up and doing the beds and things like that, and she went and misbehaved with one of the lodgers and got herself in trouble. Nobody said anything about it, not to me anyway, but Johnny's father had said to him, 'Mind, you're to have nothin' more to do with that other Nichol girl, from now on, d'ye hear..? What one sister does, sooner or later the others'll do.'

One night Johnny and me were talking in the street and I asked him if he had a pin he could lend me...lads used to stick pins down the top of their lapels because they thought it made them look tough; we'd been messing about and my collar had come away, and my mother would have gone mad if I'd gone back with it like that. Johnny slowly took one from his lapel, and just as I was reaching for it he opened his hand and let it fall to the ground. Then he stamped on it and ground it in with his boot.

'What did ye do that for?' I said to him.

'Because you're not even worth that pin.'

'What!'

'I said you're not worth it. You don't mean anything to me any more.'

You could have knocked me down with a feather...

'Oh, well...if that's the way ye feel. I suppose there's no point me bein' here, is there..? That's it then, is it...as far as your concerned, Johnny?'

'Yes,' he said, and turned his back.

'Right, that's fine by me... I'm through with you as well, then.'

He had given no explanation at all for his attitude and obviously wasn't going to, so I just walked away and that was the end of it. Why he'd done it, I hadn't the faintest idea, but I certainly wasn't going to get down on bended knee to find out. If that was the way he wanted it, then that's the way it would be. He wasn't the only fish in the sea. It was years before I found out why he'd been so nasty to me.

It was 1909 and I was nineteen and standing outside the Gazette office, looking at the notice board for jobs in South Shields; Nellie had moved back to South Shields after Sep went to Canada and I was now looking for something on this side of the Tyne, something for a woman rather than for a girl. I still couldn't read very well so must have been standing there for quite some time when suddenly a voice spoke up.

'Hello..! Is that you, Francie?'

I turned around to see Johnny's oldest brother, Harry.

'What have you been doing with yourself? How are you keeping? It's ages since we've seen you.' He was quite full of himself. 'I'm a blacksmith now, you know.'

'Are ye? That's good... Served your time and all that, have ye?'

'Aye, I have. I've got my own lodging house as well. In Barrington Street, next to the Trustee Bank... When did you come back to Shields..? You must come and see my Mam and Dad.'

No matter how poor we were, I'd always been clean and decently turned out; because of that, and because I was plucky and a hard worker, I think Mrs Robinson had always been quite taken with me. I still didn't know how they'd felt about our Lizzie and what they'd said to Johnny, all I knew was that I wasn't going to be made a fool of by him again.

'No, Harry. I can't. I'd like to see your mother and father but - '

'But what?'

'I don't want it to look as though I was pushin' meself. Your Johnny might be there. He might think - '

'Our Johnny..? Don't be daft..! Anyway, he'll be at work. He's serving his time at the shipyard to be a plater and riveter... It's only three o'clock. You'll be gone long before he gets back. I cannot go back and tell my mother I've seen you and that you're not going to come up and see her!'

'All right then, Harry. Just for a little while...so they'll not think I'm unsociable.'

And I went. And what a welcome I received! You'd think I'd come back from the dead...

'Well, well, if it isn't little Francie..! And not too little at that now, I must say. Getting to be a big girl now, eh, Henry?'

'You're tellin' me..! Come in and give us a look at ye... Big girl, all right. A fine big lass.'

'Now... Tell us what's been happening to you and your family...

We heard your poor mother died, God bless her... Here, have some tea... Come on, it'll warm you up.'

'Oh, no thanks, Mrs Robinson. I'm late already. I have to be gettin' back. Our Nellie'll be gettin' worried. I said I wouldn't be long.'

'Rubbish! There's plenty of time... You tell her you've been to see Mrs Robinson. Now don't you worry, d'you hear..? Here now...'

She poured a bit of the tea from her own mug into a saucer and passed the saucer to me.

'Drink that up. It'll keep you going till you get home for your meal.'

Anybody lucky enough to be invited to drink tea with Mrs Robinson always got it the same way, on a saucer poured straight from the mug she'd been drinking from. And if you didn't like it like that, you could bloody-well lump it because nobody stood up to Sarah Robinson, nobody except Mr Robinson, that is. And nobody back-chatted him. Henry Robinson was a quiet man and didn't like any fuss, but he was a very tough man and would easily have flattened any man I'd ever met...in the ropery, on the docks or anywhere else. He never messed about with anything or anybody; the rule was, if he got out of his chair to settle an argument, somebody went to the floorboards before he sat down again. And that would have meant Mrs Robinson as well if she'd given him cause enough, even though she was mighty herself.

'Thank you, Mrs Robinson,' I said. 'But I must go straight after this.'

'What are you doing now? Are you still selling the greens and fish? We haven't seen you round here for a long time.'

I told her I'd been living in North Shields but that I was back here now.

'Have you got yourself a job yet?'

'No, she hasn't,' Harry perked up. 'That's where I met her. Outside the Gazette office looking for one.'

'Is that so..? I'm sure we could use a hard worker. Couldn't we, Henry?'

'Aye, we could. We're always lookin' for somebody reliable for the lodgin' houses.'

Before I got a chance to answer, the door opened and Johnny was standing there looking at me. He was a lot darker now, especially around the eyes, and he'd had his hair cropped short at the sides; he was taller and prouder and very determined looking... He was a man now.

He wasn't smiling or anything but just looking straight at me. He didn't say a word, he just turned away, took his jacket off and started washing himself at the sink. Nobody said anything to him. Mr Robinson was writing something in his record book and Mrs Robinson was busying herself with the table. Johnny's muffler was lying on the floor where he'd tossed it, and he was flushing his face under the tap. His muscles were going up and down his arms as he was flinging the cold water over himself, his vest was dripping wet but he still didn't take it off. He couldn't have cared less about me, anybody could see that.

I got up. 'T'ta then, Mrs Robinson. I'll be on me way now. I've stayed too long as it is... T'ta, Mr Robinson... T'ta, Harry.'

'Look after yoursel', pet.'

I was out the door in no time. It was easy to take your leave of the Robinsons, they never wasted time setting you to the door, you just got up and got out.

'Don't forget what I told ye,' Mrs Robinson shouted after me. 'Have a think about it and let we know.'

I had no fare, it was quite dark and a long way to walk home, and I was hurrying up Mill Hill when I heard long striding footsteps behind me.

'Francie..! It's me...Johnny.'

'Oh..? Hello, Johnny.'

We walked up the hill together without speaking a word but he was obviously wanting to say something. When we got to the top he says 'How are you getting on?'

'Fine, thanks. How's yourself?'

'I'd set you home, Francie. But it'll have to be by the back ways.'

'Why's that?'

'I don't want to be seen.'

'If I'm not good enough for ye to set me the front ways, Johnny Robinson, then ye'll set me no ways at all. Ye can keep your own counsel.'

I knew in my mind that I still loved him so much I'd have gone anywhere with him, any way he pleased.

'I can't. I'm not allowed to. I'm matched to fight and I can't be seen with a woman. That's the way it is with boxers. My father would go mad if anybody told him.'

'Well, all right then...if that's the case.'

I just kept walking my normal way and he said nothing more, but he still stayed with me, maybe just a pace behind and a bit to the side, but if I'd reached out I could have touched him. When we got to Nellie's I told him he wouldn't be able to come in because our Nellie was very particular about who I went out with.

He just raised his eyebrow and made a funny expression and we sat down on the doorstep together for a while.

'When can I see you again, Francie?'

'That's up to you.'

'What about next week..? Saturday?'

'I think that should be all right. I don't think I've anythin' special on that night... What time were ye thinkin' about?'

'When I finish training.'

'What time will that be?'

'I don't know... When my dad says... About seven o'clock or quarter to eight, I expect.'

'Fair enough. Just come to the house and give a whistle and I'll know it's you.'

'I'm not a very good whistler. I can whistle tunes but I can't whistle very loud like for a dog or anything. I haven't got holes in my teeth like some of the buggers you get in the street, ones that just about pierce your eardrums.'

'Knock on the door, then. Everythin' is quite above board here... But before I see ye again, there's one thing I must know... Why did ye do the thing ye done with that pin?'

'Well, I'll tell you,' he says. 'It wasn't my fault. It was because of what my father said.'

He then told me everything that had been said about our Lizzie.

'Has your father got no sense..? It doesn't say at all that because one sister does somethin', that the others will all go and do the very same thing. Do brothers..? Is that what they do..? You should be able to answer that. Ye've got two of them.'

'All right then... But it'll be a long time before I can get married.'

'Who's talkin' about gettin' married..? I'm not talkin' about gettin' married. I just thought ye wanted see me and mebbes go out now and again.'

'Fair enough. Goodnight then, Francie. I'll see you on Saturday.'

'Goodnight, Johnny.'

When I got in, Nellie told me off for being out so late and keeping somebody talking outside at that time of night. It was half past eight.

'It was Johnny..! Johnny Robinson..! And I've got an offer of a job at his brother Harry's house.'

I didn't dare tell her it was a common lodging house, I knew she'd never allow me inside one of those places, not after what happened to Lizzie; the funny thing was that when it came down to it, the Nichols didn't seem to think all that differently to the Robinsons.

'All right then, Francie. We'll see, we'll see. But next time the lad comes, bring him in and let's have a look at him.'

She'd forgotten Johnny after all these years. She'd get a shock when she saw how he'd grown up and how tall and handsome he was.

When he came on the Saturday and I asked him in, Nellie took to him straight away; he was shy and she liked that. Johnny and I then went out and had a good time and he told me the Robinsons wanted me to start in Harry's lodging house, it was quite near Mill Street where they lived; 'mucking out', they called it, but it was just the usual cleaning, dusting and polishing...no bother at all to me.

After a couple of months of going out with Johnny, he asked if I'd mind waiting a while before getting married.

'How long do ye mean, Johnny?'

'I don't know. But it'll be quite a time yet because of the boxing... Would you wait?'

'No, I certainly wouldn't. I'm not waitin' donkey's years for you or anybody else. D'ye think I'm soft in the head or somethin'..? D'ye think I could never get anybody else but you..? Is that what ye all think..? No, if somebody comes along who's just as good as you, and I like him as much as I like you, I'll just marry him instead.'

He just shrugged his shoulders. 'Please yourself, Francie. You do the best you can. Nobody could blame you for that.' And he just walked off.

A couple of weeks later I found I was in the family way and I didn't know whether it was his fault or mine. What I did know was that Nellie had many a time told me that if I ever got myself into any kind of trouble, she'd put me out. She said they had no money to be looking after a whole lot of illegitimate kids, and the family wanted no more disgrace brought on it, there'd been enough of that already.

'I'm warning you, Francie,' she would say. 'Any of you-know-what kind of monkey business, and ye'll have to go into the workhouse. It takes me all my time to cope as it is.'

Now that it had happened, I didn't know which way to turn. My pride wouldn't allow me to tell Johnny after what he'd said the last time I saw him, and I daren't tell Nellie out of fear of what she might do. I thought JaneAnne would be the best one to go to, I had to go to somebody, and she was the eldest and had seen quite a lot one way or another... I should have had my head examined...

JaneAnne gave me her solemn promise she wouldn't tell a soul, especially not our Nellie.

'Go home and get some Epsom salts and drink a large glassful while you're sittin' in a tub of hot water. Make it as hot as you can bear and try not to be sick. Keep it in. That might do the trick.' That was her advice.

My mind was much eased so I thanked her for being a good eldest sister and giving me her advice, and especially for promising to keep it a secret.

Sep was out of his time now and earning good money as a blacksmith in Canada and he was sending whatever he could to Nellie while he was getting a house ready for her to come out to. Nellie was clever and she was smart, and as soon as she'd been able to get herself into service, she had left the fishhouse; she never did hawking or ropery work or anything like that; she was the proudest of us all

'Don't worry about me,' I'd say when she used to go on about our Lizzie. 'I'll never do anythin' like that.'

And now I had, and not only was I scared about what was going to happen to me now, I was very sorry for Nellie who didn't deserve any more trouble.

As soon as Nellie got a bit of money from Sep, instead of spending what little extra she had on herself to make herself comfortable, whenever she could she would make up a little hamper of food and take it to all the other sisters in turn; she'd never give any of them money because she knew what would have happened to it...straight down the sink in most cases.

Although I didn't know it at the time, and I'm sure our JaneAnne didn't know it either, the night of my visit happened to be the night of JaneAnne's turn for the hamper, and JaneAnne was so grateful that she blabbed, she told Nellie everything.

'When ye go up home, you're in for a shock with our Francie,' she'd said to our Nellie just as she was about to leave.

'What do you mean?'

'She's fallen.'

'She's what!'

'That's that Johnny Robinson for ye... He'll be the one. I'll bet ye anythin' ye like.'

By the time Nellie came back I was tucked up in bed trying to pretend I was asleep. She didn't say 'Are you awake?' or anything like that. Without turning around, as she was taking her hat and coat off, she says 'You're in bed a lot sooner than usual, Francie. What's the matter with you?'

'I've got a bad cold, Nellie. I'm tryin' to sweat it out of me system. I thought a good night's sleep might help is get rid of it.'

'I know what's wrong with you, Francie Nichol..! I know the secret..! You won't sleep that one off, my girl.'

'What?'

'Don't play dumb with me, Francie..! Open your eyes! I want some answers!'

'How did ye know?'

'I've just been to our Jinny's.'

'She promised..! She...'

'What I want to know is what you're planning to do about it..? It's that Johnny Robinson, I suppose?'

'He wants to marry is, I know he does... He's just frightened of his mam and dad. They want him to box...both of them. He says he can't do both.'

'Too bad..! He'll just have to be told...whether he likes it or not. You'll have to tell him yourself...and the sooner, the better. I want you to do it by the end of this week.'

'Right, Nellie. I promise I will.' I was only too relieved she hadn't told me to get out, there and then.

Two days later Johnny called to take me out and I told him everything.

'I'm three months.'

'That's all right, Francie. I don't think any less of you.'

'It might be all right for you, but it's terrible for me. I could be put in the workhouse.'

'Well I certainly can't marry you, you know that... Anyway, I've fallen in with this other girl.'

'That's fine by me, Johnny. I didn't expect you to anyway, so I'm not complainin'... If ye want to know the truth, I don't want to marry you either... I never did... I was just tellin' ye because I thought ye had a right to know, that's all... T'ta then, Johnny. I have to get back home because I've got the toothache... No, no..! Don't you bother yoursel' followin' is or anythin'. I can get the tram. I don't need you or anybody else to see me home.'

Pretending to have toothache, I sobbed my heart out into my hankie all the way home; I didn't get the tram, I just walked.

When I got home, Nellie says 'Well..? Did you tell him?'

'Yes, but I haven't got any satisfaction yet. I'll let ye know as soon as he decides.'

Several weeks went by and I never saw hide nor hair of Johnny. It was an awful time because I was getting bigger and bigger and it was becoming harder and harder to hide it. I was still working at the lodging house because it was more important than ever that I kept my job, but it wasn't the kind of place where you'd want to be showing. I'd be down on my hands and knees scrubbing the floor or reaching up to clean the gaslight, and I knew people would soon be putting two and two together.

Nellie hadn't put me out, she hadn't even mentioned the workhouse, I think it had all just been a threat to scare me off doing anything I might be sorry for, and I was certainly sorry now. I knew she was very worried about what would happen to me if she went off to Canada and left me behind, and what Sep would say if she brought me out with a bairn when they didn't even have one of their own; maybe they wouldn't even let me on the boat with it. I tried to be as good to her as I could but things were strained between us, and I was nearly out of my mind at the thought of ending up in the workhouse after she went.

Although I had steered well clear of the Robinsons, Harry must have guessed something was up because he saw me working in his lodging house practically every day, and I think Johnny had probably told him what had happened. Everybody knew Harry couldn't even keep his own water, and in no time at all Mrs Robinson sent for me. Supposedly it was to come to the house and do some cleaning for her, so I didn't dare refuse, I couldn't refuse any work now, and I certainly couldn't afford to offend M͟ ͟ Robinson because if she told Harry to get rid of me, he'd have done it like a shot and there'd have been no if's or but's about it.

Mrs Robinson set me on scrubbing the stairs first of all, and I'd hardly been at it five minutes when one of the boards came away and I found a calico bag of gold sovereigns underneath. I was flabbergasted, I'd never seen so much money in all my born days. I thought 'I wonder if she's put this here to try me..? I'm not goin' to touch it.' So I just put everything back where I'd found it, put the stair board back and carried on cleaning while I thought whether or not I should say anything. In the finish I decided I'd have to go and tell Mrs Robinson and see what happened. I didn't know if it was stolen, whether it was a secret hidey place, or whether they mightn't have known it was even there.

She didn't turn a hair. 'Just roll it up and put it back where you found it, Francie. It's no business of yours.'

A little while later I was polishing the furniture in the big room. Four rooms had had the walls knocked out to make it, and the furniture was massive; there was a huge table, high sideboards, dressers and bureaux, great heavy wooden chairs and big leather sofas and armchairs; the fireplace looked like an armoury with all the huge iron tongs and pokers. Everything took place in here; this is where they did their property and business deals, matched their fights, did their betting, eating, smoking, drinking, entertaining, sparring...the lot. If they wanted to see somebody perform, they could just put up a ring in the centre of the floor and they could have boxed, wrestled or had a ceilidh. After the little rooms I'd lived in all my life, this was like a hall.

I had climbed on top of the huge sideboard and was polishing away, and must have been breathing a bit heavily because when Mrs Robinson came in and stood watching me for a while with her hands on her hips, she said 'Is there anything the matter with you, Francie?'

'I beg your pardon?'

'Are you going to have a baby?'

Anybody else would have said it in a whisper, but she said it in this great loud voice.

'I don't know.'

'You "don't know", do you..? Well, I think you are! And I want to know who's the father of it!'

Johnny must have been listening behind the door because he came straight around.

'I'm the father of it, Mother. It's me,' he said, bold as brass.

'Oh, are you now..? In that case you had better fetch your father... Go on! Away down to the Model this instant..! As for you, my girl...for the time being you better just carry on with what you're doing.'

'The Model' was the biggest of the Robinson lodging houses and the one Mr Robinson looked after. Five minutes later he came in.

'You'll not have heard the news, have you?' Mrs Robinson says to him in this angry high voice as soon as he came in the door.'

'Fine mess this is, isn't it?' he said.

Johnny was just standing there like a fish out of water and I was still kneeling up aheight with a duster in my hand; we hadn't spoken a word because Mrs Robinson had just been standing there with her arms folded all the time.

'What've the two of yous got to say for yourselves?'

Johnny still just stood there, not saying anything.

'I'm sorry, Mr Robinson. I'm very ashamed of meself,' I said; I didn't know what else I could say.

'It's not just you, Francie. It's him as well. But he'll never work to keep you... Did you think that if you got yourself into this situation, that he would?'

'Well then, Mr Robinson, I can tell you this... If he's sick, I'll work to keep him. If he's not, he'll have to work to keep me and whatever comes along. Because I didn't do it on purpose, I can tell ye that.'

'Ye know ye'd have to become a Catholic if our Johnny married ye, don't ye? Ye do realise that?'

'Yes.'

'Are ye prepared to turn?'

'I've no objections. One religion's as good as another as far as I'm concerned.'

'That doesn't sound very promising,' Mrs Robinson says.

'When I'm in church I consider I'm in the Lord's home, whichever one it happens to be.'

'You'll have to go and see the priest a few times and satisfy him before you can get married in our church.'

'Ye'd better ask Johnny if he wants me, first... He hasn't said he does yet.'

'I don't want anybody else, Dad. She was my first girl.'

'Is that what ye want..? D'ye really want to marry Francie?'

'Yes. I don't want anybody else. I'm sure.'

'Well, I'd have to say there's none would make ye a better one, in my opinion... What do you think, Sally?'

But Mrs Robinson never smiled or anything. 'Things won't be as rosy as you two think,' was all she said.

'Right. That's that... Come down off there, Francie,' Mr Robinson said.

I'd been afraid to get down before this.

'Get yourself back to Harry's or wherever it was ye were workin'. And don't worry any more. I'll see to the weddin' and everythin'. Leave all that to me.'

When I went back home I was all happy and laughing. I rushed in and flung my arms around Nellie's neck.

'Nellie, Nellie, Nellie! I'm so thrilled! Everythin's goin' to be all right! Johnny's goin' to marry is! His father's goin' to pay for everythin'... Eeeh, I shouldn't be so happy, should I? I should be ashamed at what I've done to ye.'

'Never mind, it's done now. Just make sure nothing else goes wrong. Keep in touch with him all the time... Mind, there's one thing I have to say and it's this: all the respectable young men I know wear a collar and tie when they go out, because that's the way to treat a lady. But your Johnny always wears a muffler when he comes for you...no matter where you're going.'

'But Nellie, he's a boxer...a sportsman. None of the fellers he knocks about with wear collars and ties.'

'Well, if you told him you wanted him to, and he cared for you at

71

all, he'd wear one just to please you.'

I respected our Nellie and thought maybe she was right, and this would be a little test for Johnny to see how much he cared; although I didn't want to push my luck too far, not now that I nearly had him for my own. So the next day when I saw him, I mentioned about the collar and tie in a matter of fact way. To my surprise, he didn't make anything of it at all, he just said 'Right.'

The next day was Race Wednesday and he asked me if I'd like to go to the big race meeting with him, all the Robinsons and all the sporting people would be going.

'Eeeh, Johnny! I've never been to anythin' like that before... I wouldn't know how to go on or anythin'... I might let ye down.'

'Look, I'll tell our Harry you're not coming to the lodging house tomorrow. Don't worry, it'll be all right. You tell me now that you'll come with me, and when I come for you I'll have a collar and tie on.'

He did as well, he came with this great big high stiff collar like the toffs wear, and our Nellie was delighted; mind, he didn't keep it on for long once we'd gone round the corner. After that he never came to the house without a collar and tie, though I think he must have been out and bought himself a little soft one, or got his sister Lily to get him one, because I never saw the big stiff one ever again, it was probably floating in the Tyne somewhere. Lily Robinson knew all about fashions and she knew what to wear for every occasion; she never missed a single one, she was a lovely looking girl and well she knew it.

6

Mr Robinson was as good as his word; not only did he pay for the wedding but he gave us somewhere to live as well, a little two-roomed flat in Mill Street just across the road from one of his lodging houses, which he furnished with good quality second-hand stuff and put in a gaslight with a mantle. This was the first time I'd ever lived in a house with anything as fancy as a gaslight, it gave a lovely yellowish green light and you could turn it up or down just as you wanted and there was hardly any smell at all.

Johnny and I were married at St Bede's Church on the 9th October 1909 and dear Nellie rigged me out not only with my wedding costume and hat, but shoes and stockings and gloves as well...I wasn't in a white bridal gown or anything because I wasn't entitled to it but I was very, very smart. Nellie had hung on for the wedding and said she would leave for Canada as soon as it was over, because only then could she go with her mind settled. She must have been dying to see Sep again after all this time, yet she waited for my sake. Nellie was the only one of my family at the wedding, neither my father or any of my other sisters or relatives were there.

I was married from the Robinsons' residence, and bridal gown or not, they rolled out the red carpet. It was all show of course but they had this carpet stretching all the way from the front door, down the steps and over the pavement to the horse and carriage. I felt like a duchess.

The reception was held in the big room at the Robinsons', and it lasted for a week. There were three pianos in the big room mostly all going at the same time, fiddles, banjos, ukuleles, concertinas, accordions, tin whistles and all kinds of singers. I've never seen so much drink in all my life; the more they drank, the more there was to be drunk, and somebody was forever rolling in these big barrels of beer and filling up the huge bowls of punch. There were no taps or glasses, it was just a matter of off with the lid and in with your mug, scoop it out and get it down. Mind, there was ample food as well; there were massive bowls of steaming hot tateys, steaks, bread, cheese, and broth...nothing fancy but plenty of it. They just plonked it down on the big table and you either helped yourself or you got nothing.

The Robinsons were well off but they could be a rough lot when they wanted. I must say though that I never heard any of them blaspheme...not really blaspheme...they were too good Catholics for that; Catholics always seem to know just how far they can go, and if they go that bit further they can always go to Confession and wipe the slate clean.   They loved music, you could tell that straight away, and they liked anybody who could sing and dance. When something like the Gay Gordons came up, some dance where you jumped in and pulled each other about, they all joined in, but there weren't any waltzes or anything like that. Fiddlers and other musicians were hired and when they'd had enough, they brought fresh ones in; Irish jig fiddlers were only too willing to play till they dropped for a few shillings and as much whiskey as they could get down their throats, and when they collapsed somebody just tossed them out.

Mrs Robinson had a reputation for being as mean as sin with her family, tenants and lodgers alike, but when it came to drink, she was generosity itself. Her sons Harry and Geordie were supping for all they were worth, Lily as well, but her husband Stoker Allen thought too much about his boxing to drink himself sick, and Mary Ellen was too young.

Johnny had a lovely voice, and before Lily got too much drink in her they sang beautifully together. Mrs Robinson was the one who got everybody up to do their bit, and nobody got excused. She did all the organising of the food and entertainment. Mr Robinson didn't even see to the drink, somebody else did that. The big man just sat in his big chair smoking his pipe, taking it all in and smiling to himself. He'd be swigging from this huge mug, far bigger than anybody else's, and hardly saying a word other than 'Aye' or 'Good', but he'd be watching everybody like a hawk. Several times I saw him nod to different ones when he thought they were getting a bit out of hand, and twice he got up and laid somebody out with a blow from one of his huge fists and sat back down again without saying a word.

Mrs Robinson would lay into somebody much more quickly, she

was one of those that are always using their hands to push and shove people, and she was the very opposite of her husband when it came to going about things quietly; she couldn't, or rather wouldn't, have kept her mouth shut to save her life. She'd be yelling 'Give us a song, Lily! Howay, girl!' Then she'd start off whatever it was she wanted her to sing, herself: 'Have you... ev-ver been in love me boys, and have you felt the pain...' She didn't have all that bad a voice herself if it hadn't been so loud. And she'd break up a song right in the middle if somebody wasn't singing to her satisfaction. 'Hey, you're not singing, wor Geordie! I cannot hear ye! Come on! What the hell's the matter with you..?' Then she'd turned to somebody else. 'Come on, Mary! Sing up so we can all hear ye!' Then she'd see somebody asleep in the corner. 'Give that lazy bugger a kick! This is supposed to be a party, not a bloody sleeping contest..! Go on! Kick his arse for him. If I come over there, I'll damn quick waken him up!'

Then she'd stand up, straight as a plank with her back to the fireplace, and bang her mug down on the mantelpiece.

'I'm offering to take anybody on..!' She'd now have her fists up. 'Come on, you spineless gets..! Who's man enough to take on Sally Robinson..? Anybody..? Are you all afraid of a woman? Have none of you got any spunk in you..? If I was a man, I'd be champion of the world... You there..! Come here! You always fancied yourself, didn't ye? You think you're handy with your fists, don't you..? Well, here's your chance!' She'd be going over to the bigger tougher-looking fellers and giving them a shove. Then maybe she'd come to Harry.

'Here's wor Harry! He'll have a go, won't you lad. Get up, Harry! Now.. Try and hit me, you stupid bugger.' Harry would maybe punch her in the shoulder.

'Hit your own mother, would you..? Right..! Take that. And that...' She'd give him a couple of hard punches to the side of the head and he would step right back out of the way. She would growl and sneer at him and make a fool of him, and then she'd start singing again.

'There's a pret-ty spot in Ire-land, I'll al-ways cla-im for my land... Sing! Sing! Everybody sing..! Get me a top-up, Harry. Just put it down there.'

Five minutes later the accordionist got his backside kicked for asking for an extra half a crown.

75

I found out later that sometimes Mrs Robinson didn't touch a drink for six months, but when she did, she went to town; 'being on the ran-tan' is what they used to call it, and when she was on it neither Mr Robinson, the priest or anybody else could stop her. The priest was normally never away from the house because Mrs Robinson put a lot of money into the Church, but there wasn't much evidence of him the week of the wedding, not after the first day, I suppose he knew when to make himself scarce.

Before the week was half done, Johnny and me left. We didn't have a honeymoon or anything, we just went. It was mainly my doing, I just got sick of it all, I wasn't used to it and I wanted to get Johnny away from it. It wasn't because I wasn't a dancer or a singer and didn't like a bit of fun; because I did, there's nothing I like better than to see folks enjoying themselves. There just has to be a limit, you can't have it all night every night and to hell with the consequences; from what I'd seen of drink so far in my life, it brought nothing but grief, especially to other people.

By the time I married Johnny he was beginning to make his mark with the boxing. He'd won the Thompson Knockout Cup competition when he was only nineteen, and although it mightn't always show, because he was a very gentle feller by nature, boxing was in his blood and he couldn't get away from it. His father was his manager and whoever his father managed to set him up against, he would fight and there would be no argument about it. One week he would be fighting a feller in one place, the next, somebody somewhere else, and then maybe nobody at all for a few months because it was important he fought only the right ones. Fights had to be with fellers in the same weight class as he was, and had to be one step up the ladder each time, and such a one couldn't always be found easily, certainly not in the area. Sometimes his father might tell him he had to lose weight so he could fight somebody in a lighter division if the feller was somebody really good, maybe somebody like Jimmy Wilde that his brother-in-law fought. Other times the fight would be called off for one reason or another, and even in the ones that weren't, there was always a lot of messing about and argy-bargying.

I got sick of it and told Johnny it was no life at all for us, what was the point of being fit as a lop and strong as a bull if all you did was jump around punching air all day. I wanted him to finish his time as a riveter at the shipyards, he only had a year to do. His pal Matty Cocklin had gone to the South Bank at Middlesborough with the other apprentices, there was plenty of work there. But all he thought about was boxing, boxing, boxing.

'Why don't we go, Johnny? Ye could finish your time and make somethin' of yourself.'

'Oh, shut up, Francie. You talk too much.'

'It's only for your own good. I don't want ye comin' in all bashed up. I don't want to sit lookin' at a pair of cauliflower ears and a broken nose for the rest of me life.'

'Shut up, I said!'

'But Johnny. There's a bairn comin' on.'

'What do you think my father will say when he finds out we've left this lovely place he gave us? He isn't going to let us stay here if I give up the boxing.'

'He might. Ye don't know he won't.'

'Howay, then! We'll go round and tell him. Then you'll see.'

'Have ye not got a mind of your own or somethin', Johnny? Are ye just a little dog that does everythin' it's told?'

'Shut up!' he said, his face full of anger and his fist clenched. 'Nobody tells me what to do..! Anyway, I've got no money for the fare to go to Middlesborough.'

'Ask your mother... It's for her grandbairn, isn't it?'

'Don't be so bloody daft! If my father wouldn't give it, she certainly wouldn't.'

'All right, Johnny. We'll still go. I'll pawn my weddin' clothes and your jacket and waistcoat.'

I argued with him for ages and in the end he agreed but said it was entirely for my sake, he didn't want it. 'Fine,' I said. 'That'll do me. I don't expect any more than that.'

Straightaway that day I pawned the clothes and gave Johnny enough for the fare and pushed him to go that night before he had time to change his mind or anybody had time to work on him; I'd made him promise not to tell anybody yet because I knew his family wouldn't like it one bit. Next day I arranged to send our stuff and I followed in the train.

In no time we got on grand; Johnny started back in the shipyards, we got a canny little place, and even Mrs Robinson came to visit us. I was getting very heavy now and Johnny was so kind and considerate; he was washing dishes and sweeping up and even helping with the knitting and so on...holding the hanks for me, that is. Johnny never drank very much, he and Mary Ellen were the only two in the whole family who were like that; he'd have a drink if there was one, but he wouldn't care if there wasn't. He'd go out at night to play cards with Matty and his pals at the watchman's hut, a few games of billiards, a glass of beer, and that was all. If ever he won anything, he'd always bring it back with him and put it on the table. He was a good husband to me and I was very happy during those few weeks. He slapped me once or twice when he lost his patience, the way you might slap a bairn for being cheeky, but he never tried to hurt me; if he had, with the fighting strength he had in his body, he could have killed me with one blow. Slaps meant nothing to me, I knew the difference between a slap and a punch, and he never followed them up with anything else; I just took it as a warning to watch myself, he was a boxer and had been trained to hit fast and without thinking

One day a letter came from his father and Johnny said he had to go to Shields to see about it. 'I'll have to go right away to see what he wants, Francie.'

'When will ye be back then, Johnny...so I'll know when to put your bait up for work?'

'Well, let's see... It's Friday today. If I go this afternoon, I'll probably be back by Sunday night.'

'You'll definitely be back on Sunday night then, will ye, Johnny?'

'Aye, I expect so.'

'I'll have somethin' ready for ye for when ye come back then. I'll wait up for ye.'

He left that day and didn't come back. It was just as I had feared, all along I'd been waiting for that call to come. Two weeks went by without a word, and no money. I didn't know what he was doing or what I was supposed to do. My time was drawing near and I was really worried in case something had happened. But now he was back with the Robinsons, he seemed to forget all about me and his bairn, they all did, it was as though we'd never existed.

There was a canny old woman up the street who had treated me like a mother ever since we came to Middlesborough, and even

78

though I hated taking my problems to anybody else, especially somebody I didn't know, I was so desperate I went to ask her what she thought I should do.

'Write to him, pet. Tell him you've got no money and the bairn could be born any day now. Tell him he'll have to come back and let you know what's happening. Or what's wrong if anything is wrong. I'm sure everything'll be all right. You know what men are... He hasn't seen his people for a while and they're probably having a bit of a get-together. Maybe he's got 'flu or something and he's waiting till he gets better before travelling back. His mother's probably made him stay in bed for a couple of days... It's the right weather for it.'

'It can't be that. Johnny's never ailed a thing in his life. He trains in all weathers. I've never known a fitter man.'

'Well then, all the more reason to write. Now you sit yourself down here at this table. Here's a pencil, and I'll get you some paper. Go on now, Francie. Write your letter and we'll post it straight away. I'll put the kettle on and make us a nice cup of tea for when you've finished.'

So I wrote. It wasn't much of a letter but it said what I had to say, and I sent it. But then another week passed and still I had no word from Johnny.

This time I made up my mind to go myself. I took all the flour and bread I'd been stowing away in the cupboard and sold it to get the money for the train fare, and off I went after asking the old woman if she'd keep an eye on things till I got back.

When I arrived at the Robinsons, they were all sitting round in the big room and there was Johnny just sitting in an armchair, large as life.

I was almost in tears. 'Would ye mind tellin' me what's goin' on, Johnny? You're supposed to be my husband and I haven't seen hide nor hair of ye for weeks. I write to ye and ye cannot even be bothered to reply. You've just left me on me own, expectin' a bairn at any time, with no money or nowt. And I come here, and there ye are sittin' like King Tut, as though ye hadn't a care in the world.'

Johnny didn't say a word, he just looked over at his father.

'Sit down, pet,' Mr Robinson said. When I did, he said 'Francie, me and Johnny's had a long talk. And Johnny's decided he wants to carry on with the boxin'. This time we're going all out. He cannot be workin' in the shipyard during the day and boxin' at night. You cannot do things that way. It's impossible. He'd be no good at either the one or the other.'

'You don't mean it, Johnny?' I says, interrupting his father. 'You're not goin' to give everythin' up and stay here, are ye? What kind of a marriage is that? What about the bairn and me?'

'Hear my dad out.'

'The boxin' won't do ye any good at all. Look what it did to your Uncle Johnny.'

Johnny jumped to his feet. 'Hold your tongue, woman! I've told you not to talk about him! You're ignorant! You don't know anything!'

'But we were just beginnin' to do all right... We were gettin' on canny down in Middlesborough. You've got a good job and you're nearly out of your time... Your best pal's down there... All our things are there now...our home and everythin'.'

'I don't want to be a riveter in a bloody shipyard..! What glory is there in that?'

'Now, now, Johnny. Don't speak to her like that,' Mr Robinson says.

'I want to be a champion! My father wants me to do it. My mother wants me to do it. Everybody here wants me to do it. And that's what I'm going to do... Anyway, I'm already matched to fight next week. I've started training, so that's that.'

'What about me? What am I supposed to do..? Look at me! I cannot even work. I've got no money.'

'Pack the stuff up, whatever you want, and get back here as soon as you can.'

'But how are we goin' to live?'

'I'll see to that, Francie. Don't you worry,' Mr Robinson says. 'You'll be well taken care of.'

'I don't want to be taken care of by anybody but my husband. I want us to work for our own keep.'

'You'll have the chance to do that all right,' says Mrs Robinson. 'We're putting you in one of the lodging houses.'

'What!'

'Ye'll look after it yourself. You'll manage it. It'll be a business for ye.'

'A lodgin' house?'

'There's as good as you stays there,' Johnny says. 'So just get on with it and think yourself lucky. My father looks after lodging houses. My mother looks after lodging houses. And my brother has one. What makes you so special that you should turn your nose up at one?'

'There's many a married woman in this town would jump at the chance.'

'What if there's any trouble and they have to be put out..? Ye don't expect me to do that surely...? It's not a men's, is it?'

'My mother does it.'

'Is it a men's!'

'Yes. But anybody will tell you they're the best.'

I said no more, I just got up and walked out. I went to the station and got the train back to Middlesborough. I didn't know what to do for the best now, but at least I knew what the choices were. I'd left the Robinsons in a huff and hadn't asked for any money, or really given them the chance to give me any, so now I hadn't a penny for food, for rent, fares or anything. Then out of the blue, Scotch Lizzie arrived; Lizzie was Geordie's girlfriend and she was a real tough nut. She said she was fed up with Geordie's antics and had made her mind up to come and stay with me for a while. It was a godsend as it turned out.

'Them bloody Robinsons..! I like to see a mill as much as anybody. But fightin' comes between them and their wits. And that old bitch, 'Sarah' or 'Sally' or whatever she likes to call herself...! She's the worst of the lot... None o' them are worth a light. They're as hard as bloody nails.'

'My Johnny's different.'

'Your Johnny..!'

'I want to go back to him as soon as I can. That's all I care about. I married him, not them.' I didn't say anything to her about the lodging house because I'd been thinking a bit about it; it would be quite a responsibility, more than anything I'd ever had before and I'd pretty much be the boss of it...with a regular income, and two rooms for me and Johnny that went with it; and Lizzie had a big mouth.

'I'll go back to Shields with ye, if ye pay me fare.'

'Lizzie, I cannot even pay me own. I haven't two ha'pennies to

81

rub against each other. I mean it.'

'I'll tell ye what... See if ye can borrow the money to go into Middlesborough town, bring a hat, and I'll get we plenty when we get there.'

'What..! I won't let ye! Ye'll never do anythin' like that for my sake! I'd chuck meself in the river first.'

'Not that, ye silly bitch... I mean I'll sing.'

'How ye ganna do that?'

'Open me mouth.'

'Don't be so daft. Ye'll get yoursel' locked up.'

'Course I won't... Have ye never sung for your supper before?'

'I've never had the voice for it. Anyway, it's no different from beggin'.'

'Don't be so bloody silly! It's just entertainment. They pay to go to the Empire to hear people sing, don't they?'

'Maybe. But...'

'It's better than starvin', isn't it? Better than the bloody work-house, isn't it? And you've got an extra mouth to feed now, don't forget.'

'I know, but - '

'Look, it's Saturday today. Couldn't be better. You hold the hat, I'll do the singin', and we'll make worsels a fortune.'

I had nothing to lose so I thought I'd give it a go. Nobody would know us, it wasn't as though it was Shields; so I borrowed the money for our fares from the old woman, though I didn't tell her what for, and away we went into town that night. We went to the marketplace in the middle of Middlesborough and Lizzie stood by herself in a little square and sang her heart out; Scottish songs, Tyneside songs, Irish songs, she went through the lot. I went around collecting the coppers in a cap, the way she showed me to do, and in less than two hours she'd made enough to feed us both over the weekend and for both our fares back to South Shields.

First thing on the Monday I put the furniture on the train and told them it would be paid for at the other end. I paid back the old lady but there wasn't enough to pay the landlord, so I had to slope him, I'm ashamed to say; I had no choice.

I never forgot Lizzie for that. She was as rough as anybody I'd ever met in the ropery and she could be a funny'un at times...she could be moody and had a hell of a temper...but she had a heart as big as a whale.

When I got back, Johnny was doing what he said he was going to do, training hard, and I was put into the Robinsons' lodging house in Thrift Street. I was given my own room and told to run the whole show, and that Johnny would be living over at his father's until the fight. I had never had any dealings with lodgers in a common lodging house before, and here I was, pregnant, no man to rely on, and in charge of more than forty men, some of them as low as you could get. It wasn't as though I'd never been in a lodging house before, because I had, I'd been mucking Harry's out for nearly a year before I got married. But whereas they'd kid you on when you weren't married and just a cleaner, it was a different matter altogether when you were a married woman and in charge. I'd heard bad language often enough, I'd seen violent men before, and I knew there was nothing to fear from somebody just because they were shabbily dressed. 'Begin as ye intend to carry on, and make every one of them respect ye,' was Mr Robinson's advice, and I made up my mind that's what I'd do.

Very quickly I learned what to do and what not to do, when to get a hold of somebody and when to leave them be. Lodgers came from all walks of life but they all had one thing in common, poor though they were they had sufficient pride to pay for their own bed rather than knock on the workhouse door, and they'd never let you forget it.

At first it was fourpence a night and a few weeks later it was put down to thruppence, those were the regulations and the regulations had to be strictly carried out. This meant you got more lodgers so your beds were nearly always filled, and that you got some poorer and more troublesome ones than you might have had before, ones that would have slept in an alley, on the docks or on the beach, because they couldn't have afforded the extra penny.

In a lodging house a person could come in, get himself warmed by the big fire that had to be kept going all the time, wash his clothes, make himself a meal and leave the mess behind, and then go to bed; the next morning he could get up, get washed, make his breakfast, and then go. And you might never see him again, or not for a very long time; so you had to make sure you got your money, otherwise it came out of your own pocket. Some lodgers were regulars and came back every so often and you knew you could trust them, some were long stayers who never left the lodging house and paid every week. It was the strangers, ones who came for the odd night, that you wouldn't know how you were on with, and there were a lot of these. Some would pay as soon as they came in and you wouldn't have to ask for it, and some would pay when they went out, but some were as crafty as anything and would make it their business to get in and out without it costing them a bean. Every day you had to clear up the mess every lodger left behind; you had to empty the pail he used during the night...because he wasn't allowed to leave his room once he went to bed...you had to wash the saucepans and cutlery and things he'd used to cook and eat his meal with, you had to change his bedding, clean up any vomit, wipe up any pee, sweep up, clean the tables and clear away any rubbish he'd left, and do all the other things that the regulations required. So you didn't let him get away without paying if you could help it.

At the back of the lodging house were what were called 'furnished rooms', but they were really only one room divided into two, and they were very basic; they had a bed and bedding, a table and a couple of chairs, two sets of knives, forks, spoons and crockery. They sometimes were let to couples, sometimes for quite a while, sometimes for just a night. Nobody asked any questions about them and no marriage certificates or anything were required, so they pleased themselves what they called themselves and how they lived. Enough to say that the rent was eight shillings a week which was far more than they'd be paying if they were renting a house somewhere.

I had to pay the Robinsons sixteen shillings a week rent for the whole place, and out of the incomings I had to pay for bedding, cleaning materials, a hundredweight of coke a day, and for everything other than the maintenance of the building. So I was on a business basis with them and I wouldn't have wanted it any other way.

If I had any trouble with the lodgers, I wasn't allowed to send for Johnny or any of the Robinsons, I had to manage on my own like any other lodging house keeper. And whether I filled my beds or not, or collected all my money or not, I still had to pay Mrs Robinson her sixteen shillings. So I learned very early on that if somebody came in, made a hell of a mess and then diddled off without paying, I, and only me, would be the loser. And I learned that it was a damn sight easier to get if off them when they came in at night, before they'd done or used anything, than it was before they went out next morning with their clothes washed and their bellies filled.

Some would come in and get started making their meal or washing their clothes or whatever while you were upstairs or gone a message, so by the time you came on the scene they were already well in; in which case, I would go over to the counter and rattle my keys and shout 'Anybody who hasn't weighed in, can do so right now!' But it was easier said than done because sometimes you'd get a real bad'un, and in my first week I had my arm split with a brick when I tried to stop one getting out without paying, and in the afternoon of the same day I was badly bruised trying to break up a fight between two others. Lodgers were funny people and they were always falling out with each other over some little thing, they'd fight over a slip of paper or four inches of space. One of the things Mrs Robinson was most insistent about before I went in, was that I should never call the police; the lodgers didn't like it because the police would come in and rough them up, guilty or not, and it gave the place a bad name.

By no means however were they all hard to deal with, some of them I got on with very well and I could tell they liked me. Many of them were lonely people who had no home of their own, and many of them had nobody in the world. Certain ones, especially if they were long-stayers, would help with cleaning the pans and dishes, do the sweeping up, even help with scrubbing the floors or making the beds, and I would knock a bit off for them at the end of the week. There was a lot of brass to be polished, and ones that wouldn't scrub a floor or were unable to get down on their hands and knees, would sit there with a rag in their hands and do the whole lot while they were having a bit crack on. I never turned anybody away just because they had no money, but I'd say 'Mind ye make your own bed in the mornin'. I'm not runnin' round after ye. And don't cause any bother either, or ye'll be straight out that door.'

7

On Christmas Day little Alfie was born at last. It was still 1909 yet sometimes it seemed as though I'd been carrying him forever, so much had happened since that day I first found I was pregnant.

No matter what else you did or didn't do, if you ever missed Mass you were no good at all as far as the Robinsons were concerned, especially if you were a woman; so I'd been to Midnight Mass even though I was five days overdue and not feeling well at all. I'd taken a bad turn when I got there and had to come out and come home by myself, but I knew it would be all right; if you were a Catholic and you were ill and went to church and come straight back out again, it was all right, you had done your duty as far as God, the priest, the family and the congregation were concerned.

I'd made a spread for Mr and Mrs Robinson and the family for when we all came back from Mass, but when they came in I had to say 'Everythin's ready for ye to sit down to. But I'm afraid I can't attend to ye. Yous'll have to help yourselves. I have to go upstairs.' It was now past midnight so they were all jolly and laughing and wishing each other Happy Christmas, and I knew I could expect little sympathy, not the way I'd become pregnant; Mrs Robinson and some of the others still thought I'd done it deliberately.

I'd already sent somebody from the lodging house for the handy-woman, and I hadn't long gone upstairs before she came. As she was coming in the door, she was taking her hat and coat off and asking where the kettle was, and organising everything. She told me to take my bottom things off and squat over a pile of newspapers and rags on the floor, at the bottom of the bed, and strain whenever she said to me. Although she was telling me to stay calm, I could see she was getting worked up because the baby wasn't coming properly, and she was rushing backwards and forwards. I was hanging on to the bars of the bedstead and trying to do everything she told me and trying not to get upset, when Mrs Robinson came in. She stood there watching for a few minutes with a kind of a sneer on her face, and then went out. She couldn't have reached the bottom of the stairs before I heard her saying 'I think Francie's a goner. It doesn't look to me like she's goin' to come through.'

There was a hell of a commotion and I heard Mr Robinson thumping up the stairs and hammering on the door. 'Howay, Francie!' he was shouting through the door. 'Come on, lass! You'll make it! Be a brick!' And then I heard Johnny beside him shouting 'Aye, that's right, Francie... Be a brick! Be a brick! Don't give in, whatever ye do!' He wasn't yet twenty and I knew he didn't know what else to say. And before he'd finished the bairn started coming. It was twenty-five minutes past midnight, that'll tell you how much time it had taken since I came back from church.

The way I had Alfie was the way it would be for each and every one of my bairns...work right up to the time the waters broke, a pile of papers or rags on the floor, the kettle on, something to hang on to, and then just squat down and pray until it was all over. After Alfie was cleaned up, the handywoman handed him to me and then rolled up the dirty cloths and papers and pushed them on the fire.

None of the Robinsons, not even Johnny, seemed bothered one way or the other about the new bairn. As long as it was baptised a Catholic, that's all that mattered, and Mrs Robinson came two days after it was born to see about getting it done. I said I hadn't thought about it yet because the bairn was weakly and the weather was very cold, but she insisted it be done on the following Sunday; it had to be done quickly, she said, so its soul would go to Heaven instead of just Limbo. I didn't know much about Limbo but I didn't fancy my little bairn going there, so I agreed, even though the way I'd been brought up it wasn't proper for a woman to be seen outside of her own house so soon after a lying-in. I wasn't really up to going out myself because the whole thing had taken a lot out of me, and when we got there, what with all the standing around in the cold and everything, I fainted and the priest had to pour some of the holy water over me to bring me around before he could do the business with little Alfie.

The funny thing was, I wasn't christened myself till I was nine or ten years old. We didn't bother too much about that sort of thing in my family, Mam said she was too ashamed to take us because we hadn't any decent clothes to wear and she couldn't afford a shawl for whichever one it was. In any case, the Protestant Church didn't seem to make such a song and dance about it. But when I was older I saw this old lady in raggy clothes getting done, and when I told me mother, she took me to the same place and I was done there and then in the clothes I stood up in.

Johnny was now training full-time and there was never any more talk about serving his time, indentures, trades, plating and riveting, or anything else. From now on he was to be a professional boxer. Mr Robinson was to look after his training, his sparring partners, where he stayed, what he ate and how it had to be cooked, and even what time he went to bed at night; as well as matchmaking and all the business arrangements, deposits, betting and all that sort of thing. Mr Robinson himself didn't go out running with Johnny, he hired a full-time trainer to do it, one who would watch him night and day and strictly carry out all of Mr Robinson's orders; his name was Charley Whyte and he was absolutely devoted to Johnny. Sometimes Charley would get on your nerves, the way he was always rubbing Johnny down and snorting down his nose and shooting his fists out. 'One-two, eh, Johnny? One-two! One-two!' I think boxing came between him and his wits.

Even when he was living at the lodging house with me, Johnny would always go to his father's house for breakfast. Mr Robinson would see to it that Johnny got the proper food and at the proper time. Breakfast was his main meal of the day and like all boxers, he made a feast of it; he'd have bacon, sausage, eggs, tomatoes and onions...enough to satisfy three or four men...and then always finish up with a lump of meat on a separate plate. One day the meat would be an underdone steak two inches thick, the next it would be leg chops done the same way; it had to be practically bleeding to do any good. 'That's what puts the fire in your belly, son. That's where the stamina comes from,' Mr Robinson would say, beaming as he watched his son get it down.

Johnny would have ten minutes rest after his breakfast to let it digest, and then he'd be out on the road and he would run for miles, right along the river and then down towards the beach and along the coast road to Marsden and beyond. He would sprint for so much and then jog, sprint so much and then jog, sprint so much and then jog.

Charley would then stop him, but not to rest; he'd make him leap over walls and vault over gates, and then jump with his feet together, backwards as well as forwards.

Afterwards they might come back to the lodging house and have a rub down and a short rest, though never without Charley keeping an eye on Johnny all the time; then they'd be off to Mr Robinson's for sparring and skipping practice. One of the rooms at The Model was done out like a proper boxer's training hall, with dumbells and Indian clubs, punchballs on springs and punchbags hanging from the ceiling, and anything else they might need. Fellers would come and offer themselves for sparring partners for a couple of bob a time and Johnny would tell them, 'I pull no punches, mind. So ye'd better watch out.' Stoker Allen, who was featherweight champion of the Navy, used to get into the ring with him; so did his brother Geordie, Walter Callaghan and a lot of others, some of them famous boxers in their day, some of them up-and-comers.

Mr Robinson made Charley Whyte train Johnny harder than any whippet for the track, and if Johnny was hard on me, which he was, his father was harder again on him. Yet he put up with it without complaint, he did everything his father told him to do and I never once heard of Johnny so much as crossing a word with him. I didn't care for boxing at all, I'd seen enough beating up to last me a lifetime and I wasn't brought up to think it could ever be called a sport, but he wasn't doing it because sticking rivets in the side of a ship was a harder way of making a living, of that I was certain. There couldn't have been any fun in it apart from when he won...and he didn't always...because he wasn't even allowed to enjoy himself at the end of his day, not even with his own wife.

But I was proud to be married to him. He was very well liked, not only because he was a good sportsman, but because he was a quiet respectable man and never a big-mouth, like some of them were. He was good-natured and he'd always be singing if he wasn't having a workout; when he was a lad he sang on the stage at the Empire and won a pony and then had to show he was up to it by staying on its back while a feller with a whip put it through its paces.

For a whole month before every fight Johnny wasn't allowed to talk to me, let alone share my bed. Usually he was sent to a quiet place in the country, somewhere like Morpeth, far away from all the bars and everybody. I wouldn't see him at all during that time but sometimes he would write me a letter. But although his father never knew it, whenever Johnny was training in Shields or anywhere close by, he would creep around the back of the lodging house last thing at night, and tap on the window; but only if he'd managed to give Charley the slip.

'Francie..!' he'd whisper. 'Are you there, Francie?'

'Course I am! Where else would I be?'

The two of us would be looking through the glass at each other, both in love with each other; I'm sure of it, his letters proved it.

'Howay in for a minute,' I'd say to him.

'I cannot. My dad might find out.'

'How's he goin' to know?'

'He's bound to. Somebody'll tell him. Then I've had it.'

'Oh, come on, man...'

'No. I just wanted to make sure you and the bairn were all right. That's all I came for. Nothin' else.'

'Aye, we're keepin' our end up all right. What about you?'

'Fine...grand... Francie, I'll have to go. Look after yourself.'

And he'd be gone, and it was no use running after him. But then sometimes he'd come the next night and maybe the next, whenever he could get away from his father.

When Johnny was staying with me, even between fighting when he wasn't training hard, Mr Robinson would send around a lump of meat and tell me how it had to be cooked just so. I'd do as I'd been directed and lay it out for Johnny who would come in, sit down, and wolf it back without even looking up.

'Thanks, Francie.'

'Thanks..! Thanks, ye greedy nowt..? Are ye quite full now...now that ye've eaten the whole bloody lot yourself? What about me and the bairn? Are we supposed to sit and starve while you gorge yourself?'

'What do you mean?'

'We've had nowt.'

'Well, why didn't you keep your share? How am I to know what you've been eating and what you haven't?'

'Your father would murder is if he thought I'd eaten any of his son's precious dinner.'

90

'Course he wouldn't..! Don't be so bloody daft..! You might like to think he would. But he wouldn't. He thinks the world of you.'

'Aye..? Bit late now, then.'

Johnny would never allow me to come to any of his fights. I don't know whether it was to spare my feelings or because the family thought I might put him off, or what, but I never had any choice in the matter. He wasn't the least bit nervous or anything before a fight, the way you might have thought, it was just part of the day's work to him; he might just as well have been going to the office as to a boxing match to get his brains bashed out. I didn't know much about boxing, except what I picked up from hearing the Robinsons talking and the rest of the fellers that followed boxing, but I don't think Johnny was really cut out for it. I know it would have practically amounted to a cardinal sin to say it, but I don't think he even liked it, not in his heart of hearts. I think he did it to please his father, I think his father wanted another champion in the family like his own brother, the great Johnny Robinson, the barefist man; though it's hard to imagine a man would go that far to please anybody if it wasn't in him already. He never talked fighting talk at home, not in ours anyway, never boasted about beating anybody or anything, the way some would, and people used to tell me he would never fight in a bar or in the street. He'd say 'There's a proper place to settle anything. And that's in a ring.' Mind, that said, I never knew him have a grievance against anybody he fought, even against somebody who might have got the better of him, he always seemed to be the best of friends with them.

Johnny never even mentioned boxing when he was home with me; he was just like an ordinary feller, he read the paper and kidded about, and he loved to sing. In the mornings when he wasn't away training, I'd be frying his breakfast in the back and he'd be standing in front of the fireplace combing his hair; he was daft about his hair and never a single one had to be out of place, short at the sides for the boxing style but long and dark on top, lovely it was with his dark eyebrows and long eyelashes. And as he'd be combing away, sometimes he would whistle and sometimes he would sing at the top of his voice. It could be an Irish song he'd got from his mother, like 'Where the Praties Grow', or it could be a Tyneside one like 'Oh Bring Me a Boatman, My Bonny Hinny', and all the lodgers would waken up and listen to him. It was the happiest time of my life...standing there with the sausages and eggs crackling in the pan, seeing the bairn peaceful in his cot, and listening to Johnny. He was funny because he always sang a song right through to the finish, he wasn't one of those who start off with a great big loud voice and then fade away to nothing after a couple of lines that they've usually got wrong anyway. And if you started talking to him in the middle of it, he'd just carry on; he'd look at you and smile but he wouldn't answer until he had finished every verse. His father was always on about the quality of 'finishing', that's what the great Johnny was supposed to be most famous for, never giving quarter. I don't think my Johnny was like that, I think that's what they thought he lacked. But if my Johnny's speciality was finishing his songs, nobody could fault him for it as far as I was concerned. When I heard him in the room, or when I'd hear him outside and I'd go to the window and see him come whistling down the street, skipping and jumping, and fit as a fiddle, I used to think to myself, 'Johnny, you're lovely. You're the nicest thing on earth.'

I really, really loved him and I'm sure he knew it.

When the fighting men used to go to the contest, or even when they went to pay their share of the purse and lay the wagers, and the air would be thick with cigars, whiskey and big talk, they always liked to have their fancy women with them; they liked nothing better than to swank into a crowded room at a big hotel with a good-looking woman in their company. Johnny would take Lily, and didn't Lily just love to be at the centre of attention..! She'd get a new dress and a new hat and get all titivated up with her thick lipstick and her hair all done up and her fancy shoes and handbag and her long gloves. She even went with them when they were making the matches, when the talk would be rough fighting talk full of boasting, and a party of tough fellers with their man in the middle of them would swagger around the best sporting pubs and places, throwing out challenges to this one and that and sometimes bad things would be said. Not that Lily would have turned a hair at any of it. She'd have been in there with the father and her brother Geordie and Stoker and all the fighting men, and never a bother on her. They'd be arguing the toss about the size of the purse, the weight they should fight at, where the fight would be held, how long each side had to come up with the money, and all that sort of thing, and she'd just be laughing, she lapped it up. I think it might have got Lily started with her drinking, because she became a terrible one for the drink in later years and she wouldn't care what she said, she'd have nearly made the old woman blush.

All the fancy women would be there, but I never was. I knew how to dress myself up all right, and now we had the money from the lodging house and from what Johnny was bringing in, I had the clothes. Thin waists with big breasts to match, were very popular then and the women used to stick their chests out as proudly as any man, and no woman would have been ashamed of mine; but I don't think Johnny wanted anybody to know. I had beautiful black costumes, smart gloves, boots and handbag, and a big picture hat every bit as big as Lily's, and I wore it whenever we went to the variety hall or anywhere special, but I never got to wear it among the fighting crowd. I mightn't have been brought up to mixing with these kind of people but I had enough savvy not to say or do anything to let the side down, I knew when to keep my mouth shut and just look good.

Maybe Johnny thought the boxing crowd were too rough for me, maybe he thought I didn't deserve to go because I didn't like boxing; whatever it was, he never invited me and I never asked, I just let him get on with it, him and his family. I wasn't even allowed to watch one of his fights from the back row to give me the chance to see if I liked it or not. Maybe they thought I'd have been crying out every time he got hit, and trying to get in the ring to stop it or something. But I thought if Lily could be watching the fight in the front row with all the Robinsons, I should be there as well; he was my husband now and I had a right. She travelled all over the country with the whole party, I never even got to see him fight at St James' in Newcastle. In the middle of the afternoon I might be slogging away in my coarse apron, down on my knees with a scrubbing brush, or kneeling in the cinders cleaning out the great big fireplace with soot flakes on my face, and she'd come tripping in to call for Johnny, all dressed up like a high society lady, and away they'd go together to meet the rest of the party, all of them looking like toffs. At times, when Johnny and me were arguing about it and I was making a bit of a fuss before he went off, he'd smack me one. I admit I sometimes went on at him even though I knew he was a man of few words, and I suppose he didn't know what else to do to shut me up.

Johnny would always send a telegram to me straight after the fight to let me know how he'd got on, but it wasn't the same as being there, and when the time came that he was fighting a feller called Jerry Delaney at the Skating Rink, I told him I was going to go and see it even if I had to pay for a ticket myself. But it didn't work.

'You'd better not!' he says. 'Or there'll be big trouble.'

'Is your Lily goin'?'

'Why?'

'Is she?'

'What do you want to know for?'

''Cos I do. That's why.'

'I don't know. I suppose so... It's got nothing to do with me.'

'It's got everythin' to do with you..! If she's goin', I'm goin'..! If she can stand it, I can stand it!'

'I've said all I'm going to say... You go, and believe me, you'll wish you'd never been born!'

He thought I wouldn't go, he was sure I wouldn't dare go. But I did. I went by myself. I didn't go in, but I stood outside and peeped in through a hole in the tent.

My God, didn't they start hitting each other when the bell clanged! Hammer and tong they went, punching each other in the body and punching each other in the face, until I thought one of them would fall dead of a heart attack or something. But after that, after they'd shown each other they meant business, they took it easy for a while and I was amazed to see how light they were on their feet. Instead of just standing there and slugging it out, the way I'd seen men do in the street or in the lodging house, they would dance in a couple of steps towards each other, throw a couple of fast punches, and then dance away again. One-two, one-two, they went with their feet; and one-two, one-two, they went with their fists. Now I knew what Charley Whyte meant with all his 'one-two'ing'.

But after about six rounds it just looked like a brawl in the street, only worse, they wouldn't give up. Slaver, sweat, blood and snot was being knocked out of the two of them and flying all around in the air so you wouldn't know what was from who. By now there was blood everywhere...smeared all over their faces and arms, and some on their neck and chest. The sounds of the gloves hitting each other's bodies: 'Poof! Poof! Poof-poof!', made me feel as though I was being hit, as

94

I imagined what it would be like to have somebody that close who wouldn't stop hitting you and you couldn't escape. It was hard to see who was getting the better of it because they were both covered in sweat, both smeared with blood, and both red from all the punches. One would stagger back and it would look as though the other was on top, then he would fight the other one back on to the ropes and that one would be covering his face up as though he had nothing left in him. They'd then hold back for a moment or two and quickly wipe their face with the back of their glove, and then be at it again. It was amazing where all the strength came from. And it was even more amazing to realise that one of them was my lovely good-natured Johnny, my Johnny with the sweet singing voice and the carefully combed hair, doing all this and having it done to him; and sometimes I couldn't even tell which was him.

It was terrifying but it was really exciting at the same time. Everybody was shouting and cheering their man on. Most of them were for Johnny because I think this feller came from a long way away, somewhere like Leeds, and he wouldn't have so many on his side. And without realising it, I was shouting and yelling as well, though they wouldn't have been able to hear me above all the racket going on inside. 'If you hurt my Johnny... If you so much as mark his face...I'll kill ye when ye come out!' Then Johnny got the upper hand and I got completely carried away and was yelling 'Go on, Johnny, lad! Knock him down! Hit him now! Don't let him do that to ye! Hit him hard! Now! Now! Now's your chance! Get him! Finish him off!' And I could see his father and brothers, Stoker, his mother and Lily, Charley Whyte and all his supporters on their feet with their fists in the air, shouting like mad.

Then Delaney went on the attack... 'Oh, my God..! The swine! Me bairn's little bit face! It's such a mess... His lip's all swollen and there's a lump over his eye. And his ears are so red... He's being hurt badly...' Then Johnny almost knocked Delaney off his feet and Delaney was going backwards into his corner all the time with Johnny hitting him again and again and again. 'That's it, Johnny! Put him down! Finish him off..! Oops..! What's Delaney tryin' to do..? That's cheatin..! That's right, Johnny! Teach him a lesson! You show him, lad..!' Now Delaney was coming out of the corner again and hitting Johnny...

95

'Will it never end..? Oh, God, I hate this boxin'...'

For some reason I didn't understand, and others obviously didn't either, Jerry Delaney got the verdict and all hell was let loose..! People were yelling and jeering, and bottles were being thrown all over the place. They were piling into the ring and brawls were going on all over the place, in the ring and out of it. For the first time I was glad I wasn't inside. They were even fighting outside in the street and a crowd was attacking ones that were trying to get on a tram.

Afterwards I never said a word to Johnny about going to the fight and I still hadn't made up my mind if I'd like to go again, but a couple of days later I got the shock of my life when Jerry Delaney came around to the house and just walked in, I hardly recognised him all dressed up in his suit and hat. I thought 'Here comes trouble!' But Johnny just smiled and put his hand out and Delaney took it and they shook hands. 'You won, Johnny. I know that. You should have got the decision.'

'Aht, that's the way it goes,' Johnny said. 'Next time it'll be different.' And they both just laughed. 'How about a beer? Some of the lads are waiting for us down in the Crown. Terry McDermott's there.'

'Aye, all right then, Jerry. Hang on, I'll just get my jacket.'

A couple of minutes later the two of them went off together like old friends. I thought to myself, 'Well, well... I've heard about sporting gentlemen. And now I've seen one. I've seen two.'

More and more I came to realise that that was the way most of them were, the best sports were the boxers themselves. It was the hangers-on who caused all the trouble, they were the ones who were always aching for a fight, especially when it was somebody else doing the punching and getting hurt. I never saw or heard of Johnny as much as raising his hand in threat against anybody although some of them would have deserved it. Being a true sportsman was very important to him, as it was to his father, and I'm sure it was his father who had made him like that.

Afterwards I told Johnny I'd seen the fight and he was really annoyed. I don't think the fact that he'd lost the decision helped.

Mrs Robinson always resented the slight hold I had over her son, not that she had any cause to worry because she and her husband always had their way with him. She never showed her family much affection yet I think she was jealous because she knew I loved Johnny so much, and he loved me. I was probably giving him the love she hadn't. I think it was the way she was brought up and maybe she couldn't help it. Her family, the Cairns, were a very hard lot; her brother Johnny Cairns was a barefist fighter and you never saw him without a lemon in his mouth, he would suck it and smile at the same time. She would always be saying things to try to make Johnny think I wasn't fit to be his wife or mother to his bairns, always suspecting bad things about me and telling him. I knew it because in a big house there's always listeners waiting to make mischief. But if Johnny listened to her, he never paid much heed, at least not sufficient to say anything about it to me. He hated gossip and people who were always complaining. He would just say 'Ah, don't bother yourself... Least said, soonest mended.'

It wasn't just the love I had for him though, it was more to it than that... After I'd got married and become a Catholic, I'd tried to do things properly and behave like one, and I went to church every morning, Mass every week, and Confession every fortnight...which is more than Johnny ever did, and more than his mother except when she was off the drink...at which time she'd be the holiest, most devout Christian in the whole world.

Drink was another difference between Mrs Robinson and me. I never drank, no matter how hard she pressed me at their parties or do's; not because I was a saint or a martyr, but because I didn't like the stuff, I'd never seen any good come of it, never seen anybody talk, sing or behave one whit better after it. But she drank like a whale. And when she went on one of her ran-tans she'd disappear for days on end and nobody would know where she was; and it was just as well...because when she was on the drink nobody could tackle her.

The priest would get on to her sometimes when I was there, and hold me up as a kind of candle. 'And this girl's only a convert, Sarah,' he'd say. And she didn't like that, she didn't like it one bit. He might have thought he was bolstering me up at the same time as he was telling her off, but he wasn't doing me any good at all, I didn't want him making a stick out of me to beat her with; she was much higher up in the world than I was, and if money was important to the church, she'd done a lot more for it than I ever could.

97

One afternoon I'd taken Alfie over to see his grandmother and found her in one of her spells, not a ran-tan, just drunk. She'd apparently got herself vexed because she'd mislaid a gold sovereign, and as soon as I came in she started blaming me and saying I'd probably pinched it. In no time, it all came out; I was a no-good Protestant bastard, a whore who had produced a weakling for a son, I'd sapped all the spunk out of Johnny so he couldn't win his contests...and much more besides. Not so much out of fear as out of respect for my husband's mother, and knowing full well that if I were to force the issue, Johnny would side with his mother, I picked up my hat and coat, got little Alfie, and went home without saying a word. You just had to cross her once, and that was it, you were done for. She would never listen to anybody except Mr Robinson, and in the kind of mood she was in, she'd have been capable of anything. I would have been no match for her, drunk or sober; this was a woman who would drag a man out of his bed and throw him down the stairs if he hadn't paid or was causing trouble; anybody sending for the police to come to her lodging house would have been doing it to protect the lodgers. I could still hear her yelling her head off when I was halfway down the street.

Later on that day when Johnny had gone round to the Robinsons', Geordie had told him what had happened. 'You've got to do something about it, Johnny. It's not fair on Francie. The old woman goes too far. You don't know the half of it. She's always on to her. Francie's a good wife to you and you should stick up for her.'

Johnny didn't do anything that day, nor did he say anything to me, he just bided his time. A couple of days later his mother came around to our lodging house, drunk as a newt, and started making every kind of accusation against me, saying I'd been sleeping with the men in the lodging house when Johnny was away training and that she'd heard I'd been doing it that very morning.

All of a sudden Johnny leapt up. 'You're a bloody liar, Mother! She's been with me all day. We've been out looking at a clock. I've listened to you more than enough. Now get out and say no more!'

Instead of shutting up, she went on shouting and raving at Johnny. Suddenly he picked her up and threw her straight on the fire. Luckily for her, it hadn't been banked up and wasn't blazing properly. She yelled and she cursed like I've never heard a woman before or since, as she struggled to get her big drunken backside out of the grate; but he wouldn't help her, he just walked out. It certainly did the trick because when he'd gone and she got out of the fireplace, she looked at me with eyes like hell but she never uttered another sound, she just dusted herself down and went.

When we were in bed that night Johnny said 'Don't hate me because of my mother, Francie. I can't help the way she is.' And I put my arms around him and said it was all right, I'd married him, not her.

8

Little Johnny was born on the 7th February 1911, and there was no more fuss made over him than there'd been over Alfie. He had double pneumonia when he was a couple of months old but he got over that and never looked back. Alfie however wasn't making progress at all. He couldn't crawl, he couldn't even sit up by himself, and he took a lot of looking after. Every second week I was having to take him up to the hospital in Newcastle but they didn't seem to do anything except examine him, and when I came away he was always in a paddy with himself. I had to sit him up in a chair and put cushions and things around him so he wouldn't fall off, because he wouldn't have been able to help himself if he had; and then I had to leave him something to play with so I could get on with my work.

There were a lot of regulations from the Town Hall that you had to abide by if you kept a lodging house, and the inspectors were very strict. All the windows had to be open by ten o'clock in the morning and every lodger had to be out of his bed. The pails had to be emptied, the whole place swept, and all the dishes and pans cleaned by noon. Every week somebody in uniform would come around to inspect the premises; not just an ordinary policeman, but somebody pretty high up. They had the power to close a place down there and then if it didn't come up to their standards, and then you'd have had a real battle with the Town Hall to get your licence back. Many's the time a little something in the palm has saved somebody for a while but not for ever, and if they didn't put right whatever it was, they'd get put out of business. And if ever I'd lost the Robinsons their licence for them, I'd hate to think what would have happened.

The Robinsons' lodging houses were much like any others; some were mixed, some were just all men or just all women. I considered myself lucky that 'Thrift Street' was a 'Men Only'. Little bits of thieving always went on in lodging houses, they'd forever be pinching each other's scraps because they were hungry, or pinching little nick-nacks out of spite. Women always bickered and caused trouble and they could get violent with each other just like the men could. And when you got a dirty woman, she was usually dirtier in her habits than any man; women sometimes give up any notion of respectability and let themselves go completely, and I wouldn't like to have to describe the state of the beds I've had to clean belonging to some women in lodging houses.

Mixed lodging houses were the hardest of the lot to manage, and Mrs Robinson managed all of theirs.

Lodging houses were always in the poorest parts of the town, sometimes a whole street of them, one after the other. Poor people couldn't afford to buy their own houses or even rent rooms, and poor people who lived by themselves found it very hard to get by. A man with a family only had to be out of work for a few weeks, and unless they were very frugal and had a kind landlord...and I never met too many of them...they'd be out on their necks; and if the man drank, they'd have no chance. In such cases the family would always get split up one way or another, with some living in lodging houses, some in foster homes, and some in the workhouse; and kids that went into the workhouse often got sent to sea or to some place like Australia and were never heard of again. Even if the mother and father came upon better times, they might well have lost their bairns for good; nobody knew where they were, or nobody would tell them.

Lodging houses weren't like hospitals or barracks with great long rows of beds; some were, but most weren't; they had usually once been town houses or inns and it depended on the size of the rooms how many beds they had in them. Thrift Street had rooms with just three or four beds in, others with six or eight, and others with more. But each one usually only had one night pail and everything went in.

You could have as many lodgers as you had beds, so the beds were packed pretty close together. Even when I was full, I'd never turn somebody away on a bad night with nowhere to go, not if they looked all right; they could sleep on the floor on a mattress if I had one spare, or even on the kitchen table. If you were caught you'd be in trouble, but how could you say no to an old customer who'd always paid up, when it was maybe pouring with rain outside and he'd been going from place to place and was just about all in.

There was only one door, one way of coming in and going out, and this was kept locked and bolted to stop unwanted people getting in, and to make sure nobody left without paying; not that it always worked of course. On hot days you might have to leave the door open all day to let the fresh air in, also you had to let the lodgers who'd paid, in and out; and that was when you might get the unwelcome visitor getting in, or the sneaky bugger getting out.

Inside the door at the back was a large dining-hall we called the 'eating room' which had a kitchen joined on to it. In it was a fire that was always kept going, and an oven, a great big kettle, and umpteen pots and pans so the lodgers could make themselves a hot meal or a cup of tea when they wanted. And there was a long plain wooden table that was scrubbed twice a day with coarse sand, and long wooden crackets at each side for them to sit on. That's all the furniture there was, but there were mugs, plates, knives, forks and spoons. They didn't have to bring anything or do anything except see to their basic needs. I washed all the pots and pans, dishes, mugs and cutlery, and I put a fresh pail in every room at night and emptied it in the morning, as well as making all the beds and keeping the whole place clean. Mostly the wooden floor-boards were bare, but they were scrubbed every week and here and there I had little bits of oilcloth to cover the badly worn parts and stone flags. At least once a week the big back yard would be scrubbed, and every day it was swilled down; I'd just take off my shoes and stockings and start from the top end in my bare feet.

You could make a canny living out of keeping a lodging house if you were firm, hard-working, and did things right by the Town Hall; it was a business and like all businesses, it could be made better or worse. The lodgers were my customers; they called me 'landlady' and they respected me, and that meant a lot to me. They were all men except for the two couples that would come and go usually without any fuss at all, but by and large they did what I told them to, and that was something I'd never been used to before.

Although they were all in poor circumstances, it didn't mean the lodgers were more or less all the same kind of people, because they weren't. Some of them were very honest and would come back months later to pay you if they owed you something, others wouldn't. Thrift Street wasn't far from the docks so they'd often say 'I'll pay ye when the ship comes in, Missus.' Maybe the kindest thing you could say about some of them is that more than a few ships must have got lost.

The haymakers used to come to work on the farms in summertime and they would pay for their beds for the whole season, whether they occupied their beds every night or not; they were good business so you couldn't allow yourself to be tempted to let their beds to anybody in case they suddenly came back. When you got good ones like that, you got a good name for yourself and you'd be known as a 'respectable' lodging house and that would attract the better kinds of people. Though you couldn't afford to kid yourself; much the greater part of your bread and butter came from people who were little better than paupers, without them there wouldn't have been any lodging houses, not in Thrift Street nor anywhere else.

I encouraged regulars and long-stayers by trusting them and being as kind as I could to them; when they couldn't pay, I'd let them go for a bit and sometimes they'd pay back with a few pence interest. They were usually more considerate and reliable, and most important of all, you knew where you stood with them, which is more than you could say for strangers; they were all strangers to me at one time of course, and if you were afraid to ever take a chance, the place would have been empty. Another thing about long-stayers was that you wouldn't need to change their bed clothes quite so often; you were supposed to change the bed clothes between lodgers and generally I did, but if I saw somebody coming in who was pretty scruffy and had a fair bit of drink in him, all I might do would be to straighten the clothes up a bit and plump up the pillow.

Canny ones like Johnny Graham and Tommy Flynn, who treated the lodging house as their home, would often give me a helping hand and they would let me know what was going on between the other lodgers, they'd tell me if such and such a one was a thief, if any of them were up to any mischief, or if somebody was intending to leave without paying. I needed all the help I could get because I was left entirely to my own devices, Johnny never came in, and even if he was upstairs he'd never interfere if there was any trouble. When I first went in I'd sometimes run up to him and say 'Quick, Johnny! There's a fight goin' on! Sort it out, will ye!'

'Sort it out yourself. That's what you've been put in there for... What are you going to do when I'm not around?' He didn't fash himself in the slightest, he'd just carry on whistling and combing his hair or whatever he was doing; I suppose he'd been brought up to it, stroppy lodgers were a part of everyday life for him.

I soon realised he was right and that I'd have to learn how to look after myself, and some nights I'd get him to spar with me so I'd know how to hit somebody where it really hurts and how to duck if they were trying to hit me. I thought it might toughen me up a bit as well, but a woman's made a lot different to a man. You can hit any man as hard as you like in the chest, and so long as he hasn't got a bad heart he won't even feel it, he'll just laugh or get more annoyed; but if a man hits a woman in the chest, it's a different matter altogether, more than likely that'll be it, it'll be all over.

I got smarter though, I realised the best way of dealing with trouble was not to let it get to the stage of fisticuffs if I could help it, but to use my brains instead; I don't mean just standing back while things got damaged that I'd have to pay for, I mean not losing my temper too quickly and being careful what I said. After a while I not only got to know the natures of all the regulars but I became shrewder with strangers as well, I got so I could tell how far I could go with somebody before he'd lash out, and which ones were likely to be full of wind. But you can never be a hundred per cent sure with anybody, and sometimes I misjudged badly when maybe I should have let them off rather than stand my ground for the sake of a few coppers. I knew there was a whole lodging house either watching, or going to get to know about it, and if I showed any weakness, I was only storing up trouble for myself; there were very few who wouldn't take advantage of you in one way or another if they got the chance.

Those that hit me, I hit back, even though they probably hurt me more than I hurt them. But I was no Mrs Robinson and didn't pretend to be, there was nothing she liked better than a set-to; she'd stand up to the biggest and best of them, man or woman, fists right up just like a prize-fighter; but she was a big strapping woman and very fierce looking even before she was roused; arse over tip I've seen her lodgers going down her stairs, men and women.

Generally I'd stand my ground unless they looked as though they were going crazy and were strong with it. Then just as they were about to strike, I'd run in and fetch a couple of big lodgers. If I didn't have any, I wouldn't bring out any dwarfs or ones that were skinny as rakes, in case I got them killed; I'd just wait until whoever it was had calmed down and hope they'd see sense or that they would just go away.

You weren't ever allowed to have any sick people staying in the lodging house. It didn't matter if they were lame or backward, or full of aches and pains, as long as they could get out of their bed in the morning; that was all that mattered, that was the test of fitness. And once they were out of their beds by nine o'clock in the morning, they weren't allowed back into them before five o'clock at night. But when it was cold and you could see they weren't well, you couldn't very well go in and tip them out on to the floor. I had this old cripple feller who was always wetting his bed, even two or three times during the day when he wasn't supposed to be in it, and sometimes I got so mad I used to let him lie in it all day to teach him a lesson; but it was no good, the poor bugger couldn't help himself, I think he needed a new washer. Mind, drinking didn't help, and he used to stand by the door and beg off the lodgers coming in although it was against the law and bad for business. I'd keep going out and telling him to shoo, but quarter of an hour later he'd have shuffled back. He was no trouble otherwise and he wouldn't harm a fly, but when he paid it would always be with sticky stinking coppers that I'd have to run under the tap. Ones like him that couldn't hold their own water, or looked as though they couldn't, used to be given what were called 'darkie's breakfasts', which were straw mattresses; they'd have a good horsehair ruined in no time. I went through two or three darkie's breakfasts a week with this feller and I had to charge him extra for it; by the time they came off they were in such a state that neither darkie nor donkey would have gone within a mile of them.

Often somebody would come in and look really beat, maybe after doing some backbreaking work they'd managed to get, or maybe because they were cold and hungry or sick, and I'd let them get warmed by the fire before getting them to weigh in; then I'd get one of my regulars to show them to their bed. And some would play on it, they'd make on they were too weak or tired to pay.

One time this bloke was pretending he was deaf and dumb, and had everybody believing it, came in. He was making on he couldn't understand a thing you were saying to him, which isn't the way with deaf and dumb folk...usually they can tell what you're saying to them as well as anybody else from the front...and of course he couldn't understand a word about paying any money. I didn't know quite how to handle him at first so I just let him get on with it. He'd been occupying a bed and making his meals and doing his washing and going out and coming back for about three days, without a single word out of him and without paying a penny, when one night I was talking to one of the lodgers, and he just walked in large as life and went straight past without as much as a 'How's your father', and straight up the stairs.

'Smell that..?' the other lodger says to me. 'He must have been makin' himself understood somewhere. His breath's enough to cause an explosion.'

As the bloke got to the top of the stairs he must have missed his footing because there was a loud shout, 'Fuck it!'

'I'm not havin' that from anybody,' I says to the lodger, 'deaf, daft, or anythin' else!' And I went to the bottom of the stairs and shouted up, 'Hey! Was that you?'

There was no reply. He was just standing there looking down.

'Hey you! I'm talkin' to ye!'

He then started mumbling like somebody with no tongue.

'Did ye hear who that was swearin'?' I says to Johnny Graham, who followed me about everywhere...he was a right nuisance but sometimes I was glad of his company.

'Aye, I did... It was him... The deef'un... Supposed to be anyway.'

'Right!' I says to this one as I'm coming up the stairs. 'Ye can come down here with me and weigh in this minute! Or deaf or not, ye'll never get out of here alive!'

By the time I got up he was sitting on his bed and had a whole lot of money spread out on it as though he was going to start counting it.

'And ye can fetch some of that with ye!'

He sat there with this nasty look in his eyes, but he was just a skinny feller and he didn't look much so I grabbed hold of him and started pulling him. All of a sudden he let out such a mouthful..! It was terrible.

'Swear at me, ye bugger, would ye?' I yelled at him. 'You're not so deaf now, are ye, ye bloody fraud!' And I clouted him across the ear as hard as I could. He was so drunk he couldn't keep his balance, and I bundled him right down the stairs; over and over he went, cursing away all the time.

'Open the door!' I shouts to Johnny Graham. And the instant he got the bolts out and opened it, I shoved this feller out.

My husband Johnny had always told me, 'If ever you hit anybody, make sure you hit them hard. Because if you don't, they'll come at you harder than ever...particularly if you're a woman.'

All I can say is I mustn't have hit this one hard enough, because he went absolutely crackers; he took off his belt and smashed every window in the place, all for the sake of ninepence. Three of the other lodgers, two big seamen and a labourer, then came running down the stairs and out into the street, and caught a hold of the bloke and gave him such a hiding I had to beg them to stop. By this time Big Ginger Porter, the pollis, had heard all the commotion and come to the door.

'What's goin' on here?' he says.

I told him. 'But by the look of him he's learned his lesson now all right.'

'I'll learn him his lesson all right,' Ginger says. 'Deaf and dumb, is he..? He'll be blind an' all when I've finished with him.' And he dragged the poor bloke around the back into the yard and brayed him till the blood came out of his ears.

'Don't hit him any more! Ye'll kill him!' I was yelling. 'Please, Ginger..! Don't hurt him no more!' By now I was nearly crying, I'd forgotten about the windows and everything.

'You leave him to me, Francie. I know what I'm doin'.' But then he stopped hitting him and put a pair of handcuffs on him and took him away.

They put him in jail for three months, and as soon as they let him out he came back. I was sure he'd come for his revenge, and when he came in the door I shouted to Johnny Graham to go and fetch the lodgers. 'I'm warnin' ye! I'll have Ginger Porter down here before ye can say boo to a goose,' I said to him. 'You lay one finger on me, and he'll murder ye. Ye think he gave ye a hard time last time..? That was nothin'. He'll...'

But he had his hand in his pocket and was getting his money out so he could weigh in, he said there wasn't any other place he could go. He'd probably made a nuisance of himself everywhere else pulling the deaf-and-dumb business, so I just let him in and he was no more bother. He didn't say much but that didn't matter, he didn't have to; as long as he paid his thruppence he could keep his mouth shut as long as he liked.

Every so often two men who had it in for each other would fight it out and all hell would be let loose, things would be knocked over and smashed, and stuff would get spilt all over the floor. It was sometimes better to leave them to get on with it and get it out of their system, in which case I'd try to get them out into the yard..

'Get outside, if ye want to fight. Go on..! Get yoursels into the yard! Ye can knock each other's blocks off for all I care...as long as ye don't do it in here!'

But if they took no notice and were wrecking the place, I'd have to try and break it up; what they broke would come out of my wages. Once I went between two of them and they bust my head open with a poker; it wasn't intended for me, and that stopped the fight and they were sorry. It was too late then, but it taught me a lesson I never forgot.

One night I'd been out for a message and when I came back this great big navvy I'd never seen before was in, and he was doing this and doing that and fleeing about as though he owned the place. He stripped right down to his trousers and got himself a rare good wash, washing under his arms and using plenty of soap while he was at it, and then washed his shirt and his linings and his socks, gave them a damned good rinse and hung them up to dry by the fire, making sure they were well spread out and taking up as much room as possible. Then without as much as a nod, he makes himself a nice big supper on the stove, puts it on the table and gets tucked in.

I'd had about as much of this as I could take by now so I goes over to him and says 'You're carryin' on a lot, aren't ye? Don't ye think it's about time ye weighed in?'

'I'll weigh in when I think fit,' he says without even looking up.

'Will ye now..? Well, you'll do nothin' of the kind, mister! You'll weigh in when I tell ye... And that's right now. Else ye can get all your things ye've got hangin' up all over the place, and ye can damn-well get out..! You've had your threepenn'orth already, if anybody has!'

'Who d'ye think you're talkin' to?'

'You know who I'm talkin' to..! I'm talkin' to you..! And if ye don't get moved right now, I'll have ye put out!'

'Oh..? And who's ganna do that when he's at home?'

'Me..! I will!' I was really annoyed with the big sod by now.

'Ye'll bloody-well not!'

'I bloody-well will!'

But when he stood up I didn't know what to do, he was more than twice my size. I turned around to go into the kitchen and give him five minutes to think about it, and find something heavy to hit him with if need be, when he suddenly jumped me from behind. In a fraction he'd taken his great knobbly belt off, clunched it up in his hand and was wrapping round and round his wrist, ready to smash it over the back of my head, when two lodgers came rushing out, grabbed his wrist, and got him down on to the floor. They were a strong pair themselves and had the better of him; while one held him down, the other kicked him as if he was a football and I thought they were going to kick him to death, but he was a nasty sod and I didn't want them to stop too far short of it. Eventually he went unconscious and they dragged him out and dumped him twenty or so yards up the street and then chucked all his wet clothes and stuff after him. By now there was half a dozen lodgers gathered at the door and they hung around for quite a while and I think he must have thought better of coming back. Of course, that's not to say he wouldn't be waiting around some corner to catch me some time, and that's why I was always careful when I went out at night, especially with two long dark passages around the side. Some men cannot take a hiding and just go away and forget about it, no matter how much they've deserved it.

One Sunday night a foreigner came in and said he wanted a bed. I didn't care much for the look of him so I said I was full up, which I was, although I could have made room if I'd wanted to.

'I stop here,' he says.

'You not understand,' I said to him. 'You not stop here.'

'I'll kick you in stomach if you no let me stop.'

'Get out of it!' I said, flinging my arm out and going past him to open the door. But as I opened it and turned around, I saw this long fancy dagger in his hand.

'You not like me, eh?'

'It's not that,' I said as I was trying to edge away. 'It's just that we're full. And I'll get wrong off the police if - '

He whipped the dagger right above his head and I screamed so loud I think I must have paralysed him because his eyes opened wide and he just stood there with it in the air. I ran into the lodging house yelling at the top of my voice and then he came after me with the dagger in the air as though he was going to stab me in the heart. In one room I went, and around the beds, with the lodgers lying there petrified, and out again and up and down the stairs and out the front door and into the street. He wasn't very young and he had these long clothes on so luckily for me he wasn't very fast, but he wouldn't let up, and he chased me down one alley and up the other and down one street after another. 'My God!' I thought, 'I've had it this time! Where is everybody..? But it was a dark wet night and there wasn't a soul out, and the only light was from a gas lamp on the corner. I knew if he'd caught me, he'd have murdered me and be gone on a ship by the next morning and they'd never have got him. But when I ran back up Thrift Street for the second time the lodgers were standing at the door shouting 'Francie! Francie..! In here! In here..! Quick!'

I ran straight in and they slammed the door and put the bolt in; they'd seen him racing by and were as terrified of him as I was, he was so fierce-looking. We kept the door bolted and eventually he went away, the likes of him wouldn't hang around, the pollises would soon get on to them if they did.

Although I was sometimes able to depend on help from some of the lodgers, the lodging house was by no means full of big strong fellers just waiting by, most of them weren't like that at all. Anybody who stayed in a lodging house had a hard life, it was only a step up from the workhouse and it's no good saying otherwise. They all had problems of one kind or another, many of them were disabled in some way and were as contrary and stubborn as people like that can be. They'd fall out with each other and fall out with me and then usually fall in again. We were a kind of a family, and although it was a rough life, I liked it. Sometimes at night we'd all get sitting around the big fire with a mug of tea and sing sea shanties, or somebody would do a monologue or a funny ditty, and we'd talk about all manner of things. Some of them were old seamen who'd been everywhere under the sun, and some had been no farther than Durham; yet they would all have their own tales to tell, some of them very interesting and some of them frightening, that had happened to them or to somebody they knew. I loved to listen to them. I only had the bairns and they were too young to be much company, and sometimes I saw very little of Johnny, especially when he was away training for a big fight.

There were some really funny ones as well, and it was a rare day when you didn't get at least one good laugh at something or other, or at what this one or that one had said. Foggin was one of them. He was tall and very skinny and he never ate a thing that I ever saw, he lived on what they called 'long pulls' which were lemonade bottles filled with draught beer; you took an empty bottle into a bar and they filled it up from the pump and you took it away and drank it somewhere else. The law was very strict about liquor on the premises but time and time again I'd find Foggin lying on his bed with his long pull. I'd shout and bawl at him and threaten him with all sorts of things but it never made a ha'porth of difference, and he was too canny a feller to chuck out altogether.

'Give's it here, Foggin, ye long skinny nowt,' I'd say. 'I've told ye till I'm sick, that if I see ye with one of those in here again, you're out of here for good...' I'd then grab the bottle off him and be going downstairs with it and he'd be running after me begging me not to pour it out.

'Let's just finish this one... Please, Francie..! I'll never have another. Not ever! I swear!'

'No..! So don't sin your soul..! I've had enough.'

He wouldn't be concerned about being put out, all that mattered was the drink in the bottle.

'I'm not doin' anybody any harm. Why can't ye leave is alone... Don't waste it... Please don't pour it out, Francie, I'm beggin' ye..! I'll never do nowt wrong no more..! On my honour, I won't!'

I'd pour it down the sink or out of the window and he'd just sit and watch. He was strong, for all he was thin, I've seen him lifting very heavy things as though they were a bag of feathers, but he never touched me and never got nasty; he was as harmless as he was hopeless. Many a man would have kicked you in the belly for doing that, my father certainly would; but Foggin was as soft as muck and that's why I'd always let him come back. I once kicked him down the stairs because he'd peed all over his bed and I was really fed up with him, and I never saw him for nearly three months after it; but back he came in the end, and before long he was back to his old tricks, he just couldn't help himself.

There were some really clever fellers came in from time to time, ones that could make toys, whistles and little gadgets for the house. Others could write poetry or take up a pencil and make a lovely drawing of one of the bairns, and then later on you'd find it where they had left it lying, knowing you'd find it; or it might be one of me washing the pans in front of the window or sitting by the fire smiling with my hands in my lap.

Just as there were a lot of handywomen around at that time, there were also a lot of quack doctors. The handywoman usually had a family and lived in a house and was well thought of, but the quacks were always moving around and were regarded as rather shady characters. They often stayed in lodging houses and I nearly always had one or two...'crocuses' we used to call them...and the things they got up to would turn your hair grey, no wonder they were so careful not to let anybody see how they made their medicines up. But when they lived in your lodging house and used the kitchen to make their stinking stuff in, they couldn't keep everything a secret.

Each one had his own speciality, and some of them did quite well out of it. One would mix soap and sulphur in a tin can, roll it into little balls in the palm of his hand, and then wrap them up in silver paper and sell them for rheumatism pills. Another one used to boil sugar in pans and add these white and grey powders...I don't know what they were, I only know it had a lovely taste, because when he'd finished and left it to cool, I'd sneak a spoonful of it. It was probably just toffee and nothing else but it would have sold for the taste alone; though it did have a hotness to it that you could feel in your throat and I could imagine it might well have helped to melt phlegm away.

Another one would buy a pound of foreign beans from the chemist for a shilling...like little hard pebbles they were...and sell them as lucky beans or magic beans for sixpence each; if you bought one with a thread through it to wear around your neck, it would cost you ninepence. One feller used to get French chalk from the bicycle shop, mix it with a bit of water, put it in tins that once had something else in them that he'd only half cleaned out, and then sell it for toothpaste. Some of them were proper frauds.

112

No matter what they sold in the market, at the fair or on the quayside, they were never allowed to sell anything in the lodging house. Nobody was. No trades or trading were allowed by law, and there was a whole list of things from tanning pigskin to slaughtering turkeys, that were banned. As far as the quacks were concerned though, if anybody had pulled them up while one of their concoctions were in the pan, they could have said they were just making their supper.

I had an Indian feller who always wore a big carnation and called himself the 'Tooth Doctor'; he used to say he'd pull your teeth out with his finger and thumb, and people would think that meant there wouldn't be any pain, and they'd be damned sorry when they found that wasn't the case at all.

'Only one application, Madam!' you'd hear them shouting in the market. 'Only one application necessary!'

'Aye..! One application and your leg'll drop off!' somebody would shout back. But more than likely the 'ointment' was only margarine mixed with flour and the worst that would happen to you would be that you'd have wasted your money.

They'd sometimes call out for somebody to come up and try their new wonder medicine that would cure anything under the sun...dropsy, vertigo, epilepsy, leprosy and whatever else you were suffering from. More than likely it was something like Epsom salts and beetroot juice mixed together, but it would certainly look good in the little bottle with Latin writing on that nobody could read and that they'd probably copied off something they'd seen in a book, that sounded highfalutin.

One of their cronies would then come up, doubled up with pain and screaming blue murder. He'd then take a sip of the marvellous medicine and be cured on the spot, it wouldn't even have had time to reach his stomach. A few other stoogies would then start clapping their hands and cheering, and before long everybody would join in. The one that was supposed to have been practically at death's door would be waving his arms about, laughing and singing, and then he would run away with the quack shouting after him for his money. It would all be part of the act, you'd hear them in the kitchen rehearsing their lines and telling each other what to do after so-and-so happened and what to do if something went wrong.

113

Another feller would throw away his crutches after he'd had a spoonful of something or other. A young woman with her face covered in bandages would tell everybody she was covered in horrible scars underneath. The quack would give her a pill and then she would take them off, and lo and behold, her face would be perfect, not a mark. Everybody would gasp and rush to buy a bottle. Everybody knew it was just a big show yet it fooled those who wanted to be fooled.

One bloke that regularly stayed with me used to get a jar of water he'd tinted with some pink dye, unravel a bit of cord and drop it in. Then he'd go to the market with an old woman he'd have agreed to give a few coppers to, and after telling everybody how tapeworms ate your insides away, he'd say he had somebody who'd passed this tapeworm that morning after taking his wonder purge. Then he would ask any doubters to come up and feel it to see if it was still warm; it would look as though it was moving because he'd be knocking the trestle with his knee, and nobody would dare come up and touch it.

Some folks swore by quacks, and certain ones had a great reputation. Many would go to them for things like corns or bunions that you wouldn't bother a proper doctor for, and I think some of their remedies must have worked; some old wives' remedies did and there couldn't have been a lot of difference between them. But I think their best customers were those who were desperate, ones that doctors could do nothing for.

The marketplace would attract all kinds of other interesting people as well as the quacks, people who would swallow swords and fire, ones who'd get themselves put in strait jackets and tied with ropes and chains and then escape in three minutes. There were always frauds and freaks, and people knew they'd have to watch their money but they still went, the kids loved them. There would be raffles and lotteries and things that were always won by somebody nobody knew, and when they thought people were cottoning on to them, they'd disappear for a few months and new ones would take their place. They were never stuck for ideas about how to get your money, and some of them were really fly.

But some would be genuine enough in their way. An old feller who stayed with me a long time used to make artificial flowers out of turnip and carrot tops, bits of sweet paper and wire. He'd cut them up

114

and then tie them together so quickly and in a way you could never manage to do yourself, and in a flash he had a lovely plant that would have looked a treat in any vase.

In the next bed to him I had a tinker, and I've had tinkers so good they could have mended the holes in a cullender, but this one was little better than an idiot. He used to go around the scrap-yards looking for old pans and kettles that were completely useless, patch the holes up with gum, and then slap a bit of blackening on and try to sell them. Wherever he went he would rattle like a china shop because he had little cloth tabs sewn all over the outside and inside of his coat, and he would tie all of his old cans, saucepans, frying pans and kettles on to them. It was no wonder he was gone in the head, he couldn't have been anything else with all that rattling in his ears all day; the only time he had them off him was when he was in bed, and even then he'd have it over his bed like an eiderdown because he was dead scared in case anybody pinched any of his pans. He'd go out in the morning and go up to people in the street and ask them to drop a coin in one can or another, and by the time he came in at night, drunk as a skunk and smelling like one because he used the same frying pan he had on his back to fry his breakfast in and he never cleaned it properly, the noise was something terrible. He'd be staggering up the stairs and forever falling down and banging and clanging. One night I got so fed up with him and everybody complaining about him, that I knocked hell's bells out of him, and by the time I'd finished, his pans and kettles were all dented and there were handles and spouts lying all over the floor. I was sorry for the poor bugger afterwards but he really was a nuisance.

9

Joe was born in January 1913 and there was no trouble with him. His father Johnny had been away training over the Christmas but he had sent me a letter:

21 Oldgate
Morpeth

Dear wife

I now write you these few lines hoping to find you in good health as it leaves us at present.

I hope you and the little ones enjoyed your Xmas.

I hope that little Johnny is better now and running about as before he was bad.

Francie I hope the house has been going on all right since I left. You can tell the boys that I am alright and that I will make Lambert go for it. Tell Joe Hancock that I was at Newcastle on Saturday to see the dog match but got there too late.

Francie I hope you haven't done the hat-trick yet. You know what I mean by that, making three of them.

If Jack Lynch is there, tell him to drop me a line.

I hope you all have a happy New Year.

He came back a couple of days before Joe was born but was back and forwards to his father's most of the time because of the fight soon coming up. I'd been in labour for a couple of hours and was lying on the bed waiting for the handywoman coming, when Johnny brought in a bottle of stout. 'Here, Francie,' he says. 'Drink this. It'll do you good.'

'No, thank you, Johnny. Ye know I don't drink the stuff.'

He was so mad he took the top off and poured the beer all over me... This is what training for a fight did to him. He would have lost a lot of weight and be so on edge, a spark would have set him alight.

I was only in bed a couple of days because as well as the lodging house, I had little Johnny and sick little Alfie to see to, so it wasn't the kind of thing you could make a holiday of. Even while I was in the bed I'd have somebody fetch me a bucket of water so I could wash the nappies. And as well as suckling Joe, I suckled somebody else's bairn because the mother had no milk; I always had plenty and I'd done it for somebody when I had Johnny as well; women would do favours like that for each other.

The rats at that time were very bad; they would run up and down the curtains and across the bed, and I was terrified they would get at the bairns so I used to pull the sheets over their faces at night and then I'd be worried in case they suffocated; and you heard of horrible things that rats could do to a woman in milk. On the first few nights after Joe was born, before I was able to get up myself, I'd get Mary, the girl who'd come in to help me with the bairns from time to time, to put all the shoes, the poker, the shovel and anything else heavy she could find, on the bottom of the bed; that was her very last job every night before she went home. When she'd gone I hardly dare close my eyes and I'd try everything I could to stay awake till morning.

It wouldn't even be dark before they'd start to come out they were so bold, they seemed to know I wouldn't be able to get up and chase them. I would sit there with something in my hand waiting until there was a few of them in the same place, and then I would take aim and toss it with all my might. Then when I missed, which I always did, I'd have to remind myself I now had one thing less to throw, and that I had to make them last right through what might be a very long night. Some nights they were worse than others, sometimes there'd be as many as five or six only a few feet from where I was lying, and they were so cheeky they'd sit up washing their faces with their little paws, watching me.

When Mary came the next morning she'd gather everything up and ask me what kind of a night I'd had with them, and I'd tell her to take the poker and poke it down the big hole at the side of the fireplace and rattle it around. But she'd be too frightened to more than just tap it. But as soon as I was strong enough to get out of bed, that was the very first thing I did; I was as mad as hell with them, I'd been looking forward to this moment for days, and I shoved the poker in and out and waggled it about from side to side until it came out with a blood on the end.

'Got ye, ye little swines!' I yelled at them, and I went in with the tongs. Seven I got out, seven young'uns; but the big'uns were too sly. I had to nip their bellies in and out with the tongs till they stopped breathing...they're a lot harder to kill than you might think. But there were plenty more to take their place, the horrible things would have a new batch every month, and sometimes they would run right across my feet in broad daylight while I was sitting in a chair suckling the bairns.

Because I had to look after Johnny and Joe and feed this other bairn, as well as looking after the lodging house, and having to take Alfie up to the hospital at Newcastle every fortnight, I was finding it very hard to manage. Whenever I went I used to call in and see an old friend called Ethel, a woman who had no bairns of her own and was dying for one, and one day after I'd been hours and hours at the hospital, she offered to look after Alfie for me and take him up to the hospital whenever he needed to go; and because Alfie was so weak and the trip always so trashing for him, I agreed.

At least once a fortnight I'd go up to see Alfie, and whenever I did he always seemed to be lying on the sofa with never a stitch of clothing on him and nothing to play with, though well enough looked after and perfectly clean. I never said anything about it because I knew Ethel was very fond of him and thought she'd put him like that so I could see he was nice and clean with his hair combed and everything; but I was beginning to get a bit worried in case he wasn't being given the chance to romp about, not that he could have got very far, and I wondered if maybe she wasn't mollycoddling him too much. Ethel was one of those people who were very particular about having everything clean and neat, so much so that she seemed to spend the whole of her life going around tidying up and dusting and washing and polishing things till she'd nearly have them worn away.

One Friday Ethel came to Shields to visit somebody and she brought Alfie with her, so I said 'Why not leave him here until you've seen your friend?' And she said 'All right... I'll come for him on the way back.'

When she'd gone, Alfie, who could talk by now although he still couldn't sit up by himself, begged me not to let him go back with Ethel, and began to cry.

'Don't be so silly, Alfie!' I said. 'Ethel's your Auntie, and she loves you. It's wrong of ye to say ye don't want to go back. That's your home for a while.'

But he cried and he cried and he seemed as though he couldn't stop; normally he was a very patient little feller and never made any fuss. In the finish I said 'Tell me what's really the matter, son.' And he told me... Apparently Ethel wouldn't let him play with toys or get down on the carpet, and she was always bathing and washing him and putting him to bed early... I realised now that he wasn't just a baby any more, but that he was a little boy with a mind of his own and he knew what was fair and what wasn't. That kind of thing was no life for a little lad at all, so I decided there and then that I wouldn't let him go back, no matter what Ethel said.

'I'm sorry, Ethel,' I said when she came for him, 'but I'm keepin' Alfie with me from now on. I appreciate what ye've done, but I'm his mother and I think I should be lookin' after him.'

She didn't get annoyed or upset or anything, she just said 'All right, Francie. You must do what you think is right.' I think maybe she knew he wasn't getting any better and she didn't want to get blamed for it, and I don't really think she knew how to go on with children, although her heart was in the right place.

After that, every day when it was fine I'd prop Alfie up in a little chair and carry him outside the door of the lodging house so he could see something of the world outside; everybody that came by would talk to him, and by the time I brought him in at night his little pockets would be full of coppers.

The doctors at the hospital said he had 'consumption of the bowels' but I don't think they knew for certain what was wrong with him; all I knew was that he was slowly getting worse. Among other things, his little eyes, his nose and his ears always got stuffed up and I had to hawk them out every day, or else pus formed. One day I had him on my knee cleaning them out, when I noticed he couldn't seem to move his head properly, and as I moved his neck to let him breathe better, the little black crucifix he'd around his neck since the day he was born, jumped off its little silver chain.

'Look, Mary,' I said. 'His little cross has come off. You can hardly see Our Lord on it anymore. He's all worn away. What a shame...' Then I noticed Alfie wasn't moving at all. 'He's very still, isn't he..? I think there's somethin' the matter with him... I'd die if anythin' happened to him now.' And then I screamed.

Johnny Graham and Tommy Flynn came rushing up the stairs to the doorway but didn't come in because none of the lodgers were ever allowed in.

'What's the matter, Francie?' they were shouting. 'Are ye all right? What's happened?'

'Come in, lads,' I said. I didn't know what I was doing.

Tommy rushed in and carried the cot over to the window. 'Put him in here so we can have a look at him.'

I was just sitting there holding my little bairn, and nearly out of my mind. I knew I'd lost him and that I hadn't had him with me long enough, I hadn't had him by my side day and night the way I should have done.

'Let's have him here,' Mary said, and she took Alfie off me and laid him in his cot.

Tommy Flynn and Johnny Graham both bent over and looked at him for a long time. Then Tommy looked up, his face streaming with tears, and said 'I think ye should send for your Johnny, Francie...

We'll go for him if ye want.'

Old Tommy Flynn had been in the lodging house all the time I'd been in it, he'd been well-to-do once upon a time but had started drinking heavy and his family had put him out. He loved little Alfie, he would go out in the morning with a bundle of rags under his arm and say 'Listen here, Alfie. I've got some business to see to and I'm putting you in charge of my things while I'm away. When I come back I want you to tell me if anybody's touched anything.' Alfie would wait patiently all day till Tommy came back; sometimes one of the other lodgers would pretend they'd taken one of Tommy's spuds or a crust of his bread or something, and show it to Alfie just to tease him, and Alfie would get all excited and tell his Uncle Tommy as soon as he came in.

Tommy would spend ages with him, holding him up and trying to get him to stand, and I didn't like to hurt Tommy's feelings because he was so good to the bairn, but Alfie's tiny legs could never support his body, skinny and little though it was. Sometimes I thought that trucking with Tommy Flynn wasn't the best for him, like when he would get Alfie to fold up the dirty rags he'd collected from God knows where, and maybe share his dinner with him. He was a good man but he'd let himself go and he wasn't as clean as he might have been, and the way he prepared his food left a lot to be desired... But what could I do? The bairn loved him. Tommy spent hours playing with him, whereas many wouldn't have been bothered with what they would think was just a snotty little bairn, bar winking at him or saying 'Hello, there.' Alfie's own father was away so much, and I never had the time to give.

Alfie was buried in Harton Cemetery barely ten days after Joe was born. The lodgers clubbed together to buy him a wreath and practically every one of them walked behind his coffin. It was a very sad sight to see them all, many of them as shabby as it was possible to get.

Johnny didn't know what to say, to him death was one of those things that happened and there was nothing anybody could do about it, you just had to forget about it and get on with life. 'Don't upset yourself, Francie,' he said to me at the graveside. 'There's plenty more to get.'

'You might think that's all there is to it, Johnny. But I don't. He was mine...and he was my little china. I was the one who had him. No matter how many bairns we get, I want to keep them all...every one of them.'

When we got back home I had all the lodgers in for a cup of tea and something to eat, and they were full of gratitude; some of them were in rags and pretty scruffy, but they were full of respect and there was as much kindness in them as in anybody, you could see it in their eyes.

Poor Tommy Flynn had only been skin and bone before, but from the day of Alfie's funeral he went down and down until he eventually fretted himself to death. I nursed him and did all I could for him and I wouldn't let them take him away to the workhouse, but in less than a year I buried him.

By the summer of 1913 little Johnny was two and a half years old and his father was beginning to take an interest in him. I was managing quite well with the lodging house, Johnny was making a bit of money from his boxing, and we weren't badly off at all. Mr Robinson looked after Johnny's boxing expenses and a boxer never had to pay for his own entertainment, he just walked into the bar or wherever it was and somebody always jumped up. By now I was doing a bit of baking and selling it to the lodgers for a few coppers, so we had a little bit more coming in from that and it always helped towards buying the bairns' clothes or something like that. Johnny treated me well...I was getting used to being a boxer's wife now...and both Johnny and Joe were fine healthy kids, so I had little to grumble about.

On a Sunday morning young Johnny and his father would go over to the Robinsons', and Johnny would be as proud as anything of his little son all dressed up in his purple velvet suit with his white lace collar pressed down, spats, white gloves and little walking stick and looking just like little Lord Fauntleroy. It was grand to see the two of them going along the main street like a couple of peacocks. Johnny was very tall and his hand would be so high up that little Johnny would have to hang on and give a little jump now and again to steady himself, and he'd be half running to keep up with his father's long quick steps.

People would go up and say 'Is this your lad, Johnny..? By, isn't he a fine-lookin' little feller.'

'Yes. He's my eldest lad. I've another one like him at home.'

'Have ye started trainin' him yet?'

'It won't be long. He catches on pretty quick.'

'He'll be a champion, that one, Johnny. Ye can see it in his eye... A Shieldsman and champion of the world! Wouldn't that be somethin', eh?'

'It wouldn't be bad.'

'And yourself, Johnny..? Who's next in line to get his hammers?'

'It's too soon to say yet. My dad's got one or two up his sleeve... It'll be in the papers as soon as anything's arranged.'

'Right, I'll keep my eyes peeled. I wouldn't miss one of your fights for the world.'

'Well, we must get on. Can't keep his grandfather waiting... Can we, lad?'

'Proud he'll be an' all. I'll bet he will... I won't keep ye then, Johnny. Be seein' ye, Johnny. Take care of yoursel'.'

'Aye. Thanks. Watch yourself.'

Then one day a terrible thing happened... Every Friday I cleaned the brasses, and for this purpose I'd lift the oven door off its hinges to get at the handles, and while it was off I'd stack the chopped sticks inside to dry ready for lighting the fire. This particular Friday it was rather chilly so I'd changed the bairns into their woollens, usually little Johnny would be in his silk blouse for going up to the Robinsons', because that's where I took him every Friday morning; I thank God to this day he wasn't this time.

I'd popped down to the market to get some fish for dinner and just left the bairns behind, Johnny playing on the floor, and Joe still in his cot, and had got on chatting to the fishwife. Suddenly one of the lodgers came rushing up telling me to come home quickly; but he wouldn't say what for, so I took no notice, they were always fetching me because so-and-so had done this or so-and-so had done that, and I'd be dragged in to sort out their silly squabbles. But he came back a few minutes later, grabbed me by the arm and started dragging me away from the stall.

'What d'ye think you're doin'?' I yelled at him.

'Quick, Francie! It's the bairn! It's the bairn! Little Johnny!'

I left my basket on the stall and ran like hell to the lodging house.

When I got there my little Johnny was lying on the floor, wrapped in a blanket, smouldering, with lodgers running backwards and forwards not knowing what to do. Some were pouring water on him, some were talking to him, others were looking in cupboards for something to put on, and others were ringing their hands and saying 'Oh, God! Oh, God!'

There was a terrible smell of burning flesh and burning wool and I couldn't tell which was wool and which was him. When I'd gone out, Johnny must have been taking the sticks in and out of the oven, and with the oven being right next to the blazing fire, he'd fallen into it with his arm first, and then all his clothes had caught alight.

He was in such a terrible mess and in such agony that I didn't dare do anything in case I made it worse, so I got a lodger to call a taxi and I did what I could to make him comfortable till we got him to the Infirmary. When we got there I insisted on holding him myself while they cut away the clothing and tried to pull out the pieces which had melted and got stuck to the flesh; the trouble was they couldn't make up their minds which was which. When he was cleaned up he didn't look quite as bad as he had at first, but he still had burns all over his head and body, and everywhere his skin was a bright flaming red. But it was his little right arm that was the worst...that was terrible, and they said it might have to come off.

By the time I got home I was in an awful state. Johnny had been kept in hospital and I didn't know whether he was going to lose his little arm or whether the whole of his body would be scarred for the rest of his life, or even if he would come out of it at all. I was terrified for him and I was terrified for myself. That night his father Johnny came in and asked for some money to go to London for a few days, there was a crowd of them going down for the dog races and he needed some cash for the fare and to bet with. I gave it to him gladly and wished him good luck and I couldn't get him out of the house fast enough. The lodgers were all behind me, helping me to cover things up and distract his attention so he'd forget to ask about the bairns; they knew he'd have murdered me if he'd known about little Johnny.

Johnny was away a week but as soon as he came back the beans were spilt, somebody had told him. He'd have found out sooner or later and he had a right to know, and I had it coming to me. At first when I saw him, I was sure he was going to do me in, I'd never seen a look on his face like it. But I broke down in tears and when he saw how upset I was, he said 'Well, I know you wouldn't have let it happen on purpose. And I know you'll do your best out of a bad job. So I'm going to say no more about it.' And he didn't.

It was things like that, the way he took things so manly, that made everybody respect my husband Johnny; he was very like his father. He wasn't really the selfish man I thought him to be when I first married him, I'd known that for some time now. With the boxing, he was only doing what he had to do, and it must have been harder for him at times than it was for me; he couldn't have enjoyed all of it, not all the tedious training, the rotten wasters and blowhards he sometimes had to mix with, and especially the disappointment when a decision didn't go his way when he thought he'd deserved it and must have felt he'd let so many people down. He was only twenty-three, still not much more than a lad, and he had a lot of people to try and please, a lot of people who would criticise him if he put on a performance that was the slightest bit under par...especially if they lost any money on it. When he got older and eventually got away from boxing, he would be a good husband and a good father, I knew it. He was firm, he was loving, he was proud and he was fair; he never shrunk from anything and he never went back on his word. I'd met a lot worse in my own twenty-three years, and none better.

I went to visit little Johnny at the hospital every day, and after a while all the skin dropped off all over his face and body, and new white skin grew in its place. But his arm just wouldn't heal so I brought him home, nursed him myself and took him back to have new dressings put on. Every day for months I had to stand by and watch them pull the bandages off and little blobs of flesh would come away sticking to the lint, and have to listen to his screams; some of them were really rough and shouldn't have been put in charge of little bairns, they seemed to me to be the sternest and most impatient ones in the whole place. Sometimes you would come across a really nice nurse and think 'Thank God, there's at least one,' and then you'd find she belonged somewhere else and the one you were getting was a right bitch.

They stopped me going into the dressing room in the end because they said I always interfered. I was always wanting to hold him myself, they said, and that I didn't know how to hold him properly

125

for the doctor. But they had no curtains and that in those days, no privacy, and I'd look through the window and shout 'Don't do that! Be careful with my bairn! Do it the other way..! It won't hurt him so much!'

I was never a loudmouth, I've always been respectful, but you couldn't help yourself when you saw what they were doing to your own little bairn and he was crying out 'Ma! Ma!'

After they'd finished and I was called in to get him, I'd start loosening the bandages as soon as I picked him up.

'Stop that! You don't know what you're doing, woman! Leave him to us. We know what's best for him. You're letting the air at it. It's getting more infected because you're letting the germs in.'

They were bandaging it so tightly, and his arm was being trussed up and tied against his chest so firmly, that the blood couldn't flow properly, and it was becoming wasted and paralysed as well as septic; it was less than half as thick as the other one and there were big inflamed lumps under both of his arms.

One day Johnny was screaming so much I could hold myself back no longer, and I burst in on them.

'Give him here! I'm takin' him! I'm lookin' after him meself from now on!'

One nurse had a tight hold on Johnny while the other two pulled me back against the wall and tried to keep me there. The doctor must have heard all the commotion because he came rushing in and he played war; he said if I took Johnny away it would be entirely at my own risk and the hospital wouldn't be responsible in any way. And then he really came out with the news... He told me that in all likelihood the arm would have to be taken off, and if I removed him right now it might very well kill him.

'Ye what..? Do you mean to tell me that after all this time and sufferin' ye were thinkin' of cuttin' his little arm off...? You bloody butchers..!' It was all I could do not to take him by his scraggy neck and strangle him.

'We'll only do it if it is absolutely necessary.'

'I'll see you all in Hell before ye take any of my bairns's arms off..! What use d'ye think he'll be without an arm in this world, eh..? His father's a boxer... D'ye think he'll ever be one..? My own father's a bricklayer... D'ye think he'll make one of those either..?'

'I warn you, Mrs Robinson. I'm beginning to lose my patience. You cannot come in here and carry on like this. You're disturbing the other patients.'

'What about my bairn..! D'ye not think he's bein' disturbed?'

'Get her out of here!' he said to the nurse. 'And take the child into the ward.'

But I wouldn't let them have an inch of Johnny, not any more. 'He's my bairn and I'm takin' him, mister. Ye can say what the devil you like, but I'll never bring him back here again. Not while there's a breath left in his little body. God gave him that little arm. And I'll murder anybody who tries to take it away!'

I took Johnny and I never went back. I cleaned and dressed the arm myself every morning and every night and I never let anybody else do it, the only one I let anywhere near was my own doctor who came once a week and prescribed some ointment. I would move it up and down and from left to right, I'd hold out a novelty to make him reach out and then I'd pretend I was going to take it off him to make him grab it all the tighter, and then he would try and hide it over his head or behind his back so I couldn't get it. Any spare time I had, I played this game with him even though I knew it meant teasing him; it was the only way to make him use his arm and get the strength back. But then he took the measles and they turned into pleurisy and he almost died. I had every one of the doctors in and I was never off their backs; for two whole weeks he was very ill and I carried him around on a pillow wherever I went. Then one day he woke up and he was right as rain, the way it often is with bairns and their troubles. Gradually the skin knitted over the raw flesh of Johnny's arm and it began to get a healthy pink tinge to it, his arm filled out and he could move it any way he liked. A few months later, apart from some awful twisted skin which never quite went away, his arm was normal.

I never knew much about the actual boxing, who Johnny fought, or how well he'd done. It was there in the paper if I'd wanted to read about it, the Sporting Life and the Sporting Man were always lying around, but I didn't want to read about how he was being hit this way and that or how he 'desperately tried to rally'. Who wants to read about the man they love doing things like that? And knowing that sooner or later they were going to get a terrible beating that might leave their brains scrambled and for the rest of their lives could be going around the pubs, punch-drunk fools, begging for drinks off nobodies.

Sometimes if Johnny had had a few beers and come back in a talkative mood he might say something, but it wouldn't be gory details. He might say 'I'm going to beat Alex Lambert, Francie. I know I can beat him... Then Driscoll... After him, a couple more and then we'll be flying.' And sometimes I'd overhear him talking to Geordie or Stoker or Charley.

Johnny's father was in charge of everything, he was the one who paid Charley, and Charley always did everything Mr Robinson told him to do. It wasn't only because he was scared of Mr Robinson that Charley never left Johnny's side; he was devoted to Johnny and I think he loved him, and I have no doubts that he was a good trainer and very good for Johnny, at least as far as the boxing was concerned anyway. You only needed to see him running after Johnny, getting his towel for him, and lacing up his boots, to tell he thought the sun shone out of Johnny Robinson and that he would have done any mortal thing for him. But there was no escaping he was a funny feller in some ways. Like most hunchbacks, he was very sensitive about it, especially if you were a woman and he saw you looking at it, or thought he saw you looking at it. Sometimes you mightn't have realised you were, but he would have and he'd be quick to take umbrage. He always did his best to hide his hump but sometimes he ended up drawing more attention to it. Also he had a queer way of looking at you at times, part hurt and part wicked. He'd seemingly been born with his back that way and yet he loved all sports, especially boxing. When Johnny was away training, Charley would always be away with him, but when Johnny was home Charley always stayed in the lodging house, so I saw quite a lot of him and I got to know his little ways.

Although I couldn't tell you which fellers Johnny had fought and how many rounds he'd gone with this one or that, he was a big name now, very popular, and fighting all over. I think one of the reasons for him being so popular was because none of it went to his head, and he was friendly with everybody; whether you were important or not made no difference to him, he'd be as grateful for a pat on the back from a feller with a stall in the market as he would from somebody who owned a shipyard. He was very slim because he had to keep making the weight of featherweight, which was the most popular weight and the weight his father wanted him to make his name at, but he didn't have a broken nose or cauliflower ears or anything, he hadn't lost any of his teeth, and there wasn't a mark on him. If you'd seen him in his best clothes, you could have taken him for an Irish priest on leave.

Johnny told me that to be the best, you had to be what they called a 'punisher', you had to have a mean streak and never show mercy once you were in the ring, you only held back when your opponent went down and stayed down. But Johnny could never be like that, and I'd hear different ones say that when he had his man up against the ropes and trying to cover himself, Johnny couldn't bring himself to finish him off. Everybody wanted a knockout and there'd always be booing when both men remained standing at the end and one of them then had to be given the decision on points. They all wanted to see somebody either out for the count, or so flat out on their back they couldn't get up even if they wanted to. I'd heard that Johnny's father used to curse and swear at him when he stood back to let the other feller get up. But although Johnny did everything else his father told him, that he wouldn't do, even though it might have meant him going on and even losing the fight on points. Mr Robinson would be standing in his corner shouting 'Go on, you stupid bugger! Give it to him now! Where it hurts! You've got him! Finish him! Finish him! Finish him!'

They say Johnny's movements were beautiful to watch because he was so quick and so stylish, dancing around in his bathing trunks which he always preferred to the long baggy shorts that many of them wore. Tradesmen and labourers would pawn the shirts off their backs to go and see him fight, and trainloads of them would travel up to St James Hall or Sunderland when he was on the bill. So you couldn't help but be proud of being married to a man like that even though you'd hate to give him any encouragement.

Johnny had to fight at about 9 stone, when if it had been left to nature he'd have been eleven or twelve and still had no fat on him, he was always having to lose weight. If you were over the odds at the weigh-in, you were either disqualified and lost your stake, or you had to come to some arrangement with the other man's backers which

129

meant you got a much smaller share of the takings and less credit no matter how well you did. But to lose weight you had to train harder than ever, take more Turkish baths, eat less; and this sapped energy and made you very contrary.

If a man wasn't in the 'very pink of condition', as Johnny called it, he could be killed in a boxing ring, or he could get so badly injured he'd never be able to fight again. You not only had to hit the other feller, you had to get out of the way quick before he hit you; in and out, you had to go. In and out, in and out...all the time. You had to give the best you'd got every time, and be on the lookout for any mistake he might make, or any sign of weakness. And he'd be doing exactly the same to you. And if you were away fighting on foreign ground, you had to do your best to ignore the other feller's supporters shouting and yelling all the time; and if you won, they might have to get the police in case the crowd skinned you alive.

On Monday the 29th December 1913, Johnny was just twenty-four years old. He had recently beaten Johnny Condon at Newcastle and was out to make a match between the winner of the Delaney-Sterling fight which was to be held that very night. Although it was very bad weather with snow and sleet blowing, Johnny wouldn't put on his overcoat to go up to Newcastle; he was always stubborn like that, but you had to be very careful you didn't say anything to him in front of his family or friends that might make him look soft in any way. He and his sparring partner, Walter Callaghan, had had a workout and were having a Turkish bath at Northumberland Street baths. Johnny had gone there to take some weight off because he was already training for his fight with Alex Lambert in January.

Walter had told Johnny to come out of the bath in case he sweated too much off, but Jerry Delaney was in at the same time and asked Johnny if he'd mind hanging on till he came out and had his rub-down first, as he was on that night. Johnny had said all right, he'd wait on...with the result that he stayed in the steam for far longer than he should. By the time he and Walter left the baths, it was snowing hard and Johnny didn't even have a muffler with him; I'd given it to him before he left home but he had just tossed it aside. On the way to St James to see the Delaney-Sterling fight, Johnny and Walter called into the Crown and Sceptre for a beer and a sandwich, and Will Curley, the promoter who owned the pub, made Johnny put on his fur coat. He told Johnny he had too much staked on him on the Lambert fight, for him to take any unnecessary risks. Then they all went to St James together, and before the contest Johnny had jumped into the ring to make his challenge to the winner. That was the way it had to be done, always before, never after. When the fight was over Johnny had a couple of drinks and came back to Shields and then home to his bed.

The next morning when I got up, Johnny was still in bed; usually when he was training he was up at six o'clock. I got ready, got the bairns up, and put the frying pan on.

'C'mon, Johnny!' I says. 'Up ye get! Breakfast's nearly ready.'

'I don't want any... I'm not getting up yet.'

'Don't be daft. Your Dad'd go mad if he knew ye were lyin' there at this time of day.'

It was nearly half past nine.

'I don't feel well.'

'Well I'm goin' down to the lodgin' house. I cannot lie in, I've got to slop out and make sure our customers are all up. And if I don't get the windows open soon, I'll lose your mother her licence, Christmas or no Christmas... See you're up by the time I get back. I'll make ye somethin' then.'

I thought he must just have a bit of a lazy boot and thought no more about it. I went down to the lodging house to make sure all the lodgers were up, opened the windows, slopped out, swept the floors and then I came back..

Johnny was still in bed.

'Johnny..! Johnny..!' I was shaking him as hard as I could. 'What d'ye think you're playin at..?'

'Leave me alone.'

'I know what it is... You were drinkin' too much after the fight last night. That's what's the matter with you, Johnny Robinson!'

'A funny thing happened just before... I got up to light the fire for you coming back, and I fell into the fireplace. I felt very queer and sort of weak, so I came back to bed.'

'What..?' I thought he was just acting up. 'Come on, ye don't kid me. Don't be so bloody bone idle... Here...' I flung his clothes over him. 'Get up and put them on. I'm goin' to do your meat for ye. The liver and bacon's had it now. It's burnt to a frazzle... Wait till your

131

dad hears about it. I'm tellin' him, mind...if ye don't get up. I will, Johnny. I mean it.'

'Shut up, will you.'

'It's all right for you...lyin' there without a care in the world.'

He then got up and sat at the table but he didn't eat his breakfast, he just picked at it for a while and then sat with his head leaning on his hand. I had to see that he ate his breakfast, boxers have to eat their breakfast, he couldn't go out with a storm blowing and nothing on his stomach.

'What's wrong with it..? If it's been too long in the pan, it's your fault, not mine.'

'I feel bad, Francie.'

'Don't talk tripe! All the time I've known ye, ye've never so much as had a headache.'

'Honest. I'm not kidding.'

I didn't know what to make of it but I had to go and scrub out the lodging house and do our rooms for the New Year, so I went off to work and left him. When I came back at dinnertime, he was back in the bed.

'You're a lazy bugger, Johnny. All the work I've got to do, and here's you lyin' abed like Lord Muck... It's a wonder Charley hasn't come lookin' for ye.'

'Leave me be, will ye. Stop raising your voice.'

'Howay man, Johnny! You're only storin' up trouble for your-self.'

But he wouldn't get up, he just lay there and started talking daft. I couldn't afford to faff around any more so I went off to get the shopping in and attend to other things.

When I came back at tea-time, he was still there, and there he remained right till the next morning. And still he wouldn't get up; not to have his breakfast, not to get washed or anything.

'It's New Year's Eve, Johnny. Ye'll have to get up now. I'm goin' to see Charley and tell him to chuck a bucket of cold water over ye.'

He didn't answer.

'Ye'll have to get up and change your underwear, Johnny. Your vest was soakin' wet when I got up. Even the bedclothes are all damp... Pooh! They're stinkin'..! Howay, ye'll have to get up to let me take them off and put some clean ones on.'

I tidied the room and washed the breakfast dishes and then I had to get back to the lodging house. Before leaving, I told him he'd better not fall asleep with his gold watch in the pocket of his jacket which was hanging on the back of the bed, you could never be too careful with the lodgers.

When I came back at half past three, his jacket was still hanging there but his watch was missing, I knew it because he always had the chain hanging out of the top pocket. I looked under the bed and all over but I couldn't find it.

He was still just lying there. I shook him hard. 'Where's your watch? Where's your bloody watch! It's all we've got that's worth anythin'..! Who's been in here..? Has anybody been in?'

He just stared at me with this crazy look in his eyes, I'd never seen before.

'It's all right, Francie... Come here, little Francie. It's all right... Give me your hand. Put your head in here and feel this funny noise.'

I was really beginning to get worried and I didn't want to go too close, so I just leaned over a bit. As soon as I did, he reached out and grabbed me by the neck, stuck my head under the bedclothes and rammed my face into the mattress.

'Don't be silly, Johnny... Johnny! You're hurtin' is!'

Then I heard the watch ticking, he had it under the pillow and he was laughing in a wild, frightening kind of way. I didn't know what was the matter with him but he was acting very contrary. There couldn't be anything much wrong with him, he looked after himself too well, he was a very fit man, he never ailed anything, he'd been fighting hell for leather in a boxing ring little more than a week ago.

If ever I wasn't feeling well, and that wasn't very often because I rarely ailed anything either, my way was to ignore it, get up, get a good cold wash, and get on with whatever I had to do. Everybody would like to lie abed on some days, especially when it's cold and wet and they've maybe got a rotten job to do that day; but nothing would ever get anything done if everybody did that. Once you got up and got started you soon forget about feeling sorry for yourself.

It didn't seem to sink in with Johnny that it was New Year's Eve and all his family and friends would be wanting to see him, and that his supporters would be coming around to toast his health and wish him every success for 1914. He hadn't seen Charley for a couple of days and that was very unusual, even at Christmas time, and Charley would be wondering what was the matter. Charley normally wouldn't come to the house because he knew I didn't like it; when Johnny was out of the house Charley was nearly like a wife to him, but when he was at home I wanted him to myself.

I was pleading with him now. 'Come on, Johnny. Just try. I'll give ye a hand to get ready.' He wouldn't even answer.

'We cannot have people comin' in for their drink and bit of cake, with you lyin' stinkin' in bed.'

But he never budged, and when I went out to do my work and came back at teatime, he was still there. I began to think that maybe there really was something wrong with him, that maybe he was sickening for something. I knew it wasn't a cold because he didn't have a runny nose or eyes and he wasn't sneezing or anything... I didn't know what to do, but his father was bound to be around before too long and he surely would.

Johnny had gone very quiet and didn't seem to want anything so I thought he was maybe just resting and that he would make the effort and get up when he realised what day it was. So I straightened up the bed and then went out to borrow some wine glasses ready for all the guests coming; they'd all expect to be given a drink so they could drink to their champion.

By the time I came back with the glasses, a gang of his pals and relatives were already waiting at the door, so I fetched them all in and poured a drink for each one of them. 'Where's the man himself?' they were all asking. 'He's not drunk already, is he?' And they were all laughing and joking about it.

'He's still next door,' I said.

'Gettin' all dandied up, I'll bet.'

I went into the bedroom and whispered to Johnny, 'They're here, Johnny. We've got a houseful already.' I thought that when he heard them all laughing and carrying on, that would have got him up if anything would. But it didn't make the slightest difference. The door was slightly open behind me and he could see through into the other room.

'Has anybody got a tanner?' he shouted. 'I'm saving up to marry Francie.'

Everybody laughed, they thought he was only kidding, they didn't

134

realise he was still in bed. Then Johnny yelled 'We're getting married, you know..! Oh yes! We've decided! Somebody give us a tanner for our wedding, will ye!'

He went on shouting dafter things that weren't even funny, just stupid, and gradually they all stopped laughing and realised something was wrong. At first some of them thought he must have started early and got himself drunk, although they knew it would have been very unusual. At first, some of them shouted things back to him and tried to make a joke of it. But then he suddenly sat right up and shouted 'Get out, all of you! I don't want you in my house! Go on! Get out! You're makin' too much noise. I can't get any sleep.' And then he flopped back on the pillow.

'Take no notice,' I said to them. 'He's not well. There's somethin' the matter with him. His dad'll be here shortly. He'll know what to do.'

Everybody was shocked but they just put down their drinks and went. Not five minutes after, Mr Robinson came; whether he'd heard about Johnny or not, I don't know, but as soon as I told him how he'd been carrying on he went straight in to see him.

'I don't know what to make of it, Francie,' he says. 'How long has he been like this?'

'A couple of days, I suppose.'

'A couple of days..!'

'I didn't think there was anythin' wrong at first...'

He sat there looking at his son and I could see he was very concerned.

Every five minutes or so somebody would come to the door for Johnny, and I'd have to tell them Johnny had taken a bit of a turn and wasn't well enough to go out or see anybody. Mr Robinson sat there on the wooden chair by his bedside and never took his eyes off him.

By midnight Johnny had gone mad. He had pulled the hangings off the bed, which was an old fourposter to separate us from the bairns, pulled all the frills off the quilt and was tearing the feathers out of the pillow and scattering them all over the room. 'This bed's full of sand!' he kept shouting. 'This bed's full of sand!'

It took Mr Robinson and me all our strength to hold him down but eventually we did, and he settled. Ten minutes later he started up again, raving at the top of his voice. After a while he fell back again.

Then he started again.

It was getting on my nerves people keep coming to the door with a couple of bottles of drink in their hand, with nothing to care about but get drunk, and I was having to control myself and remember they didn't know there was anything wrong and had only come to wish us well; so I was just wishing them all the best and sending them away without saying too much. Sometimes when they came to the door they'd hear Johnny singing at the top of his voice, and must have wondered it there was a party going on and we weren't letting any more in. But if they'd listened, they'd have heard he was just singing rubbish.

I was picking up the feathers and feeling very frightened because I was thinking Johnny might be losing his mind and mightn't ever get it back; I'd seen simple people, there were plenty of those about, but I'd never seen anybody who was completely mad like they had in the lunatic asylum.

Suddenly Mr Robinson said 'You'd better send for the doctor, Francie. He's delirious. That's what this is.'

'Are ye sure that's what it is?'

'Yes. I'm sure.'

'Thank God!' I said. I was so relieved. That's what people got when they had fever, I knew that much; and when the fever passed they were all right again.

I put my hat and coat on and went straightaway, more content now than I'd been at any time for the last two days.

When Dr Dalziel came, Johnny was quiet again. He said Johnny was only suffering from influenza and that we had to keep him in bed and put hot poultices on his chest. He wasn't in five minutes before he was away again.

All night long people were calling to see Johnny, either to have a drink with him and wish him all the best, or because they'd heard he wasn't well and wanted to see him; and as fast as I was showing them out, others would be pushing their way in. All night long this went on and although I was just about beside myself with it all, I knew they were only coming because they thought the world of Johnny, and that I would have to try to be patient for his sake.

By morning Johnny was quiet and sleeping, he was soaking with sweat but both his father and I thought he seemed a bit better. Mr

Robinson said he had to go home to get himself a wash and see to a few things but that he'd be back very shortly. And he was. From the time he had first come and seen the way Johnny was, this great big solid man had sat there breathing very heavily with his head on his chest and his fists resting on his thighs, except for the times he leaned over to study his son's face.

All day long I kept putting hot flannel poultices on Johnny and rubbing him with olive oil, the kettle was on the boil all day. At one time he leapt up and said 'If you put another one on me, as hot as the last one, I'll clap it on your face!'

I'd laughed at him, it was the first funny sensible thing he'd said for nearly two days and I thought he must be getting better at last. But by the next day, Friday, he was worse than ever. One minute he was quietly sleeping, the next he was out of his mind.

I had all three of the doctors in turn, but they all said the same thing and prescribed the same treatment...poultices and bed-rest. Charley Whyte was a great help and the two of us nursed Johnny as best we could, with Mr Robinson looking on, saying nothing and doing nothing.

That night there was a tremendous banging on the door downstairs which went on for several minutes. Charley ran down but there was nobody there. He had only just come back up and sat down again, when there was a sound of shattering glass, the sound glass makes when it's smashed hard against a stone. The light from the gas light had dimmed slightly and we looked up and saw the globe had thousands of tiny cracks in it, though not a single splinter had fallen out. I think it was a warning...

Johnny's brothers and sisters kept coming in to see how he was, and by the Saturday he was so crazy they were talking about putting a strait jacket on him. By now I was completely exhausted, I hadn't been to bed for days.

'Go next door to Lily's and rest your eyes a bit. Get her to make you somethin',' Mr Robinson said. 'I'll look after him. Don't worry.'

But I couldn't sleep there, I just sat at the table with my head in my hands and started to cry. Something was really wrong, something was seriously the matter with Johnny, I knew that now. I couldn't keep on kidding myself there wasn't. No cold does this to anybody. Suddenly I heard somebody shouting 'Get the doctor! Quick!'

I rushed back. Mr Robinson was badly shaken up and was in a terrible mess with his hair all over the place and his clothes all torn and pulled out, just as though he'd been in a scrap. Apparently Charley and three of Johnny's friends who'd called, had only just managed to stop Johnny from strangling his father. They'd sent for a straitjacket but Mr Robinson wouldn't allow them to put it on.

I raced back to the doctor's house, grabbed the speaker outside the front door and shouted up.

'Can the doctor come to Mill Street straight away? My husband's very poorly! It's serious this time!'

'Is that Robinson of Mill Street...? John Robinson..?' It was Dalziel himself.

'Yes..! Hurry, will ye!'

'It's no good me coming down. I can't do any more for him,' the voice came down through the speaker tube.

'What d'ye mean..? We need ye to come! Please! Now!'

There was no answer and the speaker just clicked off.

A young feller was standing behind me, waiting his turn.

'Please, mister,' I said, and I was sobbing now. 'I'm in such a state, I don't know what he said... Will you ask for is..? Quick! Please be quick! It's me man. Johnny Robinson. He's very ill..! He doesn't seem to realise,' I said, pointing to the speaker.

The feller did what I asked and got through to Dalziel. Then he hung it up again. 'Sorry, hinny. He says he can't do a thing. It's too late. You'd best get back home.'

I ran all the way back home with the tears running down my face.

When I got there, there was nobody there except Mr Robinson. He was still sitting by the bed, very quiet. Bed linen had been torn to shreds and scattered all over the room and there were more feathers than ever all over the place. The brass bedstead was bent and twisted, some of the spars had been snapped, and the knobs were lying on the floor.

Johnny was hanging over the end of the bed, only his legs were still covered.

I heaved him back on and laid him on his back. Mr Robinson was watching me as though he was in a dream.

While I was out at the doctor's Johnny had got up and stood in front of the mirror and very carefully combed his hair. Then he had asked for a glass of water, drank it, bit a lump out of the glass, spat it out, got back into bed, and died.

'Double pneumonia' the doctor said it was, though neither he nor any of his partners had said it when he was alive. According to them it had been a heavy cold and they had never said any different, not once.

All the time Johnny was ill Mrs Robinson had never been to see him. All of the rest of his family had...and nearly all his pals, but not his own mother. It couldn't have been that she didn't care, I would never say that and neither could anybody, because Johnny had been her favourite just as he'd been his father's. It was because she was on a ran-tan, and gin would have been the thing on her mind, nobody even knew where she was.

10

When I'd come back and found Johnny the way he was, and put him back into the bed, I didn't say anything to Mr Robinson and he didn't say anything to me. He had just sat there looking at the floor and I had begun to tidy up. I'd rolled up my sleeves and swept and cleaned, and all night I swept and swept and I cleaned and cleaned, shifting things round, putting them back and shifting them again, dusting them, polishing them and then dusting and polishing them again.

First thing next morning there was a knock on the door. When I opened it, the handywoman was standing there with her little case.

'What do you want?' I said to her.

She just smiled and put her hand on mine and then walked over to the bed where Johnny was lying. She pulled away the pillows from under his head and straightened him out. When I realised what she was doing, I rushed over to the bed and felt Johnny's face. It was a cold as ice.

'Oh, Johnny, Johnny, Johnny! Oh, me Johnny! It's true... It's really true... You've gone, haven't ye, Johnny..?'

All the time, the handywoman was quietly going about her business, gently doing what she had to do, and I hardly noticed when she closed the door behind her and was gone.

Mr Robinson had just sat very still in the corner, looking on and never saying a word to anybody.

'What'll I do, Dad?' I said to him. 'Whatever am I goin' to do now?'

'Sit down, pet. Bring your chair over here... Francie, I've got three daughters... One is good. One I won't mention. And one is special. And the special one is you.'

'Don't say them things, Dad. They're all your bairns. They're your own flesh and blood.'

'I know that. But I'm going to tell you somethin'... You're not

140

goin' to have anythin' to worry about any more. The way I intend, ye'll be better off as a widow than ye ever were as a wife... And I'm not sayin' that because I didn't love my son. You know that...

'You look after the lodgin' house the way you are now, and I'm goin' to see that it's put into your name... As for the two bairns, they can come to the Model Lodging House and help me with the books when they get on a bit. I'll see them all right. I'll treat them as if they were my own bairns. Neither you nor them will ever want for a thing.'

As we were talking, Charley Whyte came in with the priest who was very upset and kept apologising over and over again and it was obvious he hadn't given Johnny his Last Rites. The day before, somebody had brought him but he hadn't thought Johnny was poorly enough. And now he was sorry, but there wasn't much he could do now.

'He was such a fit man... Only the other day I - '

'Well it's too late now, Father,' I said. 'But my Johnny wasn't a bad man. No just God will put him in Hell. I'm certain of it.'

'I'm sure you're right, Francie,' he said. 'But I'm going to say a few prayers all the same.' And he got his little book out and said a few prayers and we all joined in.

There was a little service at the church for Johnny that night, but it was bitterly cold and Mr Robinson wasn't too well and had gone for a lie-down at Stoker and Lily's straight after. Later on he came over.

'Now remember what I told ye, Francie. I don't want you worryin' about a thing. Go and order whatever ye want for the funeral and choose any headstone you want. I'm payin' for everythin'. Tell them to send all the bills to me.'

Just then Mrs Robinson came in with Mary Ellen. Mr Robinson turned straight on her.

'And what kind of a mother d'ye think you are, eh..? You're no mother at all..! You've been so bloody drunk for so long, ye didn't even know the lad's been bad...never mind dead... I'm takin' my name off any door that has yours on it. I don't want to be associated with ye any more.'

She didn't say a word, she just sat there for a while and then she and Mary Ellen got up and went.

After a while Mr Robinson said he had to go over home for a while, he didn't say why but I think it must have been to lie down because he didn't look well at all, and I was left on my own for the first time. I'd been sitting there for about half an hour when old Mrs Hancock from the market came in with a sandwich and a pot of tea. The only way for me to heat any water would have been to put the fire on, so I hadn't even been able to boil a kettle. Because of the time of year it took a long time to get buried, and I was scared to light the fire in case it would turn poor Johnny, I'd already poured two bottles of whiskey down his throat and still he was turning.

During the dark and freezing cold days Johnny lay in that room waiting to be buried, hardly a soul came near the place. I still had to go and see to the lodgers and I still had to see to the bairns, and sometimes I had to leave Johnny by himself. Every time I came back into that room, it was like realising for the first time that he was really dead; and sometimes I even kidded myself I saw him smiling and that maybe he was just asleep after all and would get up in a while, or I would look back over my shoulder at him and think he'd moved. I hardly knew what I was doing or what day it was as I waited with him for the hours to tick away, I just slept in a chair because the bed had been taken down to make room for the flowers and wreaths that were arriving by the score every day. Geordie came once or twice to see his brother but he only stayed a very short while. The Robinsons seemed as if they couldn't cope with the situation, it seemed to me they had never taken sickness or death into account. And now that Johnny, the favourite of the whole lot of them, had gone...just like that...they didn't know what hit them.

Some people probably thought that because Johnny was a prize-fighter, we would have plenty of money. But it was the promoters and backers who made all the money, Johnny never got what was shown on the bills; eighteen pounds was all we had saved from his share of the takings from all of his fights, and neither of us were spendthrifts. The night after Johnny died, a man kept banging on the windows and doors shouting 'Open the door! Open the door! I've got somethin' to tell ye!'

It was a strange voice to my ears and I kept shouting back, 'Go away whoever you are! Go away and leave us alone!'

For an hour or more he knocked and banged, until at last, Big

Ginger Porter must have been passing by and heard him. Ginger grabbed him by the neck, turned him upside down, and shook him until all the money came out of his pocket, and then kicked him all the way down the stairs and out into the street.

'Open up, Francie!' he shouted. 'You're all right now. It's only me...Constable Porter... Get the bairns to pick up these coins. They're yours now. I'll keep an eye on ye. Don't worry, he won't be back.'

The next night somebody else came and did the same thing. This time I knocked hard on the fireplace wall to waken Stoker who lived next door, and he came rushing out and up the stairs. But whoever it was had gone. The third night, the same thing happened again and it was really getting on my nerves. But I was mad as hell, so I thought 'I'll have ye mesel' this time, ye bugger! Either that, or you'll have me!' I grabbed the poker, opened the door, and rushed into the pitch dark swinging the poker. 'Whoosh! Whoosh!' I went until I connected with something.

'Ow!' this voice yelled, and this feller grabbed hold of me and the two of us struggled as he lifted me right off my feet and into the room. As he came through the door, his face was familiar as one of the ones who used to hang around Johnny, and this made me so furious that I dropped the poker and clawed at his face with both hands until my hands were sticky with skin and blood. He cursed and swore but let me go and ran out and away up the street.

All that night I couldn't get his face out of my mind; and then I remembered who he was. First thing next morning I got somebody to mind Johnny and the bairns while I went out. I found where the swine lived and knocked on his door.

His wife answered.

'Is your husband in?'

'Who are you? What d'ye want?'

'You'll find out soon enough. Get him! And get him right now..! Because if ye don't, I'm bringin' a policeman to this door. And, mark my words, he'll soon have him out.'

She went in and was ages coming back, and I was just about to go to the police station, when she came back with him right behind her.

He had his face hidden and said in this meek voice, 'I'm very sorry, Francie. I didn't realise it was you... I thought it was somebody else... I thought... I'd had a few beers and I...I must've got lost...

143

Honestly, I...'

'See the sod's face, missus..? Him..? D'ye know how he got those marks on his face..? He came to my house and tried to get me last night, he did... The bloody swine!'

'I told ye, Francie. It was a mistake...'

'It was a mistake, all right..! A very big mistake..! And if you ever make one like that at my door again, I swear it'll be the last mistake you ever make! Because I'll poke your rotten bloody eyes out!'

The funeral procession left from my house at two o'clock on Wednesday the 7th January 1914 and went through the main streets of South Shields which were lined from one end to the other with people who had come to see Johnny pass by for the last time, ordinary people who had admired Johnny Robinson as a boxer and loved him as a man. It was the biggest funeral Shields had seen for many a day, landaus pulled by black horses took him to the cemetery at Harton, and all the boxing and sporting public followed it to the graveside. There were all kinds of tributes in words and in flowers, but none of them brought him back. And when the last old boxer and supporter had limped away, Johnny was the only one left behind. Everybody said they were shocked, nobody could believe it; they talked among themselves and shook their heads and said it was terrible. But it was true, no matter they'd seen him just a fortnight ago in the pink of health, no matter they were just talking the other day about him taking on Sterling and giving him a trouncing, no matter he had a wife and two bairns that loved him and who now had nobody. And when I saw his coffin lowered into the grave, I knew it too.

The reception afterwards was at the Robinsons', and me and the bairns were supposed to stay there for the following week until I'd pulled myself together and things got sorted out. Mrs Robinson said the best thing would be for me to give Joe and Johnny to her for her and their grandfather to bring up.

'No, thank you, Mrs Robinson,' I said. 'They're Johnny's and my bairns and I'll bring them up meself. No matter what happens, they're not leavin' me.' I knew she didn't like it, and that night when I was sitting in the kitchen suckling Joe, I asked Geordie if I could have a pot of cold tea...what with all that had happened this past week, I wasn't making sufficient milk.

'Give the bitch a jug of piss! That's good enough for her!' I heard Mrs Robinson yell.

I put the bairn down, fastened myself up, packed my things and went home.

Mr Robinson had looked ill at the funeral and had taken to his bed as soon as he'd got home, he'd had nothing to do with the reception afterwards. So as soon as I'd attended to the lodging house next morning, I went over to see him. I hated going over to the place now that Johnny would never again be there, and I wouldn't have gone except that I thought the world of Mr Robinson. There had been so much of him in Johnny and I felt he was the one contact I had left with him.

He was pleased to see me when I went in, and asked if I'd rub his chest with mustard ointment, which I did gladly, and I wiped his face and hands with a damp cloth and tidied him up; he was such a huge man that the sweat just poured off him. He wouldn't have the doctor because he said he had no more time for them, especially after Johnny, and nobody seemed to be bothering very much about him; like Johnny, he was one that never ailed anything. I had to keep going back to do my work at the lodging house and see to the bairns, but whenever I had half an hour to spare I'd pop over to see how he was, give him a rub and a wipe and a drink of hot milk in a little cup with a spout that I'd got; he was so bad he couldn't drink without dribbling...and I knew he could never abide anybody who did.

One afternoon he said 'Francie, tell Sally to come up. I want a word with her. Tell her I want her to fetch a solicitor so I can put things right for you and the bairns.'

When I went down and told Mrs Robinson what he'd said, she shouted up, 'Harry, you're bloody mad! You don't know what you're talking about.'

Old Mrs Cairns, Mrs Robinson's mother, was sitting there and she said to her, 'Sally, I think you ought to do what he says, hadn't ye...and send for the solicitor?'

'He doesn't want a doctor, yet he wants a solicitor..? Huh..! No bloody solicitor's getting past me!'

'When he gets up, he'll murder ye.'

'He doesn't know what he's saying. That's just the fever talking...making him sentimental, it is. In a couple of days he'll have forgotten everything.'

I don't know whether he would have forgotten or not, but Mrs Robinson didn't bring anybody, and a few hours later I think he had more on his mind than that. I'd been up with him and told him I had to go and buy a black hat out of respect for Johnny, or soon I wouldn't be able to show my face in the street.

'Where's it you're goin' to?'

'Just to Mordains in Frederick Street. I'll not be long.'

'Ye don't want to be goin' out this time of night. Let it wait till tomorrow.'

'I cannot leave it any longer, Dad...it's not right. I'll go the back ways. I'll be there and back in no time.'

'If ye do, I'll not be here when ye get back.'

'What d'ye mean?'

'I'll be with Johnny.'

'Don't talk so silly, Dad! Come on... It's not fair to talk like that. And ye know it's not.'

'If you go out of here, I want ye to turn me over first.' Every time before I went out I had to turn him on to a certain side. 'Turn me so I'm facin' Johnny,' he would say. 'I feel nearer to him on the other side.'

He was very hard to shift with being twenty stone or more, and I'd have to take my shoes off and climb on the bed and get him to put his arm around my shoulder, and then I'd heave and heave till I got him far enough over so he was content. Then I'd wipe him down again because all the effort of moving would have him soaked in sweat.

'All right,' I said. And I did what he asked... 'I'll have to go now, Dad. Or they'll be shut.'

'Ye'd better give's a kiss before ye go,' he said as I was going out the door. 'Because this time I won't be here when ye get back.'

'Now, now, Dad... You're only sayin' that to make me stay. You'll pull through. Nothin' could kill you.'

But he was right... The shop was shut when I got there, and by the time I got back he'd gone. It was only half past five when I went out, and I'd been out no more than three quarters of an hour, yet they were already washing and laying him out by the time I got back. It was only five days after his son, and I couldn't believe it.

They wrote 'Pneumonia' on his certificate but that didn't mean a thing, they'd put that on Johnny's and Johnny's illness had been a lot different. Everybody knew Henry Robinson had died of a broken heart. But they never put things like that down.

With Johnny and his father gone, any doubts I might have had about being entirely on my own from now on, were ended when I was sent Johnny's funeral bill on Mrs Robinson's say-so. A few days after I got it, I plucked up the courage to take the two bairns and visit Johnny's grave for the first time. It was a bitterly cold day and I was carrying Joe with a few flowers tucked in his shawl. My eyes lit up when I saw the beautiful greeny black headstone and cross that had been put up, and I went round to the front to read it.

JOHN
The Dearly Beloved Son Of
HENRY & SARAH ROBINSON,
Who Died Jan. 4TH 1914,
Aged 24 Years

My eyes filled with tears so bitter they scalded my eyes, and I could hardly keep them open as I read the words over and over and over again. There wasn't a mention about me and the bairns; not a word, not a single letter of my name or theirs. You'd think the body lying there had never been married and had no bairns at all, never mind three of them. No mention about leaving a loving or grieving wife behind, the way you usually see on gravestones. Anybody reading it would think I never existed, that I was nothing, that I was no more than his whore. I was kneeling down scratching at the soil with my fingers, trying to talk to my husband, trying to talk to the man who had loved me above everybody but God, trying to change things in some way, begging Johnny to come out of his grave and hold me or say something.

I hadn't noticed a man that had been standing back a bit, but now he came up.

'Come on, lass. Get up.' He helped me to my feet.

'I'm that man's wife, ye know. And these are his two little bairns.'

'I know,' he said. 'I can imagine what you're thinking.'

'You seem like an educated man,' I said to him. 'So can ye tell me this... Is there any law to stop me puttin' my name on there? And my bairns...his bairns..? Do I have any rights to do it, do ye know?'

'I don't know that you can do that. They mightn't let you touch the stone if it belongs to his family. But you can go to the undertakers and get a little stone of your own, and get them to write on what you want. They'll even put a bit poetry on for you. Then you could put it here.'

'How do I know they wouldn't just toss it out of the way?'

'Oh, they couldn't very well do a thing like that...even if they've paid for the grave.'

'But they didn't..! I'm havin' to pay for it.'

I could see he was really shocked.

'Would it cost very much money, d'ye think?'

'I'll tell you what... You go down to the mason's and tell them what you want, and I'll pay for it. I'll give you my name and address, and you give it to them. You don't know me, but I knew Johnny very well. I made plenty out of backing him. I owe him something for it.'

I thanked him very much but told him, 'No, I could never do that. He was my husband. You're just a stranger.'

A few days later I found out that Mrs Robinson had had everybody in the family up to see the headstone they'd put up, I was the only one not invited.

I went to the mason's, like the gentleman had suggested, and got them to put a few words on a piece of stone shaped like a heart on a trunk of a tree; it had little Alfie's name on it as well. It would take a long time to pay for it but I'd do it and I'd do it without asking anybody to pay a penny towards it.

Now that Mr Robinson and Johnny had gone, Charley Whyte was left at a loose end and he became a right nuisance. Mr Robinson was brought up on fairgrounds, with his father having the travelling boxing booths, and he was used to people that other people would call freaks; he'd lived amongst them and knew they were human beings like anybody else and that some of them were very good at some things. He'd always said Charley was a damned good trainer and that's why he put him with Johnny. But most people didn't think the way he did, and many thought a hunchback would be useless to train anybody for any sport, and that it didn't look good to have one hanging around. So Charley now found it very difficult to earn his keep, and I don't think being over forty years of age was a help.

I used to be glad that Johnny had somebody to take care of him and wait on him hand and foot, even though it might have spoilt him a bit, and I know that Charley was really more dependant on Johnny than Johnny was on him. But all that had now come to an end through nobody's fault, and Charley had to get on with his life just like I had to get on with mine. I'd bought him a suit for the funeral because he'd nothing decent to wear, it was only a second-hand one for about twelve bob but it looked all right. And I gave him money for drink from time to time, even though I could ill afford it, because drink seemed to be the only thing that seemed to help. But I think he took it the wrong way. If ever I was doing something or talking to somebody, and he came in, he'd expect me to drop whatever I was doing, or interrupt whoever I was talking to, to attend to him; and if I didn't, he'd stamp off in a huff. He also became very jealous and followed me wherever I went, inside the lodging house or out of it, and I realised he was trying to take Johnny's place with me; so I had no alternative but to put him out. A few weeks later I heard he'd lost his senses so I brought him back to look after him. I nursed him for five days, but in the finish I couldn't stand it any more, he took any kindness the wrong way, and I had to have him taken away to the madhouse. Soon after that he died and they sent for me to have him buried, I was the nearest thing to a relative the poor feller had.

In just over a year, I'd lost a son, a husband and a father; I knew Mr Robinson wasn't my real father but he was more of a father to me than my own had ever been. Things had been hard enough before, but at least Johnny had brought some money in; and although he never interfered in any trouble at the lodging house, knowing that he was never very far away had always made me feel safe. Because everybody knew I was married to Johnny Robinson, it stopped them from trying anything; after all, I was a young woman alone amongst all those men, and men are men no matter what their calling. I knew I could expect little support from Mrs Robinson, and I couldn't turn to my own family because most of them were worse off than I was.

I think Mrs Robinson wanted something belonging to Johnny, maybe because she was his mother, because through different ones...Harry, Geordie and the sisters at different times...she tried again and again to get me to let her have Johnny and Joe. But I'd seen the way she was bringing up their cousin Harry, after his mother had left his father, and I wouldn't even leave them there for a weekend. Everybody knows you have to give kids a clout now and then, but she used to box his ears so hard, and she was such a big tough woman, that many a time I've seen the blood running from them and his nose as well. She used to have him up and down to the hospital at Newcastle because of this awful running nose he had, but I think it was due to all the bashing about she gave him. It was the sort of thing you'd expect from some fathers, but never from mothers.

The rooms the bairns and me were living in, as well as the lodging house, were owned by the Robinsons...which now meant Mrs Robinson. I was paying her sixteen shillings a week, but from the two furnished rooms I let out I was getting eight shillings apiece, so that paid for the rent. There were forty-seven beds in Thrift Street Lodging House and they all cost thruppence a night, and if a lodger paid a full week in advance, he got one free night. Out of this I had to find all the lodging house expenses...the hundredweight of cinders every day, summer and winter, the firewood, cooking things, cutlery, crockery, cleaning stuff, bedding and laundry. What was left was what I had to live on.

As time went on, things seemed to be getting harder rather than easier, and as I walked the cobbled streets back and forwards to the lodging house every day, sometimes I'd be extra tired and slip on the wet and fall to the ground, and it would seem like the very stones under my feet were turning against me. I was lonely with only the bairns for company, it always seemed to be drizzling or foggy and the days seemed without end and so did the nights. But as I scrubbed and swilled, as I humped sacks and cooked meals, I thought and I thought how best I could feed and clothe my bairns, what was the best way to keep them healthy and bring them up decent, and most important of all, how could I keep them and not have them taken off me by the workhouse or anybody.

I made up my mind that I'd give less time than ever for talking or playing with them, for taking them to the park or the beach or anything like that, no matter how much I might want to. I'd bring them up to be honest and decent and hope that God would take care of the other things, and that when they grew up they'd one day understand. It wasn't my way to be a dampener on anybody's enjoyment; quite the opposite, I'd always been cheerful and loved a good laugh, a singsong or a bit carry-on. But if I had to choose between work and play, there was no doubt in my mind which came first.

The Town Hall people were forever concerned about epidemics, and I know it was their job to be, but sometimes it was hard to believe they weren't just being awkward for awkward's sake. They were always changing the regulations for the sake of public health, but they always made life harder and never easier; I never knew a single change that was welcomed by anybody, lodger or keeper; not a single change that saved either time or money; and if people's health was any the better for it, I must say I never noticed the difference.

You now had to have your buckets of slops emptied and the yard swilled out by nine every morning, instead of ten, and all your windows open even if it was blowing a gale or they were covered in frost. Worst of all, the rooms had to be lime-washed four times a year. The idea behind it was to keep down the bugs and fleas, but it was a horrible job; it used to make your face, your arms, your hands, and anywhere else it splashed on, red and sore. Inspectors came every week and if they saw as much as a matchstick on the floor, they'd tell you to bend down and pick it up. Mind, I always kept my place very clean in any case and most of the inspectors I had were kind; they might have taken backhanders from the Robinsons and other lodging-house keepers, but they never took any from me, and if ever I offered, they'd say 'If you've anything to spare, Francie, give it to the bairns.'

But one day a new man came. 'Scrub this. Scrub that,' he went on. 'I'm not satisfied with this. I'm not satisfied with that. Do it again. And then when you've done it, do it again.'

Every bed-frame had to be scrubbed, be they iron or be they wood, all forty-seven of them. I don't know whether he was just starting the job and trying to impress his bosses, or whether he had it in for me, but back he came day after day until I was nearly past myself. I daren't offer him a tip in case he had me up for bribery, because if anybody would, it would be him; on the other hand, I didn't know whether he was mad because I hadn't offered one. I didn't know what to do to satisfy him. This particular morning I was really worn out when he came in, and before he could say a word, I said 'I don't care if ye take the place off is, mister. Ye can do whatever ye like. But I cannot keep this up on top of everything else. Ye'd put somebody in an asylum, you would. There's no need for it. I'm goin' to find someplace else.'

But he couldn't have cared less; even if I got another place, he said, he'd come and make me do exactly the same. All the lodgers knew what was going on and they knew what a time I'd had what with losing Alfie and Johnny and everything, and they went mad; they started clashing all the pots and pans together and throwing them into the street and making such a commotion the police came.

'What's going on here?' they said. I told them my side of things, the inspector then said his piece, and the lodgers said theirs. Eventually the sergeant sent to the Town Hall for the chief inspector. When he came I told him everything. 'Find any fault ye can, sir. Go on, have a good look around. I'm at my wits' end with this gentleman.'

'What!' he said, he knew me and he knew I always kept a clean place. 'This is ridiculous..! Don't worry, Francie. I'll see this never happens again.' He was a real nice man, this one, and he said he'd see if he could pull a few strings and get me a place of my own, a smaller place, maybe in Holborn where they were cheaper.

'I'm very grateful to you, sir,' I said. And a few days later he did come up with something, but it was too dear and it had already been condemned, so it would probably have been more trouble than it was worth.

11

Nellie had emigrated to Canada in 1911 and even though I wasn't much of a letter-writer we'd always kept in touch, as we promised each other we would; if I hadn't kept in touch with her, nobody would and she'd have lost contact with the family altogether. I had written to her after Johnny died and she had written straight back telling me to come to Canada. Sep now had a good job and they were doing well and they would pay mine and the bairns' fare out and arrange everything from their side. She made it sound like heaven on earth and it seemed such a wonderful chance to make a fresh start in life, that I said yes I would. The thing about a place as far away as Canada, was even if you wrote straight back it took a long time for the letters to go back an forth, and before we could arrange anything, world war broke out. It was a long time before I got an answer from Nellie to say that although she'd done everything she possibly could, it was too dangerous to get on a boat just then and that in any case the Navy had taken over all shipping.

Canada wasn't going to be the answer to my problems so I thought I'd just stick in where I was and see if I could get a lodging house of my own. There were quite a few around and it depended where they were, what kind or class they were. Those on the docks were what we called 'skid-enders', and had mostly sailors and 'trade' in them, and I wouldn't want to have anything to do with those. Mr Robinson had had a very big one in Mill Street for men and I certainly wouldn't have minded that one, but there was no way I could have afforded it even if Mrs Robinson had been prepared to part with it. She wouldn't even let me have Thrift Street and I was already in it. There were two others in Thrift Street owned by Grants but they were hanging on to them.

Holborn, which was known as 'Old Shields', had umpteen lodging houses, and I would keep my eyes and ears open to see if anything came up there. Holborn was a kind of Arab quarter, but I never had anything against Arabs or coloured fellers of any kind, although some lodging houses wouldn't have them as lodgers at any price. I had ones that were as honest and as clean as anybody, and I had ones that were just the opposite, the same as you got with people with fair skin. The main trouble with having coloured fellers was that the other lodgers didn't like them, and if there was only one, they'd more than likely gang up on him. Some of the lodgers were the scruffiest buggers in the world and yet the same ones would complain if a darky came in because they said darkies never bothered to wash themselves.

I once had two and they were as black as you could get, but they were big and strong so they were generally left alone. Every Sunday morning three or four of their mates would come to see them and they'd all gather round and sit on the floor...although it was a stone floor it was clean enough to eat your food off...and they'd play music and sing for a couple of hours. It was really pleasant, just quiet stuff, and it was entertainment for the rest of us as well. These two used to have a very thorough wash at least once every day, and wash their feet two or three times a week. I knew it was really none of my business and I certainly wasn't complaining, but I couldn't help asking them why. They looked at each other and laughed and the biggest one says to me in this very deep voice, 'Well, Ma'am, the reason is 'cos we smell like niggers if we don't.'

Another reason why many lodging houses wouldn't take coloureds was because they all knew about one who used to tie his wife to the bed and do all sorts of things to her. He was put out of the country for it, even though he didn't want to leave Shields and he didn't want to leave his wife who was a Shields woman.

Arabs especially were very religious and every time before they had a meal they'd go and fetch their prayer book and read so much out of it; then as soon as they'd had their meal, they'd go and wash their hands, get the prayer book again and read a bit more. I hadn't been brought up to say grace before meals or anything, there were never enough of what you might call 'meals' to make it worthwhile; and I never knew what these fellers were saying; but it did your heart good to see it and hear them at their worship. When they eventually went, that was the end of it and I was sorry; they'd brought their God into the lodging house and I think the place was the better for it.

I nearly adopted one once. He was about fifteen when he first came, with only a pair of carpet slippers on his feet, and I felt really sorry for him; I think he must have jumped ship but I couldn't understand a word he said and neither could anybody else. He was with me for about five months and he never had any money. I'd get him to do little bits of jobs around the place but he was never much good, you couldn't trust him to do anything properly. When he learned to say a few words he'd say 'I pay back, missus. Some day.' I think he might have come from a well-off family somewhere in the world because he had a little box with lots of important looking papers in it, all in a foreign language. One day he said 'Me got ship. Go now. These for you.' He was handing me the box with all the papers in. 'Much money,' he kept saying. 'You take.' But I said 'No, I don't want your papers, son. Take them and everything else that's belongin' to ye. I want nothin'.' He might have needed them for when he got back to wherever he was going, they might even have been pinched and could have landed me in a lot of trouble; at best, it would have looked as though I was taking advantage of the poor lad. Anyway, he went without me ever knowing what was in them and I never saw him again, though I often wondered what they were.

I always felt sorry for bairns that weren't looked after, even though I had enough to do looking after my own, and when this quack who was a heavy drinker once came, I only let him in because he had this poor half-starved lad with him. The lad must have been about fourteen but runty, though bonny and ever so canny. He got on so well with my bairns that I used to feed him, look after him and try to be a mother to him when his father was away. However the father soon realised I had a soft spot for the lad because he sometimes used to go away for weeks on end without saying where he was going or when he'd be back, and would leave him behind in the lodging house without a farthing in his pocket.

Willy was old enough to have left school, and I'd have trusted him anywhere with Joe and Johnny because he was so sensible and good-natured, so I asked him if he would like to stop with me, and he said yes he would. 'Well, ye'll have to ask your dad to make sure it's all right with him,' I told him. So he asked his father and his father agreed, and I made him part of the family. I brought him upstairs to live with us, I fed him and clothed him and fitted him out with a proper little white jacket and boots and got him a job as a painter's apprentice. They were delighted with his work and said they'd be happy to keep him on and let him serve his time, so I got him a little suit for Sunday best as a reward. Then one Friday night he never came home from work and I was worried sick in case anything had happened to him. Had he fallen off a ladder or had somebody stolen his pay off him and he was frightened to come home without it..?

But it wasn't anything like that. His father had seen him on the Thursday and told him to put all his clothes on and parcel up his suit and things so I wouldn't know what it was, and then he had met the lad after work when he'd got his pay, and taken him away. The lad didn't tell me, I just heard about it, and it broke my heart that he would do such a thing. When he hadn't come home that night I'd sent two of my lodgers around all the lodging houses but they couldn't find him. A few weeks later he came back himself with scarcely a stitch to his back, dirty and half starved, and full of apologies saying he'd never do anything like that again. So I took him back in, cleaned him and fed him up and got him a new set of clothes...although of course he'd lost his job by now. A few weeks later he did the same again, and again he came back with nowt; and again I took him because I thought his father must have been forcing him. But then the same thing happened again and again, and each time we found him, or his father sent him back, he'd be hungry, dirty and in rags. I felt I couldn't blame the lad for doing what his father was telling him to do even though it was wrong, and he was so little and lost-looking I was sure he had no life at all when he wasn't with me. But it got so that I couldn't stand it any more and in the finish I said 'Willy, you're old enough to realise what you're doin' to me...and to little Johnny and Joe. If your father is makin' ye do wrong, tell me, and we'll go to the police about him. Otherwise I'm givin' ye one more chance. If ye do it again...if ye go away without sayin' anythin', ye'll have to stay with your dad and not come back here ever again.'

He did go away and I never saw hide nor hair of him or his father again. It really broke my heart and at first I was half praying he would come back; but he didn't, and I didn't send anybody looking for him this time as I'd said I wouldn't, and I couldn't go to the police because he wasn't my bairn. So whether he was just cute, and in on it with his father all along, and the two of them did it in other places as well, wherever they found somebody softhearted enough, God knows. But I loved him like he was one of my own and I hope he came to no harm, though I doubt it.

I had heard that my sister Lizzie was forever in and out of the workhouse and going from bad to worse in her habits, so I made up my mind to find out where she was and go and see her; Nellie always asked about her in her letters. I found her in Middlesborough and she seemed to me to be going crackers. She'd taken up with this feller who had something to do with the church but didn't do anything in the way of real work that I could see, certainly nothing that brought any money in, and they seemed to have bairns scattered all over the place, some looked after by this one and some by another; Lizzie herself was in an awful state.

There was only one thing you could say for Lizzie, filthy though she was and bad as she might be, and with her looks all gone, and that was that she was one of the hardest workers you could ever come across. It was always men's work she did, she was no use at housekeeping or anything, and she fetched and carried at the docks or loaded wagons at the brickyards, side by side with anybody. My father had once got her a job as a brickie's labourer and she worked on the building sites a long time. Whatever money Lizzie and her feller had, came from Lizzie's hard labour; the kind of men Lizzie got, she had to keep.

When I'd found her and got her on her own, I says 'Are ye married to this feller, Lizzie?'

'Yes, I am.'

'When..? Where were ye married?'

'That's my business.'

'Look, Lizzie,' I said to her. 'It's your business all right, I know that. But I'm still your sister, and I'm worried about ye...we all are... Jinny, Alice, Lily, and Nellie as well. Surely to God you're not livin' in sin again..? Why can't ye get yoursel' married..? Ye said he was a widower. Well, if he is...and he loves ye, let him marry ye and take responsibility for ye.'

'Ye don't know what you're talkin' about, Francie. Ye think ye know everythin' but ye know nowt. I've never seen Jinny and them for years. You're all too busy lookin' after yourselves to bother about

157

anybody else.'

I could see I was getting nowhere so I said 'Look. Let me take Maggie.' Maggie was her eldest daughter and was twelve and ready to go astray. 'I'll feed her and clothe her and she can look after my bairns while I'm at work.' I could do extra work over and above the lodging house if I had somebody to mind Joe and Johnny. She agreed so I brought Maggie away with me.

Maggie wasn't a bad lass and once you'd shown her what to do, she'd do it. Like her mother, she had a few rough edges, you couldn't expect much else under the circumstances, and like her mother she wasn't afraid of hard work. She now minded the bairns and kept the home tidy, and I started making snacks and selling them to the lodgers. I'd make buns, and with each one I'd give a little packet with a teaspoonful of tea, a teaspoonful of sugar and a bit of dried milk, enough to make a pot of tea, and sell it for a penny. Lodgers couldn't afford to buy a whole packet of tea, a whole bag of sugar or a whole bottle of milk; and even if they had, it would have walked long before they'd had a chance to use it up.

These snacks went down so well that I started getting off-cuts of beef and other cheap tasty scraps from the market, and making bowls of soup which I sold for a ha'penny a bowl, tuppence a basin. Soon people from outside the lodging house heard about my cheap but good food, and they began to come with their pennies and their basins. So I stuck a notice in the window saying 'Good Soup and Fresh Buns For Sale Inside.' Then I began making 'threeha'penny starvers', like my mother used to make, and other such things that looked nice and tasted good...'starvers' were dry oven-bottom bread sandwiches with a slice of corn-beef, and they were most popular of all. There were three public houses near the lodging house, one practically either side of us and one straight across the road, and the workmen used to come in for a starver to have with their gill of beer.

Things were really beginning to look up, when one night the feller Lizzie was living with turned up. He asked for money to 'buy the bairn'...by this he meant pay for an abortion. I asked him if it was our Lizzie he was talking about and he said 'No, it's one of my girls.'

'What have ye come to me for then?' I said to him. 'Go to one of your own relations.'

Then he said it was Lizzie. He was such a slimy character and I hated him so much for what he was doing to my sister, that I picked up a kettle that was boiling on the fire and I rushed up to him. 'Get out..! Get out, ye sod! And don't ever come back here with your wickedness!'

A few days later Lizzie came asking the same thing and threatening to take Maggie back if I didn't give her the money. I wasn't going to have anything to do with bargains of that sort and I told her I wasn't.

'In that case Maggie isn't stayin' here a minute longer...just so you can rake it in.'

'Please yourself,' I said. I parcelled up the few clothes I'd bought for Maggie, and gave her the shillings I'd been putting aside in a moneybox. I'd been doing Lizzie a favour if she'd but realised it, but I never saw Maggie ever again and I never saw Lizzie for a long time either.

There was an old cobbler's shop joined on to the lodging house and for a long time I'd been thinking to myself, 'If only I could get that shop, I could bake all kinds of things and sell it in the window.' With the lodging house fire being on all day every day and the oven red hot, it was a waste not to be making it pay for itself, and I was there all the time to keep an eye on it. On top of the baking, I could buy bags of flour, tea, salt, sugar and other basic groceries that could be split into small lots, and sell little packets of it that couldn't be bought anywhere else. Most shops wouldn't be bothered with selling by the teaspoonful, but I would; I'd make it a shop for poor folks that only lived from one meal to the next, and there was a lot of them near where I was.

An old lady called Mrs Prince had a busy little grocery just across the road and up a bit, and she rented the old cobbler's shop from Mrs Robinson, as a store. She must have known what was on my mind because one day when we were chatting on she said 'You know, that little cobbler's shop would be just right for you, Francie...to sell your buns and things in... I've got a good business going here to occupy me, and don't really need the cobbler's shop as well. I've really only been keeping it to make sure nobody opened up next door to me. Anyway, I'm getting on now and won't be bothered with it for too much longer...There's lots of odds and ends that would be very handy to help you get started. There's some good strong bins and a whole lot of glass jars. A pair of scales that only want a drop of oil and they'd be perfect. There's all the shelves you could ever want. There's even a few sacks of potatoes and lentils. And a good bit of flour...good stuff, it is as well... I don't need any of it. You can have it. And I don't want anything for it. All I want is to see you doing all right.'

'What about yourself? Won't it spoil you if I started..? It wouldn't be fair on you.'

'Look, hinny. You need the money...I know that. I've got enough to get me by. Anyway, I'm not doing the sort of stuff you'd be doing. We won't clash. Don't you worry about that. There's ample business round here for both of us.'

'Eeeh, thank you, Mrs Prince... And how much will ye be wantin' for it..? For everythin'?'

'Let's see... Eight pounds..? Is that all right for you?'

'That's fine, thank you. I'll away for the money and be straight back. I'll ask Mrs Robinson to lend is it. After all, it's for the good of her own grandbairns.'

But Mrs Robinson refused to lend me any money.

'Where on earth do you think I can lay my hands on money that sort of money, Francie Nichol..? Do you think I'm made of money or something!'

'I can really make a go of it, Mrs Robinson. I know I can. If ye'll only lend is the money, I'll pay every penny of it back. As it comes to me, I'll see it goes back to you. As sure as God's my judge, I will.'

But she wouldn't be budged, and I wasn't going down on my hands and knees to beg her, so I went back to Mrs Prince and told her I'd had a think about it and decided it wouldn't be such a good idea to take the shop after all.

'Why? Whatever's the matter, Francie? Only this morning you said there was nothing in the world you wanted more.'

'I know, Mrs Prince. But I've thought it over and... Well, that's it. I'm sorry. '

'Oh, come on now, Francie. You're not being perfectly honest with me, are you..? It's too much for you... That's the truth. Isn't it..? I can tell... Look, pet. Answer me honestly: do you really want it or not..? Yes or no..? I want the truth.'

'Mrs Prince, I'd love to have it..if only I could get the money for it.'

'You can have it then. If you like you can pay me so much a week or nothing at all. It doesn't make any difference to me. I don't really need the money... Go on! Take it!' She was shaking my wrists with her tiny little hands. 'You can move in tomorrow if you like. And if ever you have any troubles and want to ease your mind, there's nowhere else you need look than right here. My door will always be open for you.'

Some people on this earth are good and not even related to you, and sometimes hardly know you... I accepted her offer for the loan and moved into the shop that very afternoon.

Every day after I'd finished my duties in the lodging house, I'd go into the shop, taking with me the buns and things that had been baking or cooking while I'd been busy with my chores; and in between customers I'd make up the allocations in tiny paper cones, from stuff in the bins and big jars. Gradually I increased my bulk orders so that I was getting discount and this made things even better. Then I started selling things like little packets of cigarettes and sweets, all small quantities that were very cheap. The shop wasn't a gold mine or anything, but it was thriving. Even the Robinsons shopped there; in fact, they ran up so much credit I had to call a halt and they didn't take too kindly to it. Mrs Robinson in particular would walk in as though she owned the place, and just help herself; she thought because she owned the cobbler's shop, she could do whatever she liked. I wouldn't care but she'd put the lodging house rent up by a shilling a week even though the two furnished rooms had been condemned and had had to be pulled down, which meant I had seventeen shillings a week less coming in. The little shop was nearly having to support the lodging house, but I needed the rooms in Mill Street which went with the lodging house, because that's where me and the bairns lived.

12

On the 21st July 1915, Johnny's sister Mary Ellen was married to Walter Callaghan, Johnny's old sparring partner. As always, the reception was at the Robinsons'. Mrs Robinson had made a big splash of the wedding and there were hundreds of people there, many of them boxers but all kinds of other sporting people and business people as well. She loved anything like this; not only that her youngest daughter was marrying a boxer and a Catholic...she couldn't have prayed for anything better than that...but feeling so full of her own importance among all these people. She hadn't learned any more manners since the last wedding, Johnny's and mine, and the drink and tough talk flowed as thick as ever; this time there was no Mr Robinson to keep her in her place, and she was the queen of everything.

The Callaghans were well known as fighters. Walter had fought Jimmy Wilde, the world champion, at Newcastle the year before, and his brother Tommy was an all-rounder...boxer, runner, footballer, cricketer and wrestler...who they called 'Stoker Callaghan, the Iron Man of Jarrow'. When the father, old Tom O'Callaghan, and his wife Jane who was a schoolmistress, had come to Jarrow from Ireland, he had decided to drop the 'O' from their name because he thought they would stand a better chance in life if people thought they were English, and all of them had kept it like that except one of the them, the eldest, Jack. When Jack grew up, he put the 'O' back in his name. 'I was born 'O'Callaghan' and I'll die 'O'Callaghan,' he told me. 'If it was good enough for them over there, it'll have to be good enough for them over here. I'm an Irishman, not a damned German.'

Mrs Callaghan was a real live-wire, always talking and busying about the way you'd expect a school teacher to be, but Mr Callaghan was the quietest man I ever met; in fact, I can't remember ever hearing him say anything. If you went into a room where he was, even in his own house, he'd get up quietly, keeping his eyes away from you, and walk out. He was never rude or anything, I think he was just very shy. His head was always burrowing into a bible, he must have nearly known it by heart .

At the party after the wedding, people had kept pushing Jack O'Callaghan at me, and me at him; Mrs Robinson was the main one. She kept saying 'Go on, Francie. There's Jack O'Callaghan standing on his own over there. Why don't you take a plate of sandwiches over. Go and talk to him, man. He's a nice feller. Suit you right down to the ground, he would. Make a good Catholic father for the bairns.'

'I didn't come here seekin' a husband, Mrs Robinson. I came for Mary and Walter's weddin'. If I wanted a man, I could find one meself.'

'Huh..! Did you hear that, Lily..? Because she's all dressed up she thinks no man can keep his eyes off her... Give her a piece of cake in a bit of paper, and tell her to wrap it up and keep it. It might bring her luck. She'll be glad of it one day. Mark my words.'

Although I'd known Walter through Johnny and the boxing, this was the first time I'd ever set eyes on Jack O'Callaghan. He had a mass of curly hair, like all the Callaghans, and like the rest of them, he was quite good-looking. And from the little I had to do with him, he seemed canny enough, he was nicely spoken and very polite. But he was no Johnny Robinson, and nobody could fill Johnny's place as far as I was concerned. Yet as the night went on, he kept coming over more and more often and chatting on for quite a while.

'Go on, woman! Get after him!' Mrs Robinson kept nudging me with her great hard elbow every time he went to get himself another drink.

Johnny was her son and she should have been the last person in the world to be doing this, I thought. But she ruled the roost now and she bossed everybody. She owned all the lodging houses and other property and businesses, and she was head of the family. At one time she could only go so far because Mr Robinson would eventually put his foot down. Not any more. With him gone, nobody dare stand up to her. She wouldn't only shout and yell and call you worse than muck, especially with the drink in her, she'd lay into you with her fists or with whatever came to hand. Her lodgers, men and women, were terrified of her. I've seen some bad men in my time, and they can be frightening, but a terrible woman is something nobody can deal with, she can rob him of all his pride in a few seconds.

By the autumn of 1915 the war was well under way and they were calling people up all over the place. Geordie Robinson and Stoker Allan had joined up and been sent abroad, and so had Tom and Walter Callaghan. Ones that hadn't joined up or been called up, were having to work in factories making guns, bombs, explosives and things like that. There were some of course who found excuses not to go and do their stint, and some of them did well out of it, but by and large they had to be pretty thick-skinned because people round about where we lived used to hate them. If their men folk were away being blown to bits, they didn't see why other people's shouldn't be getting the same treatment or at least be there helping them. The women were the ones who got themselves so worked up, and it wouldn't matter if the men were 'conchies' who wouldn't fight because they didn't think it was right, or whether they were just too scared to go and fight. My man was dead already and my bairns were too young, so that was one worry I didn't have. The same ones probably wouldn't have approved of Jimmy Callaghan either, because Jimmy and his pal Joe Morgan were supposed to be queer. Jimmy was just a little feller and he and Joe were cooks in the merchant navy, but when the ship they were on was torpedoed and Joe couldn't escape because his legs had been crushed under a funnel, Jimmy, who could have jumped overboard with the rest of them and been rescued, chose to stay with his pal, and the two of them were drowned together. I wouldn't have anybody say anything to me about Jimmy Callaghan after that, I don't care what.

One night a big crowd smashed up Sieber's pork sausage shop in the market; they were canny enough people, the Siebers, and they'd been here for as long as I could remember. I don't know where the rest of the family went but Mrs Sieber escaped from the house and came knocking on my door. I'd rather she hadn't because they were shouting and screaming outside and I was certain somebody was going to get killed before the night was over, they were dying to get their hands on somebody. I didn't like the Germans either, and I didn't know what they'd do to me if they found her at my place.

'I don't want anythin' to do with it,' I told her. 'Ye've no right to come to my door. I've got bairns here. I don't want any harm comin' to them.'

But she was crying and in an awful state and I couldn't send her away, so I let her in and she stayed the night. All night I was wondering if I was a traitor or not, you were always being told to be careful who you sheltered or talked to, so you wouldn't be 'giving aid and comfort to the enemy'. By the next morning the gangs had gone and all was quiet and she left. Later on I was told she'd gone to some relatives somewhere.

Though I say it myself, I wasn't bad to look at. I was twenty-six and in my prime; I was big in the right places, had a healthy complexion, long brown hair, and I could turn myself out very well; so I wouldn't have wanted for attention if I that's what I'd wished for.

A few days after the wedding Jack O'Callaghan started calling at my little shop. He'd buy a packet of Woodbines for himself and then a packet of sweets or a little toy for the bairns and ask if he could give it to them himself. Then he would call in the morning and in the afternoon of the same day; never to see me, he said, only the bairns. I'd be serving somebody in the shop and he'd ask if he could pop up and see them, and then when I went in he'd be crawling all over the floor with them, or have them on his back and be chasing them around the yard, or mending their spinning tops or whatever.

It was obvious he thought of himself as family now that his brother had married my sister-in-law, and I'd sometimes go up to the house for a minute and he'd already be there, without coming to the shop to see if it was all right; large as life, he'd be, making himself quite at home. I wasn't a fool, I knew he hadn't come to see the kids, no grown man would do that, and I'd say 'It's no good you comin' in here, Jack. And expectin' me to make ye a cup of tea and sit round chattin' as though I hadn't a care in the world. Because I cannot. I'm far too busy for that sort of thing.'

'I was only making sure they were all right, Francie. I'm only reading them a story. There's no harm in that, is there?'

I would look at my two bairns, one on one of his knees and one on the other, and I'd think 'Am I bein' too hard on him..? Maybe he just wants to do it because he's kind and can't help himself.' I could see the kids loved the attention they were getting, and I didn't need anybody to tell me they would be better off with a father, and sometimes I'd think about it and I'd think about the value of having a man always about the house. What would become of the kids if anything happened to me? Times were hard and more than anything it was people that made them so. I'd known what it was to grow up without a proper father myself... Two working in the house would double the incomings and double the money that could be spent on food and clothes and homely comforts. It would double the bairns' chances of living long enough to be men who could be proud and stand on their own two feet and not owe anything to anybody. But I knew inside that Jack wasn't right, and I had a sneaking suspicion he thought I was a lot better off than I really was; I certainly hadn't told him I only rented the lodging house and the shop, and didn't own them.

I knew that as far as most people were concerned, a man on his own was on his own because he'd left a no-good, idle woman, or because he hadn't found one good enough for him yet; a woman on her own was either a hag that no decent man would be seen dead with, or if she had kids and had been deserted, she must be a sloven or a slut. Even women saw it that way, especially those that were married and comfortable. The only way out of it, the only way to get any respect, was to marry a decent man; that's what people expected of you, that's the only way you could prove you were respectable.

Because I worked such long hours in the lodging house and in the shop, Jack O'Callaghan was staying to all hours; he'd be up in the house with the bairns and I'd either have forgotten he was there, or hadn't even known it. I'd be very tired when I came home and I'd have the rooms to do and the kids to take care of, and I couldn't be bothered with silly chatter and I didn't want it. He was more in the place than my husband had ever been. Johnny had never been one to get under your feet, and I'd got used to that; this feller never seemed to be anywhere else.

'Haven't ye got a home to go to?' I'd say after he'd long run out of anything sensible to say and was just talking for the sake of it and I could see where it was all leading.

'I only came to see if the bairns were all right, Francie. I know how you worry when they're on their own.'

'I appreciate that. But they've been abed long since. And it's high time you were gettin' back and goin' to your own. I've got things to do that I can't get on with when you're sittin' there.'

'I love you, Francie. I want to marry you, woman. That's why I'm here. I've been waiting for a chance to talk to you on your own.'

'Well, if that's the way ye feel, ye'd better go. And ye needn't come back neither. I certainly don't love you, and I never could. I barely even like ye. I don't know ye. I think far too much of the husband I lost to think about anybody else... From now on I want you to stop followin' me around. Don't come to the shop. And don't come here any more. I don't want your business and I don't want anythin' else from ye.'

But he wouldn't go, he just kept on and on... 'If only you'd marry me, Francie, love would come. I know it. It would grow. Nobody loves them bairns more than me. It's like they were my own. And they need a father.'

'Well you're not their father! And neither you nor anybody ever could be! They're Johnny Robinson's bairns. And nobody could take my Johnny's place. Nobody!'

'But it's years now... I'm only thinking about the bairns, not myself. Can't you see that..? What if somebody came and took them away...or did something to them while you were at the lodging house..? You'd never forgive yourself...would you now..? And you... What about you yourself..? This is a rough area. You don't know who's hanging about after dark. All those foreign seamen coming out of the pubs...and darkies and Arabs coming out of doorways when you least expect it.

'I've been offered a good job at the munitions factory, and I'll be getting a good wage. All that would be for you and the kids. What with the war and all that, times are going to get harder and harder. All the papers say that... And if anything happened to you, Mrs Robinson would have your bairns like a shot. You know that full well. She wouldn't let them go to the Charity... And she can be pretty tough, as you well know... A grand old lady, maybe. But not soft on them like you or I would be...

'What about it then, Francie..? Just give me the chance to prove it to you. You'll see that all I've been telling you is the gospel truth. All I'm asking is that you think it over... All right..? Now that's not much to ask. Is it..? So I'm not asking for an answer now... Even if you said yes right now, I'd say "Hold on. Wait till you've thought it over. Be sure." Nobody could be any fairer than that, could they...? Do you think you will, Francie'.

'No!'

After that he wouldn't stay away and he kept pestering me and pestering me so much, along with all my relatives on both sides, that I wondered if I was right to keep on saying no. He hadn't gone away to the munitions factory he kept talking about, and was working as a barman at a big hotel and probably making a canny bit money what with his tips and things, and this day he asked if he could take me up to Newcastle for the races. I'd refused him every time until this time, and I thought 'I'll just give him this one chance, and see what he's like.'

So I went, and we had a lovely time. We saw the horses racing each other around the track and we bet sixpence on a couple of horses that came nowhere, then we went to a tea shop and had tea and scones; and all the time he was treating me to this and that and asking did I want an ice-cream or did I fancy a bar of chocolate, and behaving himself like a proper gentleman. All the way there and all the way back he was doing everything he possibly could to make me enjoy myself and make me feel as though I was somebody, and I wondered if maybe I'd been judging him too harshly.

The very next morning he came into the shop and said 'Well, Francie. Do you like me any better now? Now that you've seen what a good time I can give you.'

What could I say to that..? It was what you might expect a young lad to say, and I laughed. And then he laughed. 'There...you see? When I'm good to you, you can't help liking me. Own up. You can't, can you?'

And I thought 'No, that's right. Nobody could.'

From then on Jack O'Callaghan began to make ground, treating me to things and all the time taking more and more little liberties with the kids and with me, sometimes things I could never put my finger on, but nothing very much and not doing any real harm that I could see. Then it happened that if he missed coming for a day, the bairns were asking where he was. So in the end, for their sakes rather than my own, I said yes. And on the 9th of February, 1916, Jack and I became man and wife, and I became Mrs F. O'Callagan.

I was still looking after the Thrift Street Lodging House and still managing the little shop downstairs, but some time ago Mrs Robinson had put the rent up for the rooms in Mill Street, and I'd had to give them up and move into one of the rooms in the lodging house. But when we got married, Jack decided he wouldn't join us yet because he said it was too crowded with the kids and all, although he eventually told me there was no way he would ever live in a lodging house; so he stayed with his mother and the rest of his family in the big house they had in Woodbine Street, and only came down to the lodging house when he wanted me.

Then I started having problems with the shop... Milk had always been one of my best sellers but they were always bringing in new regulations about it. Like most shops I stored it in a big marble dish, and even though I kept it covered with muslin to keep the flies out, a bit of dust would still settle in it. The regulations then said it had to be kept in urns and that the urns had to be carried outside and ladled in the street, it was supposed to kill any TB germs if you did it that way. I know the idea of keeping germs away from food was for the benefit of people's health, but some of the things they made you do were so silly you wouldn't credit it. They put pressure on the sanitary inspectors, and the sanitary inspectors got tough with us. The big concerns could buy and sell the inspectors, and eventually small shops were stopped from selling fresh milk altogether, and you'd be lucky if they'd allow you to sell even bottled stuff like Puroh. But then I had even worse problems.

There were always rats everywhere...in the lodging house, in the rooms in Mill Street, in the alleys and especially down by the docks...but the shop was plagued with them. They were so bold they'd just look at you for a couple of seconds and then get on with whatever it was they were doing, it was as though they were just laughing at you. You had to be damned lucky to catch one and the traps were filthy things that were nearly as dangerous as the rats, and I'd be terrified in case any of the bairns got caught in one. And even if you did manage to get one, the others would know and they wouldn't make the same mistake. People would tell you to put this down or that down, but nothing seemed to make any difference. I tried umpteen cats, but half the time they were a bigger nuisance than the rats, and most of them were afraid of anything bigger than a skinty little mouse. No matter what I did I couldn't get rid of them and they were becoming so big and fat through eating my stocks, that their bellies were practically trailing along on the ground.

One afternoon I had a crowd outside my window laughing and cheering at two rats bowling an egg, and I knew right then that the business was finished. Nobody wanted the place and my stocks all had to be destroyed. By the time I'd settled up with Mrs Prince, there was hardly a penny left.

Mrs Robinson had been putting the rent up a little more every week for the lodging house until I was paying twenty-one shillings; I'd lost the rent for the two rooms that had been condemned and the rent for the room I occupied with the bairns, and now she put the whole place up for sale.

'How much do ye want for it?' I asked her as soon as I found out..

'Your money wouldn't buy it, Francie Nichol,' was her answer.

Although my proper name had been 'Francie Robinson', a lot of people just called me 'Nichol', and that's what Mrs Robinson called me all the time; I don't know why, maybe I wasn't 'Robinson' long enough for her to get used to it, maybe she thought I wasn't good enough for the name.

'Ye'd sell the roof over your grandbairns' heads...and ye'd sell the ground beneath their feet. Yet ye won't take their mother's money,' I said to her, really mad. 'Why..? What's it to you if I have it, if ye don't want it yourself?'

'It's not a case of that. I want shot of it altogether. I'm not renting it out any more. You'll have to make yourself known to whoever buys it, if you want to rent it.'

A few days later she sold it to two Arab brothers. When I found out who they were, I went to see them to ask if I could rent if from them, and they said yes but I'd have to go with them to the Town Hall to get the licence changed.

'Right,' I said. 'Let's go and do it right away.' I was worried in case they'd let it to somebody else.

The three of us were walking along the street when one of the inspectors I knew quite well came up to me and said 'What do you think you're doing with the likes of these two, Francie?' I told him.

'That's as maybe,' he said. 'But you're not walking along the street with them. I know these two only too well... You take that road,' he said to them. 'And she'll take this one. Now get going..!'

When they'd gone off, he said to me, 'You want to very be careful of those two, lass. They're no good. The least you have to do with them, the better.'

All the same I met up with them at the Town Hall, beggars can't be choosers, and we arranged to get the licence made over. Less than a fortnight later, one of them murdered the other, and in less than a month after that he was hanged. That put the kibosh on the lodging house.

All of us, including Jack, then moved to rooms in John Street. By this time Jack had left the hotel and had got the job at the munitions factory, which he thought would prevent him from being called up by the Army. The War wasn't going anything like as well as everybody had hoped, and they were calling up all able-bodied men unless they had a job in a vital industry like coalmining, shipbuilding or armaments.

Working in a munitions factory, it turned out, was far harder work than Jack was used to, so he left and went away to see if he could get a job somewhere else where he wouldn't be known. I wasn't getting a penny from him, I had no business at all now, and the only work I could get was cleaning other people's lodging houses. It brought in nowhere near enough money, and out of what there was, I was having to pay somebody else to mind the bairns. At the end of every day when I'd finished my work, I'd take the bairns and go along the quays to see if I could get any jobs doing out the cabins of boats or cleaning in any of the hotels. But it was hopeless, and in the end Mrs Callaghan said she'd take me and the bairns in exchange for me keeping house, and I had no choice but to accept.

Very quickly it turned out that Mrs Callaghan was no better than Mrs Robinson, for all her refined ways and fancy talk and her husband spending so much time studying the bible, and I was treated like a skivvy. She was spiteful like Mrs Robinson, but at least Mrs Robinson was never sly, she always came straight out with it, whatever she had to say. Not this one, though; she was forever talking about you behind your back but making sure you heard it all the same. Mr Callaghan never treated me badly, but he never did anything to stop it either, and I had to do the washing, cleaning and cooking for the whole house.

Nothing was ever to Jane Callaghan's liking, and she would tell

Long Row, 1889, the year Francie was born.   *(South Tyneside Libraries)*

Thrift St, 1898.   *(South Tyneside Libraries)*

Frederick Street in 1906.

(South Tyneside Libraries)

Lower Thames St. *(South Tyneside Libraries)*

Ha'penny ferry plying between North & South Shields. *(South Tyneside Libraries)*

East Holborn, the old Arab quarter.   *(South Tyneside Libraries)*

Henry Robinson's Model Lodging House, now deserted.   *(South Tyneside Libraries)*

Fresh fish selling, without any trappings. *(South Tyneside Libraries)*

The rag trade, without any either. *(South Tyneside Libraries)*

East Holborn, not long after Francie had married Johnny Robinson and taken on the Thrift St lodging house. *(South Tyneside Libraries)*

Johnny Robinson, Featherweight Champion of the North of England, 1913.

(J. Robinson)

Francie with little Johnny on her right, Joe on her left.   *(J. Robinson)*

Johnny with a group of Tyneside boxers, their trainers and backers.

(J. Robinson)

Mrs Sarah Robinson, heavyweight. *(J. Robinson)*

Francie and little Edmund.   *(J. Robinson)*

Left to right: Johnny, Francie and Edmund; Joe standing.   *(J. Robinson)*

Francie and Joe.   *(J. Robinson)*   Johnny.   *(J. Robinson)*

Young Francie and Dave (Jock) Duncan.   Edmund.

    (J. Robinson)   *(E. O'Callaghan)*

Johnny and Evelyn's wedding, with Joe as
best man and Nan Smithwhite, bridesmaid.

Newly married Edmund and Nellie.
(J. Robinson)

Joe is best man at the wedding of his friends, Tommy Whitfield and Ada Sullivan,
in 1935, the year before Johnny's, and three years before Edmund's.   (J. Meeks)

The William St shop, on the left near the corner. *(South Tyneside Libraries)*

Edmund, R.E.M.E. *(E. O'Callaghan)*   Johnny, R.A.S.C.   *(J. Robinson)*

German bombs begin the demolition of Thrift St.   *(South Tyneside Libraries)*

Waiting to see what's left when the bombs are cleared.   *(South Tyneside Libraries)*

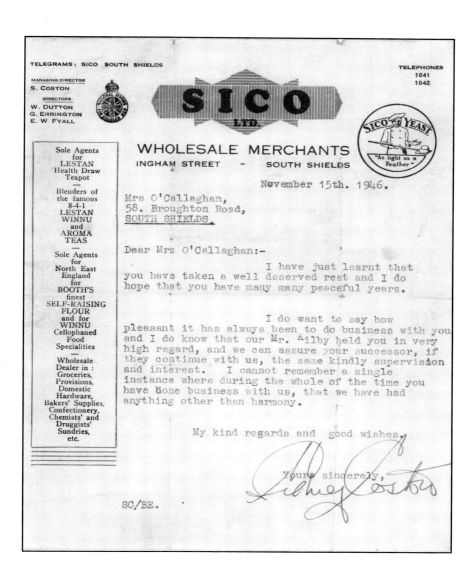

TELEPHONES
1041
1042

MANAGING DIRECTOR
S. COSTON

DIRECTORS
W. DUTTON
G. ERRINGTON
E. W. FYALL

SICO LTD.

WHOLESALE MERCHANTS
INGHAM STREET - SOUTH SHIELDS

"As light as a Feather"

November 15th. 1946.

Sole Agents
for
LESTAN
Health Draw
Teapot
—
Blenders of
the famous
8-4-1
LESTAN
WINNU
and
AROMA
TEAS
—
Sole Agents
for
North East
England
for
BOOTH'S
finest
SELF-RAISING
FLOUR
and for
WINNU
Cellophaned
Food
Specialities
—
Wholesale
Dealer in :
Groceries,
Provisions,
Domestic
Hardware,
Bakers' Supplies,
Confectionery,
Chemists' and
Druggists'
Sundries,
etc.

Mrs O'Callaghan,
58. Broughton Road,
SOUTH SHIELDS.

Dear Mrs O'Callaghan:-

           I have just learnt that you have taken a well deserved rest and I do hope that you have many many peaceful years.

           I do want to say how pleasant it has always been to do business with you and I do know that our Mr. Kilby held you in very high regard, and we can assure your successor, if they continue with us, the same kindly supervision and interest. I cannot remember a single instance where during the whole of the time you have done business with us, that we have had anything other than harmony.

           My kind regards and good wishes.

           Yours sincerely,

SC/BE.

An unsolicited testimonial in the form of a letter, a source of great pride to Francie.

Francie with her sons Johnny and Edmund, in 1950, five years after the war.

(J. Robinson)

Francie and grandson Joe, her biographer.   *(Daily Express)*

Francie and Joe at Marsden, discussing their book.   *(Daily Express)*

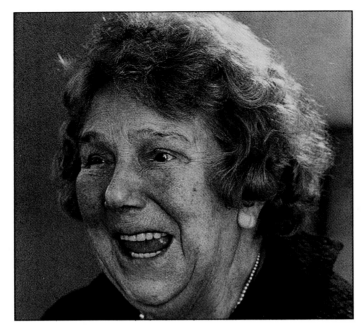

Francie at eighty-five, still able to see the funny side.   (*J. Robinson*)

Francie, at eighty-six, retraces her steps of seventy-five years ago in 1900 when, as a girl of eleven, she carried her baskets of greens and fish.   (*J. Robinson*)

me off in her schoolmistress voice, full of airs and graces, even though you could soon tell she came from nothing herself. I was probably the only servant they'd ever had and the whole lot of them made the most of it.

I'd baked bread for years, and sold it to many who were glad to buy it, but it wasn't good enough for the Callaghans because it wasn't the way they did it, and one day we had a big row over it. Mrs Callaghan had said her piece and I'd said mine, though I wasn't in a position to say very much, and she'd gone out; but she must have had a think to herself because she came back in and said 'And another thing... If you expect another meal in this house for you and your litter, you'd better get those fancy sheets of yours out and get them pledged. Money doesn't grow on trees here. Now you're living under this roof, you'll have to pay your way like anybody else. That's the way we do things in this family.' And then she stormed out again before I could say anything.

There was never any mention of Jack, not a word about the wonderful son that nobody was allowed to say one word against, I don't even know if they knew where he was, I certainly didn't. None better than Jack walked this earth, according to Mrs Callaghan. Yet five of her other sons, Edmund, Tom, Walter, Peter and Jimmy had sufficient backbone to go away and fight for their country; Jack was the only dodger.

I pledged the sheets because I was living at her house and didn't have any choice; and because I had so much to do in the house, I didn't have any time or energy to go and find a job that would have given me some money and a bit of self respect. I felt like nothing, I felt absolutely worthless. There was three sisters in the house apart from the mother, and I waited on them all. I didn't even live with them in the main part of the house, my place was down the stairs in the servants' quarters.

One day Johnny and Joe were playing beside me in their little tartan frocks while I was possing the washing, and Mrs Callaghan came up and said 'You would think those children lived in the workhouse, the way they're dressed.' It was true their frocks were shabby and threadbare, but at least they weren't dirty, and I didn't have anything else for them to put on, I only wished I had, but I was so infuriated I yelled at her.

'What more d'ye expect is to do! Go on the streets..? Is that what ye want..? Will that make yous content?'

'You're not looking after them properly.'

'Could you do any better..? Could you bring them up decent, with a husband ye hadn't heard from for months...and didn't even know where he was..? And he wasn't sending ye so much as a button?'

I thought she was going to choke but I knew one thing, she wouldn't dare lay a hand on me, she was no Sarah Robinson; and she couldn't get out of the yard fast enough to go in and tell the rest of them and have them fussing around her as though she'd taken a fit.

I knew the market people very well, I'd known them ever since I was a kid hawking fish and greens, and then again through Johnny.

Joe Hancock had been one of Johnny's best pals, and his father, old Mr Hancock, had long been a good friend; I bumped into him quite by accident one day when I was down the market getting some potatoes for the house. We got on talking about this and that and he asked me how I was managing at the lodging house. When I told him I was out of it and what had happened, he was very sorry.

'Look, hinny,' he said. 'Why don't you take over my fish-and-chip shop..? It would suit a hardworking businesswoman like you right down to the ground. It's a great goer but I'm getting too old for it. My family's always on to me to retire. Our Joe doesn't want it. He's fixed up already.'

'Eeeh, I don't know anythin' about runnin' a fish-and-chip shop...' But I liked the idea straightaway.

'You're quick. You'd get the hang of it in no time. There's nowt to it but common sense and hard work. Give it a week and you'll know all you need to know.'

The shop was right next to the place where the sailors got paid when they came off the ships, and they always used to go for something to eat straight after. Hancocks' was so big, you could get your fish and chips and bring them away with you, or you could sit at tables in the shop and eat them in comfort. It was probably the best fish-and-chip shop in town. It was situated between four or five bars and the roughest of the rough used to go in, but you couldn't be choosy when you were in business; these people had to eat like anybody else and their money was as good as anybody else's.

Mr Hancock said to go away and think about it, but not to take too long. I could have it for £50, which was really the very least he could ask for it, and I should see if I'd be able to raise the money. There was no way I'd get it from Mrs Robinson, I'd starve before I'd ask her for anything again, either for myself or for the bairns, but Mrs Callaghan might be a different kettle of fish. She was by no means as well off like Mrs Robinson but she might have something put by for a rainy day, and she was always saying the Callaghans should have had their own business, almost as though it was a disgrace.

There was no way I could raise the money myself, so it was Mrs Callaghan or nothing, and as I was walking back I was working it all out; I'd ask her to put up the money, I'd do all the work, and we'd both be equal partners and share the profits fifty-fifty.

When I got back and told her, she was even keener on the idea than I had hoped, especially when I said we could have if for £50, which she realised was very cheap for a place like that. I told her the £50 wasn't for the property but for the business itself, so we'd still have to pay rent, and we'd probably need another £25 or so for a few repairs that needed doing and for stocks of fuel, fish, potatoes and oil.

'I know, I know,' she said. 'I'm not stupid. I've been studying into this sort of thing for a lot longer than you think, my girl.'

She had sufficient money herself to buy the business and was able to borrow the rest from an old friend, but she insisted that she wasn't going to be just a 'sleeping partner', she wanted to take an active part. So the arrangement we made was that I would prepare the fish and potatoes and do all the frying and work the shop, while she'd do the buying of stock and keep the accounts. And neither of us would take a single penny out of the profits until all the money had been paid back to whoever she'd borrowed it from...who I later found out was a friend of Mrs Callaghan's called Mrs Barnett. Mrs Callaghan insisted the business would be in her name since she'd put all the money up, and I wasn't in a position to quarrel with that.

I was pregnant with my first bairn by Jack O'Callaghan now but I still managed to do my job, and in no time the business was going fine; we hadn't needed to do anything to get customers in because they were already doing that when we took over.

Edmund was born on the 10th of October 1916, and was a proper little monkey right from the start. He would throw a tantrum every time I went out, but I had no choice but to leave him at home with

Johnny and Joe so that I could go down to the shop. First thing every morning I would clean, peel and slice the potatoes while Mrs Callaghan was away buying the fish; then as soon as she came back I'd clean, bone and cut the fish. When I'd finished I'd hurry home to see to the bairns and give them their dinners and do what ever needed to be done up there before coming back to the shop to set up the fryers. I had to leave the bairns at the Callaghans' for long periods of the day, and they weren't very patient with them; it was a good job Edmund was their first grandson and nephew or they'd have probably mangled him.

Every day I had to traipse back and forwards from Woodbine Street to the shop, and it was a long way. Mr Hancock saw the way Mrs Callaghan was forever bossing me around in the shop as though it was her business and I was just the assistant, and he knew I wasn't happy having to leave the bairns at the Callaghans' all day, so he said he and his wife would move into the downstairs flat behind the shop, and me and the bairns could take theirs, rent free. He said it would be company for him and his wife, but there was no doubt in my mind who'd be the ones to benefit, and I thanked him very, very much. They moved out that weekend and we moved in, and it was wonderful for me. Not only did it save the time and slog of going back and forth to Woodbine Street so many times a day but I had some privacy at last and could check the bairns my way and bring them up to do what I thought they should do and be Robinsons, not Callaghans.

Mrs Callaghan obviously saw it as a blessing for her as well; not just because we were out of her hair, but because I could spend more time in the shop and she could then cut the hours of the girl we had in to help. The business was going so well it was impossible for one person to look after all the frying in the shop and keep running into the back to do another batch of spuds or another box of fish at the same time, so we'd had to take on a girl, just as the Hancocks had, even though they had both worked full time in the shop themselves.

After the shop closed for the night the girl and me would do the cleaning up, which was a big job; all the fryers had to be cleaned out, the fry got rid of, the counter, tables, shop and floor to be scrubbed, the condiments to be cleaned, the used aprons, which were always in a right mess, to be washed, and everything in the back to be put away and left spotless; not a bit of grease had to be left anywhere or the rats would be in. But now that I just lived upstairs, as soon as the last customer went Mrs Callaghan would send the girl home, which meant that I had to do all the cleaning up myself.

Mrs Callaghan brought the fish from the market but she never ever stayed to gut and clean it, nor did she peel a single potato, or do any of the frying or cleaning up. She was too full of herself to do any of the real work. She wasn't above raking in the money though, and she never allowed anybody but herself to put any in the till; the closest the girl and me ever got to the customer, was wrapping up their chips and putting them on the counter.

The business was going like a bonfire and had been going like that for months now, but because I wasn't allowed to handle any of the money or have a look at the accounts, I didn't know where we stood, I didn't know how close we were to paying off the debt, or whether we'd already paid it. I was told nothing at all and Mrs Callaghan resented me asking. If the debt was paid off we should now be sharing the profits and I had a right to know what they were, and we should be on a different basis now; it's hardly a partnership when one's scrubbing on their knees in ignorance while the other's sitting on their bum counting the money. I mightn't have known much about algebra or geometry but I knew how many beans made five.

All I ever got out of the business was my wages, and they were the barest of the bare, but now she saw I was getting a bit restless and making a point of looking to see how much was being clocked up in the till, she started bringing me a few groceries which she would plonk down on the table, the same way she plonked my wages down, as reluctantly as if she was paying taxes. 'There you are, Francie,' she'd say. 'I thought I'd save you a journey.'

But I didn't want her groceries; to anybody standing there it might have looked like charity I was getting. I wasn't seeking charity and I didn't want it. If I wanted groceries, I could go to the market and choose them myself and pay for them out of my own money, if I had the money that is. Buying for the business was one thing, and I'm sure she did that all right, but buying for me and my little family was a different thing altogether; I didn't want her knowing everything I bought, and going back to them at the house and saying 'Ye'll never guess what she's spending her money on!'

One Friday after she'd done her usual thing...coppers for wages and a cabbage and a loaf of bread and a few things like that plonked down on the table, and me supposed to fall on my knees with gratitude and she going to church on Sunday and thanking God for making her such a saint...that I said 'What d'ye take me for, Mrs Callaghan..? D'ye think I'm a fool or somethin'...? Not able to spend me own money wisely?'

'What on earth do you mean?'

I knew she'd take that tack, all high-horse as though she'd never do anything to hurt a soul; and I was ready for it. I told her that from now on I wanted all of my wages and I wanted them in my hand. I didn't want a penny of it spent on anything I didn't go out and buy myself. And that if the debt was now paid off, I wanted my share of the profit, in cash; not barter, not a quarter of tea, not a bar of soap, a box of matches or anything else she had a mind to bring in.

'We haven't quite paid back the loan yet,' she said in a huff.

I hadn't seen any books or anything because she kept them up at the house, and when I said I was entitled to know how we were doing, she got angry and said it was a personal loan and a private arrangement between her and 'a friend'. There was nothing else I could say so I just had to leave it at that; at least now she knew I wasn't satisfied with things and she'd been reminded it was my business as well as hers, and it might make her change her tune a bit.

Then Jack turned up. He still hadn't got himself a job but he had the wherewithal to come in drunk. He moved straight in with me and now that he was away from where his mother and sisters could see him, he started drinking like a fish and using me badly. He took his hands to me at the slightest excuse; he slapped me, he punched me, he pulled me around by my hair and would shove me against the wall and yell so loud, the beery spittle would splash all over my face. The more drink he had, the cruder, the nastier and the more violent he was. Before he went away I'd thought he was lazy and a bit too fond of the drink, but now I saw him as something different altogether, and I was scared of him. He would brag to his friends in front of me that 'If a woman back-answered me, I'd take her bloody arm and break it over my knee.'

He had also taken it upon himself to teach my bairns manners and would pull them up by the loops of their ears for speaking at the table even though they weren't saying anything bad. And because he didn't like the sound of little Johnny's fiddle when he was practising one night, he snatched it out of his hands and smashed it to smithereens over the corner of the table right in front of him and the lad was broken-hearted.

Edmund was just a baby and such an imp that he had to be fastened into his bed and blocked in with barriers made from chairs and tables, so he couldn't get out and do himself an injury while I was working in the shop; the stairs were steep and he could have fallen down when I was in the back and I mightn't have known about it. Mrs Callaghan knew I had to do it and yet she'd complain to people that I wasn't looking after her only grandson properly, and she'd tell this one and that what a neglectful mother I was and that I tied my bairns up all day. But I put up with it, I was in this business as well and I wasn't going to give her any excuse to get rid of me after all the graft I'd put into it, not when we must very soon be making a profit.

However, one day when I was sitting out in the back with my hands in freezing water, peeling spuds and gutting fish and working as hard and as fast as I could, and Mrs Callaghan was in the nice warm shop, resting her backside on the fryers with her arms folded, running me down to Mrs Barnett and telling her what a rotten mother I was and that I never cared a hoot for my bairns, I couldn't stand it any more. I knew what a good and respectable woman Mrs Barnett was, and I wasn't going to have things like that said about me to her. So I came out of the back and said 'Well, if that's the way ye feel, Mrs Callaghan, ye can keep your bloody shop...and your bloody business! Ye can go to hell for all I care. And ye can take your fish and ye can take your chips and ye can all fry together... And I'll go and give my bairns the love I know they should have been gettin' while I've been here slavin' for the likes of you!'

I knew I shouldn't have said all that, I knew I was only giving an even worse impression of myself to Mrs Barnett; but I couldn't help it, I was nearly beside myself with bitterness.

I ran upstairs and cuddled all the bairns to me, they were all crying because they'd heard me screaming down in the shop. 'I love my bit bairns,' I said to them. 'I love all of ye. I know you're only little, but ye must try to understand that I'm only tryin' to do the best I can for yous all. You're too young to understand. All I'm askin' is that ye be patient a while. We'll get by. Don't worry. Things'll get better. Your mam'll look after ye. You'll see... There, there...'

Just then the door burst open and O'Callaghan came flying in.

'I heard what you've been saying to my mother, you cheeky bloody bitch..! Nobody talks to my mother like that! Least of all, somebody like you..! Take that..! And that..! I'll teach you, you bloody whoor!'

Well, he knocked me down and he kicked me from one end of the room to the other and I thought I was never going to get back on my feet again.

'Don't you ever open your foul mouth to my mother again! She's a better woman than you'll ever be! My mother's a lady...! You're just a slut..! A harlot..! A fuckin' filthy dirty bitch..! You're just a bit of shit, that's what you are..! A useless, good-for-nothing bit of shit!'

By this time he had me on the landing and was kicking me with every word he spoke, and I was sure my insides were going to come bursting out. Just then Old Mr Hancock came running up the stairs, and I think he probably saved my life. He pointed at O'Callaghan.

'I'm warning you, Mr O'Callaghan! If you badly use that lass once more, I'm fetching the police. You're always knocking her about. We are always hearing you... Me and Mrs Hancock. But I'll tell you this: I know people around here...all kinds of people. And if you don't leave her alone, and the police don't do anything, I'll get somebody to come up here and break every bone in your body..! Now get off my premises..! Go on! Get out!'

O'Callaghan went out with Mr Hancock right behind him, and I heard the two of them going down the stairs and Mr Hancock's voice telling him off. Poor Mr Hancock was a quiet sort of a man and I knew he hated anything like this, you could see it was too much for him and he'd been very close to tears. But even an old feller like that got the better of O'Callaghan, because underneath it all he was nothing but a coward.

Two nights later there was a little tap-tap on the door. I thought 'Who's that..? Is it poor Mr Hancock coming to give me notice because he's fed up with all the carry-on..? Or is it O'Callaghan come sneaking back like he always does, full of apologies and promises that aren't worth a light?'

But it was a polite woman's voice. 'Can I come in, Francie..? It's me, Mrs Barnett.'

I opened the door and let her in.

'Whatever's the matter, Francie?' she said. 'You seem to have changed from the person you were.'

'That's what she...Mrs Callaghan...would have you believe... That's because she's your friend.'

'I know that. But the way you went on the other day... She was deeply upset by it. '

'The truth is, I'm sick of my life, Mrs Barnett. I lost a good man and got one in his place that's just the opposite... And now I've got his bairns to raise, as well as my own... Nobody knows what it's like. Everybody thinks because he's a handsome lookin' feller with all that wavy hair, that butter wouldn't melt in his mouth. But it takes more than a few waves to make a decent man. I'd sooner have one that was as bald as a coot if he was good to is.'

I told her what had happened to me since Johnny had died, and how badly the Callaghans had treated me when I was living there, and what O'Callaghan had done to me after the row I'd had with his mother.

'Did they tell ye that when they sent ye..? I bet they didn't.'

'Nobody sent me, Francie. Mrs Callaghan doesn't even know I'm here. I'm here because of you, not her.'

Mrs Barnett was a wealthy woman, her family owned a chain of grocery stores, and she looked the part. She looked around the room, taking it all in. Then she heaved a big sigh and said 'Poor Francie... What a life you've got... What an awful, hard life it must be... I'm really sorry for you and those little children... Can you not do any better than this?'

'How can ye say that, Mrs Barnett..? Ye know I can't...'

'Wouldn't you like a business of your own, Francie? I know you're a hard worker... If you were working for yourself, you'd probably do well.'

'I'm goin' to show ye somethin' I've never showed anybody because I'd be too ashamed. But I know you're a good woman and I don't want ye to go out of here thinkin' anythin' but the truth.'

I went to the mantelpiece and took down the jug I had there and handed it to her, it was stuffed with pawnshop tickets.

'Go on, empty them out.'

She very carefully took two or three out and looked at them in the palm of her hand.

'Go on... Look, there's lots of them.' I poured them all out on the table.

'There... Do those look like gold bonds? Are they proof enough to you of how well off I am since I went into business with your friend Mrs Callaghan?'

She carefully put the ones she had in her hand down on the table.

'Never mind those for a minute... Do you think you could manage the responsibility of a shop on your own...with the children and all that?'

'I once did. I had my own shop and it did fine... But then it fell through what with one thing and another. It was part of a lodging house and the lodging house was being condemned and...'

'It's clear enough you don't get on with Mrs Callaghan, Francie. Anybody can see that. But I have to tell you that she and I have been friends for a very long time, and I wouldn't say or do anything to hurt her... But supposing...just supposing...you were to leave this place to Mrs Callaghan and get your own business. Jack could work there with you and the two of you could work side by side and build a future together. Then - '

'But I haven't got two ha'pennies to rub against each other, Mrs Barnett. It's all very well to say "Get a place and - "'

'I'm asking would you like a business of your own if you could get one?'

'Would I like a business..? I'll say I would..! I'd love a little business..! There's nothin' in the world I'd rather have... When ye have your own business, every hour ye put in ye get back twice over.'

'Listen to me, Francie. I'm going to come back with Mr Barnett tonight, to see you...and see if we cannot help you in some way. But I want you to promise me you won't breathe a word to anybody.'

Mr Barnett had an important job to do with shipping. That night the two of them came back and the three of us had a long talk. They listened to all I told them and they were very kind and sympathetic, and I listened to everything they had to say in return.

'If you can find a little business you think would suit you, we'll lend you the money,' Mr Barnett said. 'But you mustn't say a word to a single soul, especially not to Mrs Callaghan because she's Mrs Barnett's friend. She must never know where the money has come from.'

'What about Jack?'

'If you don't tell him, he won't know either. We'll keep it as a private arrangement between our three selves.'

'Oh, thank you both... I'll pay every penny back as soon as ever I can.'

'Where's Jack right now? I haven't seen him for a while.'

'He's around all right. He was here the other night. Mr Hancock had to put him out. I heard Mrs Callaghan say he's goin' to Bristol, or some place to look for work.'

'Well, maybe now's the best time to act... Look for a place as soon as you can. But don't be too hasty...make sure you get the right place, then snap it up. Whatever it is, we'll back you till you get on your own two feet. We'll help you with initial capital, with whatever repairs might be needed...furnishings, stock and whatever else you need. Don't you worry about a thing. All you have to do is find the right place.'

I promised to do as they advised, and the next day as soon as I finished work I started looking. Sometimes I carried Edmund in my arms with the other two walking by my side, other times Mrs Hancock would keep an eye on them for me and I would slip out on my own. I went looking every day, no matter how tired I was, no matter what the weather. I knew I had to get something quickly. It was only fair to the Hancocks to tell them I was looking for something else but I told them no more than that, and they understood.

The most interesting place I found was a rundown fish-and-chip shop on the corner of Gilbert and Frederick Street. I didn't want a business that was already a big success because it would have cost too much, and this place looked to be just what I was looking for, just a gossip shop with very little trade. It was far enough away from Mrs Callaghan's shop, yet handy enough for me, and it had great possibilities because it was a very busy area and there was no real competition nearby.

For some people, a packet of chips just saw them right after they'd had a few glasses of beer and it would keep their hands warm till they got home if it was a cold night. A young feller and his lass might share a packet between them and it would help their courting along. But for many people, a packet of fish and chips was the main meal of the day. There was no cooking needed, no fire or oven needed, and no dishes or knives and forks to wash up afterwards; you just screwed the paper up into a ball and chucked it away.

Each night after I'd put the kids to bed, I'd slip out for an hour to watch the goings-on in the Frederick Street shop, from across the road. At the time when business should have been at its best, it was dead; hardly anybody went in, and those who did stayed far too long. After a while I'd stroll past the shop pretending not to look in the windows but jotting down notes in my head all the time; a drunk in the corner and two women with their arms spread over the counter chatting away for nearly half an hour; only one fryer on the go, the other two idle; the owner leaning against the fryer with her arms folded. It was the same thing night after night, no way to run a business at all.

One night I went into the shop about nine o'clock and waited to be served. There were only two people standing there and one of them seemed to be a relative from the way they were talking, but the owner didn't pay me the slightest attention; there was no 'Hello, missus. Cold out, isn't it?' or anything like that. I might as well never have existed as far as she was concerned. She was talking to a Mrs Butler about a Mrs Wilson's niece who was called Flora who was going with this queer feller from Hartlepool who had hurt his leg in the docks when he was unloading the sugar from that ship with the funny foreign name from Norway or Russia or some place like that and...blah blah blah blah blah.

I could only see three tiny little boilers, no proper pans or fryers or anything, and there were potato peelings all over the floor. Anybody could see right into the back where two cats were squabbling over a bit of fish they'd pulled out of a box. The whole place, both shop and kitchen, was such a mess it's a wonder the Corporation hadn't closed it down. The lino was so worn away you could see the holes in the floorboards where the mice probably went in an out. Piles of dead flies lay like blackberries in the corners and along the front of the cracked window which was so steamed up you couldn't see through it in most places. The fly-paper hanging over the fryer didn't look as though it had been changed for months. The counter was scruffy and greasy, the holes in the salt pot were solid with dirt, and there was no vinegar or pickles to be seen. 'Surely nobody would paint walls that colour,' I thought. 'That yellow never came out of a paint tin.'

The old lady at the front of the queue must have got fed up because she just turned and went out and nobody made any attempt to stop her.

'Are ye servin' tonight?' I said.

'That's what we're here for,' she said, a bit cheeky, and winked to her sister-in-law or whoever it was.

'I'll have a ha'porth o' chips then, if ye don't mind.' That was the smallest portion you could get.

'Bring your own paper, did ye?'

Bring your own paper..! I think you'd want to bring your own chips, never mind the paper.

'No. I didn't realise ye had to.'

'It's just handier for us if ye do.'

She wrapped the chips in a skinny bit of paper and they were practically coming through the bottom by the time I got them outside. They were soggy, they were full of black eyes, and they were clay cold. I put a couple in my mouth and when I bit into them they burst like pea pods filled with dripping. I spat them out and chucked the rest away.

'Good, good,' I thought to myself. 'Trade must be bad if that's the best she can do. She surely cannot expect much for that place.'

I waited outside until she closed up and then I tapped on the window.

She came to the door and lifted up the little curtain and shouted through the letterbox: 'Who's there?'

I told her I'd heard rumours she wanted to sell up and that I was here to talk business.

She opened the door and let me in.

'Well,' she said. 'It is, and it isn't. Sometimes I want to sell it and sometimes I don't.'

'Well you should make your mind up one way or the other. Because I could be interested in buyin' it if the price was right... How much would ye want for it?'

'Ooh, let's see... It's worth at least thirty pounds... And then there's the stock.'

'Thirty pounds!' I thought to myself. It cannot be any business at all if that's all she wants for it.

'Have ye any books to show what's what and how you're doin'?' I says in a very matter-of-fact way... I'd have just bluffed me way through if she had, but she hadn't any.'

'I keep it all in me head.'

I thought 'Aye, well that won't take up much room, there's next to nowt here.'

But it wasn't what the business was now that mattered, it was what I could make of it.

'Right,' I said. 'I'll give ye thirty pounds for the place and five pounds for the stock. Thirty-five pounds all told. Will that do ye..? That's if ye make your mind up here and now. Because I've got somewhere else to look at.'

'Fair enough,' she said.

'Right. I'll be back tomorrow to make arrangements.'

I went straight to the Barnetts'; Mr Barnett wasn't there but Mrs Barnett said not to worry, she would handle it.

Not only were the Barnetts willing to lend me the £35 for the business and the stock, but they offered to lend an extra £45 to put in new counters, a new big window, proper fryers with their own burners, condiments, completely redecorate the whole place, and bring the stock up to scratch. I wasn't sufficiently known to get stuff on credit yet, because Mrs Callaghan had handled all that side of things, but things would be different from now on.

'How long will I have to pay it back?'

'That's entirely up to you. Pay when you can.'

'What about interest? How much of that will ye be wantin'?'

'We don't want any. We just want to help you out.'

I couldn't have asked for a better arrangement than that and I thanked her from the bottom of my heart. She then took me to the bank and gave me the money, and then I went straight to the woman in the fish-and-chip shop and we got everything transferred to my name that same afternoon.

13

As soon as I took over the shop I put up a notice I'd got somebody to write, saying the business was now under new management and was presently closed 'for modernisation'... That sounded good, that would have them all curious; word would very soon get around when they saw all the workmen going in with their white overalls and ladders and tools. Everything I didn't want, I threw out and got a few bob for this and a few bob for that wherever I could. From then on I never let the workmen alone until they'd done everything just the way I wanted, and with hardly giving them time to draw breath.

I'd already ordered half a ton of potatoes from my old employers', Gilroys, and that gave me no end of satisfaction; it wasn't a great quantity but I had to crawl before I could walk. And then I went down to the market and ordered my fish and a barrel of best cooking oil...you cannot make good chips with cheap oil.

When everything was ready, I opened up, I didn't wait for any fancy date or the beginning of the week or anything; everything was finished by noon on a Wednesday, and I was open at 7 o'clock that night. By that time my first batch of fish was fried, my first batch of chips was sizzling, my new pots with fresh salt and vinegar were all set out, pickled onions, pickled cabbage and pickled beetroot were all in a line, the main light was put on and the door was open and fastened back; and I was behind the counter, hair done up in a bun, clean clothes, new apron, sleeves rolled up, and a big smile on my face.

Next to nothing happened. Two came in for a penn'orth of chips and that was all, no fish. Nobody at all came the second night, and only three on the third. At the end of the week I'd only taken in about two bob. I thought 'Eeeh, God! What have I let meself in for? What am I doin' wrong? Has the previous owner said somethin' or what? I owe all that money to those kind people, and I'm goin' to go broke.' Every day that week the bairns and me had fish and chips till it was coming out of our ears, and nothing else.

I knew if anything went wrong this time, I'd have only myself to blame; I'd got everything arranged just the way I'd wanted it, I'd had help from two Good Samaritans and O'Callaghan was out of the way and so was Mrs Callaghan. But I wouldn't let it go wrong, I wouldn't let anybody have the satisfaction of seeing me make a fool of myself. I'd work harder, stay open longer, sing louder, until they'd nearly be forced to come into the shop...even if it was only to see what was going on. And when they did, I'd give them good value for their money, I'd make them want to come back.

Before a month had gone by, I got my wish and the business was going champion and I was as happy as Larry; I couldn't stop singing then.

I knew there'd be a hell of a row when the Callaghans found out; although I'd often enough threatened to leave Mrs Callaghan's shop...hers and mine it was supposed to be...I'd never been able to, and she had traded on that.

The day after I'd got the shop, which was a Friday, I'd found a room in Gilbert Street and moved out of the Hancocks'; they were very good about it, as they always were, and I arranged with some blokes from the market to come at half past seven in the morning and cart my belongings off to Gilbert Street so that I wouldn't have any scenes with Mrs Callaghan. When she went into the shop on the Saturday night, the place was empty, the potatoes were still in the sacks and the fish still in the boxes just as they'd been delivered. She'd apparently gone stark staring mad and all weekend the Callaghans had been looking high and low for me. When somebody eventually told her where I was, she came storming into the shop like a headmistress coming into her class.

'Where on earth did you get the money from for all this?'

But she didn't scare me, I'd put up with much tougher women than her, and now I was on my own territory.

'Sorry, Mrs Callaghan. But I've had enough of you and your shop. I told ye last week, ye can do what ye like with your business. And I meant it... Whatever ye work for, ye can keep. And now that I've got my own place, whatever I work for, I'm goin' to keep. Now we're both in the same boat... Now ye'll see whether I look after my bairns properly or not.'

She was fuming but she couldn't do a thing. I wasn't going to tell her where the money came from and nobody else but the Barnetts knew; even the Hancocks hadn't asked, and I hadn't told them.

The very next day O'Callaghan came to the house. Where he'd been and what he'd been doing, I neither knew nor cared; as long as he was out of my hair, that was all that mattered. I thought he'd be in a hell of a temper because he must have been to the Callaghans first and found out about everything. Instead, he was all smiles.

'Can I come in, then?' he says, sort of joking. 'How's my bonny bairns?'

I thought he'd be all for beating me up for leaving his mother, but he was trying to be all nice and reasonable; in he went and had a word with all the bairns and gave each or them a little something he'd brought. Sooner or later I had to say something about the shop, so I told him I didn't really own it, that it belonged to somebody else although my name was up, and that I was just looking after it for them; and that if any damage was done, the owners would have the police around in a jiffy, and whoever it was would be liable for damaging property that didn't belong to them... But he just smiled. 'Never mind about all that... Come on, Francie. Give's a kiss. I've missed you, love.'

Hard work was the way to succeed, that coupled with fair dealings and a firm hand; I was generous but not daft, and I gave good service. Elbow grease kept the place spotless and I never had a rat near the place; a few little mice you'll get anywhere, and you can't stop the odd fly from flying in the door, but there was no place cleaner, I'm certain of it. I got rid of all the drunks and I discouraged all the lingerers...ones that would come in and expect half an hour's gossip in return for two penn'orth of business and were so full of themselves that if they'd had their way, they'd have had a queue a mile long behind them.

All the fish had to be fresh that day, and I bought only the best potatoes; if I got more than three or four bad'uns in a sack, I'd send the whole lot back. In no time people were coming from all over, but only after tea because nobody wanted fish and chips before then. This meant the mornings and afternoons were wasted, and a shut shop is the worst kind of advertisement. So I hit on the idea of opening in the morning and afternoon to sell fresh fish, fish that people could take away and cook for themselves, cheap but good fish-cuts that were very filling. And that went so well I started doing crab, mussels, whelks and things like that. And then I started doing every kind of lemonade you could get...Tizer, Dandelion and Burdock, orangeade, orange-crush, orange-squash, strawberryade, limeade, ginger beer, icecream soda, sarsaparilla...anything. And that went the same way.

By now I'd got to know my customers so well that I got to know their different wants as well as their different troubles; I got to know what they could eat and what they couldn't, what their man liked and what he didn't, and who could afford a bit extra and who couldn't. Whenever I gave the poorer ones their chips, I'd always put in a big lump of batter...it was the closest they ever got to tasting real fish; it cost me nothing and they really appreciated it. Kids loved it.

'Can ye give's a bit batter, Missus?' they'd say.

'There's some already in.'

'Thanks very much.'

'Threepenn'orth o' chips and batter twice.'

'Rightio,' you'd say, giving the greedier ones some because they'd asked for it and were entitled to it, but not nearly as much as you'd give to those that needed it.

'Wor Billy'd gan mad if there was ne batter on.'

'Don't worry. There's piles on.'

'Grand. Ta, Missus.'

I was always looking for ways to sell more than they came for if I knew they had the money. 'Tell your ma I'll have a nice bit of haddock comin' in tomorrow, Brian. Lovely an' fresh... Don't forget, now!'

'Rightio, Mrs O'Callaghan. I won't forget. T'ta.'

'T'ta, son.'

'Would ye like to take a jar of pickles wi' ye for Mr Jackson..? They're really lovely. Just in today. Look at the size of them! Ye'll never see bigger than that... Ye wouldn't be able to get them in the jar... New from Gillies across the river. I've just had one meself, and by, they're good..! Ye can pay tomorrow if ye haven't got enough with ye. Or ye can settle up when ye come for your chips tonight... I expect ye'll be in after the pictures?'

'Hey, Billy... Come back here, a minute. I've got somethin' for ye.

Here, look... Why not take the missus a bottle of this..? Lovely and sparkly it is. It'll wash the fish down nicely and help her digestion. I bet she'd really appreciate it... Only three pence a bottle... Here, I'll put it in a bag for ye. There y'are now...'

'Here, Mrs Charlton... For the cat... Divvent tell anybody. If ye come back tomorrow early, I should have a bit more. As long as I know you're comin', I can save somethin' for ye. Will ye be wantin' your four kippers again tomorrow...so I'll know to put them by?'

Now that O'Callaghan was back living with us it wasn't very long before he was back to his old ways...except that now he found he had money on tap; he wasn't having to work for his drink anymore, he just reached in the till for it. At first I thought he must have a job during the day and that's where he was getting the money from, and as long as he wasn't bothering me, he could just get on with it. I was too busy to notice what was really happening, and to tell the truth, I never dreamt he'd do such a thing, it was stupid as well as anything else; it wasn't until I found my takings were right down even after a busy day, that I began to check the till and realised. He'd been crafty in the beginning, just taking the odd shilling so I'd be none the wiser, but then he got so greedy and careless he was practically emptying it.

It came to a head one night when he came in extra drunk and was all over me in the shop. He was so bad I'd been able to push him right into the back, a kid could have done it; but by the time I'd finished and cleaned up, he'd stopped playing the lover and now he was the 'big tough husband'. He'd found out one way or another that the fish-and-chip shop belonged to me, he could read very well and I think he'd found the deeds or something, and he was shouting that I'd tricked him while he'd been away looking for work to support me and the bairns. He said that in any case what belonged to the wife, belonged to the husband, and that if he wanted to put his hand in the till at any time to take out what was rightfully his, neither the law nor anybody else would stop him.

From then on he was terrible. He drank however much he wanted, when he wanted, and he never raised a finger in the shop or in the house. On top of that, whenever he wanted his way with me, and he was always drunk when he did it, I just had to let him or he'd have smashed up the shop, the house, and me along with it.

I tried to keep him out of the shop; I thought that if he didn't have to work, if he had all the money he needed for drink and he had me as well, that that would have been enough and he would see the sense of keeping out of the way when I was working in the shop. But he was so stupid when he was drunk, that he would come in and start grabbing me and trying to pull my clothes off and it would be so embarrassing that many a time I could have nearly died. The customers would get all upset and wouldn't know what to say or whether to go out or what, and some of them were afraid of being insulted or hurt themselves. Sometimes he would walk in, empty the till and walk out without a word, and I wouldn't have enough to give change; I'd have to serve somebody else first and keep the one who should have been first, waiting.

I then started hiding money, but no sooner would I find a new place, than he would find it, and when I went for it there wouldn't be a penny left.

Eventually the Barnetts found out was going on and one day Mrs Barnett came in. I hadn't told her anything; I couldn't, not after all she'd done for me, and with her being O'Callaghan's mother's friend.

'Has Jack O'Callaghan had his call-up papers yet?'

'Not as far as I know... Why?'

'I don't want you to say a word to anybody, but I'm going to write an anonymous letter to somebody. Just you hang on, Francie. Keep your chin up. We'll see if something can't be done.'

Well-to-do women in particular hated the thought of any able-bodied man being left on English soil while the rest of them were away fighting and being killed in France, and I imagine Mrs Barnett would have been one of them.

Scarcely a week had gone by before a letter came to the house saying O'Callaghan had to report to such and such a barracks because the Army wanted him. He was in a right stumer when he got it, but as far as I was concerned it wouldn't do him any harm, it might even do him some good. All his brothers, as well as the Robinson brothers, were away doing their share, so why not him; he certainly wasn't doing the war effort any good here. I didn't want to see him shot or blown up or anything, but I was glad to see the back of him when he went, relieved to know that every other night I wouldn't be coming out of the back with a basket of fish, to see him disappearing

191

out of the shop with all the money from the till in his pocket night after night. For all that, I knew it was an awful thing to have on your conscience that you'd sent your husband to war, and I don't know how many other wives might have done it. I didn't send the letter myself, nor did I ask anybody else to write it; but I didn't stop it either, and forever after, Jack and the other Callaghans thought I'd done it and never forgave me for it.

Now I was left in peace, the business really got going and went from strength to strength. When O'Callaghan had been here, he wouldn't let me hire any help because, like his mother, he didn't like wages going out; but now I was on my own there was ample work for two, and I hired a girl and she was worth every penny.

I'd made up my mind from the start that nothing extra would be bought for the shop and no improvements made, until every penny of the money was paid back to the Barnetts and I was in the clear. I'd been doing very well for a time, but had fallen behind because of O'Callaghan. But within three months of him being called up, I did it, I settled every penny. Straight after, I began putting the profits back into the business to buy all-around windows, have decorations done and other things to make the place look as attractive as possible and to try and get back any customers I'd lost through O'Callaghan.

In another few months I was able to buy brand new fryers that looked better and did the job better, and I started buying fish, oil, potatoes, pickles and everything in bigger quantities and at better discounts. I got a beautiful tiled counter, had the front window especially designed for a fresh fish window...a fish-and-chip shop window was just a pane of glass to look through and see who was inside, it did nothing for business. The kind of fish and the kind of cuts that sold in poor districts, was something I'd known about since I was a girl, and as soon as I got this display window and got a greater variety of fish, my fresh fish business jumped right up and I was as well known for my fresh fish during the daytime, as I was for my fried fish and chips at night. There are lots of fish, like cod and blackjack, that are good to eat and don't cost much; and if you give people plenty to choose from, they're more than satisfied, they don't want to see a whole lot of dear fish that they can't afford.

My old friend Lizzie Flood came in to look after the bairns while I slaved away in the shop, and it was slaving but it certainly wasn't slavery; I was only too happy working for myself and seeing the benefit of it. First thing in the morning I'd go and buy the fish and then I'd come back and get the bairns ready for school while Mavis, my help, was starting on the potatoes. Then I'd do the fish myself and lay the fresh out nicely in the window; and then while it was doing its work attracting people, I'd be in the back cleaning and gutting and helping Mavis with the potatoes. The little bell would go any time anybody came into the shop, and I'd just slip my fish apron off and put my clean serving one on, and be in the there in less time than it takes to bat an eye, with a big smile on my face. 'Good mornin', hinny. Now, what would you like..? I've got so-and-so and so-and-so. Or, if you prefer it, I've got a nice bit of so-and-so.'

When the fish-and-chips started after 7 o'clock, and they'd just be coming in ones or twos, kids usually and old folks that went to bed early, I'd be selling, cleaning and frying all at the same time. Gradually it would build up towards the time when the pictures came out and the pubs closed, and then I wouldn't be able to get the fish and chips out and wrapped up fast enough, and I'd fetch Lizzie down because the bairns would all be asleep by now, and the two of us would be going at it hell for leather. I did this every day and night of the week but Sunday, and thoroughly enjoyed myself doing it. God was good to me then.

Fifteen shillings a night were the average takings when the business first began to pay its way. Now, with chips still at a penny a packet and fish at two pence because prices never went up in those days...a loaf of bread, a postage stamp or a tram fare stayed the same for years and years...I was sometimes taking twenty pounds a day. I was the first one in South Shields to get a queue rail put up to control the customers coming in and keep some kind of order in the shop. People liked to stand in a queue, they'd wait patiently and gossip for an hour if needs be, provided nobody else was getting served out of turn; and that's the way it always was in my shop, no favourites, nobody pushing their weight around. Francie O'Callaghan was the boss here, and everybody knew it. Mind, I was never nasty with anybody, I knew they were all my customers whether they were living in sin or doing this, that or the other, and I was there to serve them. But I'd been in lodging houses too long to let anybody come in and rule the roost the way you'd see it in some places where

193

everybody was scared to breathe because some drunken bigmouth has come in with his mates. I'd be short and quick with the likes with them.

'Right. You and you. What d'ye want?'

They'd then say what they wanted and I'd give it to them so fast they'd hardly have time to think; but I'd keep my hand on the packet till they handed over their money.

'Go on, now,' I'd say firmly if they were taking their time to get out of the shop. 'Ye've got what ye came for. Now get yourselves home. There's other people want to be in and get theirs... Next, please!' And usually they'd just beat it. The one thing I never did, was to get into an argument with them; if they wanted to shout something cheeky on the way out because it made them feel big, you just let them get away with it, otherwise you'd have them back in and you'd never get rid of them.

Everything to do with the shop, all expenses, were paid in cash, and by the end of 1917 I had nearly two hundred pounds saved in a bank account...a real bank account like all the big business people have...not just a few stamps on a card in the post office. Over and above that I had seventy-five pounds in a little cloth bag hidden behind the mirror in the house; and seventy-five pound felt grand and heavy when you lifted it down, clinking, to put more in.

Ever since Nellie had got herself established in Canada, she had sent postal orders to me for my father, although it had sometimes been interrupted by the War, and now I was in a position to help him and my sisters and their families. I hadn't time for visiting or such like, but they used to come to the shop every week and I never sent any of them away empty-handed; and as people you help regularly often are, especially if they're your family, they were pretty ungrateful. I gave JaneAnne a job helping me with the weekly wash on a Monday morning for a few shillings...you couldn't have trusted her with anything that took any more brains...and I always gave her enough fresh fish to take away with her for herself, for Kilcaddy and for my father, but I found out later that she used to go back and tell them I'd only given her the rotten fish I couldn't sell. Naturally I wasn't going to give away the stuff my customers wanted, but that hardly means what was left was 'rotten'. Also every week I'd send a hamper of groceries around to them to make sure my father didn't

194

starve, so God only knows what she made of that; more than likely she told everybody I'd won it in last Christmas's draw and it had gone stale, or the mice had been at it.

As the years went by and my father had got older, he became quite harmless; everybody knew him as 'Old Nickler' and thought he was a bit of a character. He was still a drinker, but only when he was cute enough to get it. With very little coming into the house from either him or Kilcaddy, and our JaneAnne not having the savvy to make anything go very far, there'd be little spare for drink and he'd have to outsmart Kilcaddy to get his hands on it.

He was still a bonny feller with his crop of white hair and rosy cheeks, and I think he fancied himself as quite the ladies' man, he probably always had. He was always quick to laugh at anything funny and had quite a winning way with him when he wanted, I think that's why my mother always thought there was still some good in him. But drink always came first with him; even long after my mother died and he wanted a woman's company, he'd never waste money on one. He believed drink took away from a woman; if they wanted to earn his favours by buying him a drink, that was all right; but not the other way about.

I would hear about my father's shenanigans through Kilcaddy who used to follow him all over and spy on him. Kilcaddy sometimes earned his drinks in bars by telling tales about my father and going into all the gory details; ones he thought suitable for my ears, he'd tell me, but mainly to make on he and JaneAnne had such an awful lot to put up with. Everybody except Kilcaddy himself and our JaneAnne must have known my father was much craftier than Kilcaddy was, and that he'd make up stories for Kilcaddy to tell, and pretend he was doing one thing when in fact he was doing another, just to make Kilcaddy look an idiot. It was like a cat and mouse game the two of them were always playing, where all that mattered in life was outsmarting each other.

But my father didn't always get the drop on Kilcaddy. On one occasion he'd gone out and Kilcaddy must have known he was up to something, and decided to follow him. Whenever my father wanted to do something on his own he'd go a very roundabout way, dodging down back alleys, darting through the front door of a pub and out through the back; and he must have thought he'd lost Kilcaddy. But this time Kilcaddy had stuck to him like a leech, and when he finally came upon him, my father was in this back yard with his fancy woman and the two of them were laughing their heads off as my father was telling her what a fool Kilcaddy was.

Kilcaddy had kept out of sight and bided his time. The lady-friend climbed on to an old handcart and lay on her back while my father chocked up the wheels with two half bricks; she then pulled up her skirts and the old man took his trousers off. And there they were, as brazen as could be, when Kilcaddy ran out from a doorway, grabbed the shafts and turned the cart over.

'That'll teach ye to try and make a fool out of me, ye dirty old bugger!'

The woman had scarpered and Kilcaddy says to my father, 'Howay, I'll treat ye to a gill. It'll do ye more good.'

'Ye know what you can do!' my father says as he was fastening his belt. 'I'll be the judge of what's best for me. Not you or wor Jinny... Daughters..! They're the worst thing that can happen to ye. That's how ye end up with damn fool son-in-laws like you!'

Kilcaddy had no real malice for me father, and I doubt if my father had any for him; they had lived together off and on in the same house ever since my father and me had parted in Foster Street.

JaneAnne and Kilcaddy were among the poorest of my relations, and whereas poverty brings out the kindness in some people, it brings out the meanness in others, and JaneAnne was one of the mean ones. Every Saturday I'd send young Johnny and Joe over to see their grandfather, with three shillings and sixpence baccy money, plus the little hamper. He cared nothing for the food, but was always anxious for the money which he used to buy drink with, and he'd wait for the kids to come with what he called his 'allowance', and get more and more impatient by the minute. Meanwhile JaneAnne would try to waylay the boys and take the money off them. Whichever one got it first, my father or JaneAnne, would tell the bairns not to say a word to the other one, and they'd argue black was white they hadn't seen a penny, only the hamper. Then the bairns would come back and tell me I'd been blamed for not sending anything.

My father was never afraid of work and would walk miles to collect scrap wood, hump it back home, chop it up, bundle it up, and then go from house to house till he'd sold every last stick. And now I had my own shop, I'd give him any of the damaged wooden crates that the fish came in; he would then chop it up in the back and tie it into bundles and I'd sell it in the shop for him. He worked at his little firewood business all day every day and sometimes he might walk a long way and end up with next to nothing, but it never put him off; next day he'd be up and at it just the same.

His eyesight was getting so bad that I worried for his fingers, especially when his aim would be off because of the drink. It had got so bad he could no longer read coins if they were put out in front of him, though he could tell what they were when he picked them up, even though they might be nearly worn away, and he was cute enough to know exactly how much he'd taken that day, and how much he'd spent. At the end of every day he would count his money out on JaneAnne's table so that he could pay for his board, and sometimes JaneAnne would shove a shilling under a hole in the oilcloth with the side of her hand. Then an argument would start about whether he was a shilling short or whether he'd put it down and it had vanished; he once told me in the shop that he didn't dare let them know how blind he really was because they'd have whipped every penny he had. 'Now I know what they mean by "robbin' ye blind". The two of them'll say "Look for yoursel' if ye don't believe we", the crafty buggers!' All the same I knew that as soon as he got back he'd be telling them what a hard time I'd been given him. I don't know whether he made it up or just imagined it, I don't think he knew himself half the time.

For all his ways, my father was never a vain man, certainly not where clothes were concerned, and he'd accept cast-offs from any-body. To him clothes were a waste of good drinking money and he'd go around with his wheelbarrow, with his clothes practically hanging off his back and his shoes all split at the sides and taking in, rather than spend any money buying them. Sometimes he'd come into the shop with his shoes squelching, and I'd say 'Dad, your feet must be frozen.'

'Aye, they are. But nebody cares about me. "That's just me father", they say to theirsels. "No need to bother about him. Let the oul' bugger gan an' hang hesel', and the sooner, the better".'

'Why don't ye treat yourself to a pair of second-hand shoes, instead of drinkin' so much?' I'd say to him. 'The amount ye spend on drink, ye could easy afford a pair.'

'Cos I think at my age I'm entitled to a drink. And it's got bugger-all to do with you!'

I knew it was pointless giving him money and telling him to buy something, so I'd send him some warm underwear and get him a pair of good strong shoes. 'When they're worn, I'll get them soled and heeled for ye. And when they're finished altogether, I'll buy ye another pair. But I'd better not see them hanging up in the pawnshop, mind. Or I'll never give ye another thing.'

I'd send the bairns around with a parcel of old shirts and socks and vests of Johnny's that I'd patched up and darned and that were strong and warm, but he only got what Kilcaddy didn't want. Young Johnny won a huge pair of ex-army boots in a school raffle, and I made him take them over to his grandfather; they were miles too big but the old man was so proud of them he never had them off his feet, and every morning he would shine them up before going to seek his firewood. He was a funny old bugger.

One time he took ill and I sent a basket of hard boiled eggs round to help put him right, and for some reason as soon as he ate one, he was sick as a dog. Immediately he looked up, vomit dribbling from his mouth, and said to JaneAnne that I was trying to poison him.

'Right from the start, wor Francie's been the cheekiest of the lot... And that's sayin' somethin'..! I've a good mind to call the pollis... God knows why she's tryin' to do me in. I've got no money to leave.' With me being the youngest, he'd always find fault with me first.

Not long after Johnny died, when I had the little shop in Thrift Street, Bob Charlton once came in and grabbed hold of me. I clouted him as hard as I could and told him I remembered him of old, and that this time I was going to make him pay, I was going to tell our Alice all about him. I hated the man and I always had, and later that day I got somebody to mind the shop and was getting ready to go over to see Alice, when my father came in and asked me where I was going. When I told him, he said 'Don't, Francie. They've got a lot of bairns. Think of wor Alice. She's your sister. She has a hard enough time as it is.'

I was fastening my boots at the time and I stood up quickly to say something to him, not realising he was leaning forward so nobody would hear, and my head smashed against his nose. His nose broke and there was blood everywhere, and by the time I'd got him cleaned up and a couple of customers had come in, I forgot about Charlton and I never got to go. That was the first time I'd ever heard my father say something considerate about any member of his family.

14

When the war ended, Jack O'Callaghan came home to find himself in the money. I had over £400 in one account and nearly £80 in another, one in the bank and one in the post office. I could never bring myself to put it all in the one place, I don't know whether I thought if a bomb dropped on one I might lose all my money, or what, but that's what I did. On top of that I had nearly £100 hidden in the house. The £80 was the allowance the Army had sent me on behalf of O'Callaghan, twenty-nine shillings a week it was.

O'Callaghan hadn't been farther than Kent, and much of the time he was at Rippon which was closer still, so I'd seen him off and on throughout the War, I'd even got somebody to mind the shop and had gone to his camp to see him a couple of times and taken him something. Nobody must have told him how well the shop was doing, I certainly hadn't, and as soon as he got back and saw, he demanded to see all the account books, bank books and everything. I showed him the post office book with the £80 but I kept the bank book under the washstand in my bedroom. He reckoned the £80 was part of his Army wage and therefore was his to do with as he pleased. But it obviously didn't satisfy him, because by the time I'd finished my work in the shop that night, he'd turned the place upside down and found the bankbook, and he nearly went crazy when he saw everything was in my name and not his.

'I had to, Jack. With you being away, and the War and all that.'

'You're a sly bitch, you are... Here's me away fighting for you and the bairns, and all the time you're back here, safe and living in comfort, with nothing better to do than scheme how to cheat me. Don't you realise, you stupid fool, that in this country a man owns everything his wife has down to the clothes on her back!'

The truth was that I'd done what I thought was best for all of us; I'd wasted nothing and spent nothing on myself.

He took me by the throat and shoved me against the wall and I thought he was going to strangle me, my tongue was so far out of my mouth; his face was nearly purple and all snarled up, and his fist was up in the air ready to smash into my face. And this was on his first day back, this was the homecoming... It wasn't from a feller who'd been gassed or wounded or tortured half out of his mind... There were fellers coming back every day that scarcely looked human. O'Callaghan didn't even look as though he'd been away.

By the following morning his mind was made up that he was going to buy some property, a nice home that nobody could take away. He might have been right, but I didn't think so. I believed that after war comes famine, and we might need the money to keep ourselves; and because I was the one who'd sweated to earn it, I felt I had a right to have a say in the matter. But he wouldn't listen. I knew I'd have to do something to pacify him, so I told him I'd make everything over in joint names. That would be a start as far as he was concerned, so we went to the bank the very next day.

When we got there O'Callaghan made such a fuss in front of all the clerks and everybody with his arguing and shouting, because he wanted to have all the say regarding the money and the business, that I said 'Ye can keep the lot, Jack O'Callaghan! I'll sign all the money over to you for the sake of keepin' the peace. After that, you're on your own...'

I felt worse about the scene in front of all these people who had liked me and respected me, than I did over the loss of the savings.

When we came out of the bank he wouldn't even pay my tram fare back to Frederick Street. He now owned all the money and every penny of it was in his jacket pocket because he had refused to leave a single penny in the account and had closed it down. We were walking back chewing the rag every foot of the way, and I had stopped when we came to the fare stage; all the excitement and disappointment had taken my breath away and I was pregnant with another one of his. But he just walked on.

'I've no money to waste on things like trams. If you want to take the tram, you can pay yourself... And another thing, now I'm in charge, get rid of that Lizzie Flood. She's worse than useless.'

'She's not! She's a good worker and she's a canny lass. There are times I couldn't have managed without her. She's looked after your bairn as well as mine, and been kind to them all.'

201

'Aye, well those days are gone. Get rid of her tomorrow. I don't want to get up and see her silly-lookin' face on the premises. She's a drain on the assets.'

'In that case, you're goin' to have to help. Because I cannot keep a fresh fish business goin' durin' the day, and a fish-and-chip business goin' at night... and look after a home and four bairns on my own.'

I couldn't stand up to O'Callaghan, he had the law on his side, so I had to let poor Lizzie go. She'd not only been a great help but also a good friend all these years, and I felt very ashamed.

For the first couple of weeks I think the novelty of it appealed to him and he would work in the shop for a while and then go in the back and peel potatoes, whatever took his fancy, and I would just do the other things. But like all novelties, it soon wore off and he was spending less and less time in the shop and more and more in the pub. Considering what he took out of the till...because the rest of the money he kept for what he called his 'capital'... O'Callaghan must have been the highest paid fish-and-chip shop hand the world has ever known, and what little had been saved by getting rid of Lizzie, had far more than been balanced out by what he was drinking. In any case Lizzie was a far harder worker, and she didn't care what she did, whatever you asked her to do she did gladly. Not so with O'Callaghan, he only did what he fancied and very little even of that.

You couldn't keep something like a fish-and-chip shop going without a hell of a lot of hard work, the same hard work from morn till midnight every day of the week; Sunday was the only day you weren't, and even then sometimes you had to go down to do something or other. And nobody can just drink whenever they want and work whenever they please, not in the fish-and-chip business.

If O'Callaghan wasn't a worse man for drink than my father, he was every bit as bad and he behaved in the same rotten way, with one single exception...my father worked for every drink he ever drunk, O'Callaghan didn't. My father worked every day so he could drink at night; I worked day and night so O'Callaghan could drink day and night. O'Callaghan would go to the Buffaloes Club for a few beers first thing in the morning, and then go down to the fish quay to buy the fish. For some reason he liked buying the fish and he would walk around with a bottle of rum while he bargained; they called him the

'Rum King' down there, and he liked it, he was proud of it; he even used to take Darkie, the pony we had for the cart, into the bar with him. O'Callaghan liked all kinds of animals, I will say that for him...except for cats.

Little Francie was born in December of that year, 1918, and Jack had sat downstairs drunk and singing his head off while I was having her; not that he needed an excuse to get drunk. He'd come back from the quay, drop the fish off at the shop and then go straight to the Buffs until teatime. Then he'd come in rolling drunk and his tea would have to be ready dead on time. After tea he'd have a kip for an hour and then go out for another session. On top of that I had to lay on nine bottles of beer and a bottle of red wine every day, and woe betide me if I ever forgot; the first thing he did when he came back at night, was to count them. I'd be serving in the shop and you could hear the clicking and the pop-popping as the tops kept coming off, with him swearing at them all the while; that sort of thing wasn't good for business, customers would be looking and wondering what was going on... But it went on year in and year out, with me doing the working and worrying, and him doing the drinking and swearing. The only way I could manage was by hiding money here, there and everywhere, and hope he wouldn't find it before I'd had a chance to spend it on the bairns or for something for the home. And all the while, the bairns were growing up with this.

15

By 1920 Johnny and Joe were young lads, and such good pals it did your heart good to see them together; they'd be coming up the street, tired out after playing all day or after finishing school, and their hair and shoes, especially Joe's, a proper mess, and their arms would be around each other's necks like old soldiers.

They'd be about ten and eleven yet so different you'd wonder what each saw in the other's company. Johnny was little and skinny and Joe was big and stocky, Johnny was the scholar and Joe the dunce. Johnny was strict and strong-willed, Joe was soft as muck. But when it came to fighting, and they were always at it, there was nothing to choose between them. Although Joe was big and strong, Johnny was tough and lightning quick and he would never ever give in.

I wished they didn't have to be fighting all the time but I suppose that's the way God had made them, and I knew that if I stopped them fighting at home they'd only do it somewhere else. So if the two of them had decided that the only way they could sort something out was to have a fight, I'd make them do it in their own backyard. If ever they fought in the street, some kids would be shouting for one and some for the other. 'Go on! Give it to him, Joe!' 'Knock him out, Johnny!' Joe would tell me that both he and Johnny hated the kids who were egging them on against each other, and often as not they'd both turn on them, with him and Johnny fighting on the same side.

One day at school a lad from a higher class than Joe had swung him around in the yard and punched him; the two of them had then started scrapping and a master had seen it, come out into the playground, and told them that if they wanted to settle it they'd have to do it properly. The master had then got two pairs of boxing gloves and arranged a proper boxing match for the afternoon playtime. When the time came the yard was packed with kids who wanted to see this big kid, who was a proper bully, in a fight with Joe Robinson, and all the masters were there as well.

The boys then took off their shirts and stripped to the waist in true style, squared up, and then Joe knocked this other kid out in the first round and all the kids were yelling and cheering. From then on, nobody tangled with our Joe. Both Johnny and him had always been such good boxers that they used to put on exhibitions at Johnson's Ring...they were called the 'Midget Wonders' and did three rounds. I didn't see any harm in it because they were just lads, and if fighting was in their veins I'd rather it come out this way. I never went to see them myself but I was told they were very popular and got well cheered for their efforts.

Johnny was a very good scholar and I always had reports from school saying how clever he was at reading, writing and sums. But Joe was absolutely hopeless and according to the School Board Man, he was hardly ever there. I used to march him to the gates and see him in, and after school Johnny would meet him at the gates to bring him back; but God only knows where he'd been in between. Joe got in with the rough lot all his life and none of the hidings he got either at home or at school made a ha'porth of difference. But one day I found he'd been with a pinching gang, and after I'd lynched him for it I locked him in a dark cupboard for a few hours; he didn't do it any more after that so I don't think he'd liked it very much. He was a funny lad; even though he was wild and daft, he'd get very upset if he thought Johnny or me were really mad at him...or even if he thought we were really disappointed in him, something like that would quickly bring him to tears. Mind, he quickly forgot it and the next day it would be as though nothing had happened; he was different from the rest of us in that way. In some ways his hide was as thick as an elephant's and you could say or do anything you liked and he would just laugh; in others, the tears would be rolling down his cheeks in no time and for next to nothing.

Johnny was forever getting him out of scrapes. Joe loved to get into fights, whereas Johnny only fought when there was no other way. Their father would have been proud of both of them.

However no matter how good a professional boxer our Johnny might one day have been, or whatever ideas he might have had in that line, were put paid to very early in his life when a terrible thing happened... It started when he was only seven, though I never knew the

205

half of it until much later on when it was too late to do anything... Johnny had just begun at his new school in Derby Street and hadn't known anybody yet, so he'd been standing in the playground waiting for the bell to go, when two kids started throwing stones at him. Being the stubborn lad he was, he wouldn't budge an inch, and he'd just stood his ground till one of the stones hit him in the eye. He was crying when a lady teacher found him by himself with his hands over his eye.

'Who are you?' she says. 'And what's the matter with you, bubbling your head off like that! Don't be so soft! Go on! Get to your place in the line before I clip your ear and give you something to really cry about.'

This had made Johnny feel very ashamed, and even though he could never see properly out of his right eye after that, he never told me; Johnny hated anybody to think he was soft.

About two years after, and still I didn't know a thing, Johnny had gone a message for me across town and was following a man smoking a pipe up the stairs on a tram. The man had stopped halfway up and knocked his pipe on the rail to put it out, and the red hot ash had teemed into Johnny's eyes. By the time he got home, he could hardly open his eyes and the right one was completely shut and all red and swollen.

'What's happened, Johnny?' I said as soon as I saw him. 'Have you been fightin'..? What've ye done to your eye?'

He told me about the pipe ash in the tram, but only that, nothing about what his eye was like before it happened. I bathed both his eyes in milk and the redness and the swelling seemed to go down.

'It's all right, Mam,' he kept saying. 'It's getting better. It doesn't hurt anything like what it did.'

'Are ye sure, pet..? Ye wouldn't tell me a lie, would ye?'

'No, Mam. Honest. It's nearly all right.'

And it did seem to get better and he said no more about it, so I just got on and forgot about it; kids often got red eyes with styes one thing or another, and like with scabby noses or runny ears, they usually grew out of it.

One night about eighteen months later, I was working in the fish shop and I had to go out into the yard for some potatoes, and as I passed the lads' bedroom window, I heard this quiet sobbing. So I went in the house and opened the bedroom door very quietly, and when I did I found Johnny stifling sobs into his pillow, he was shoving it into his mouth. He was a lad who never cried.

'Whatever's the matter, Johnny? What's the matter, son?'

At first I thought O'Callaghan had hit him. But when I lit the lamp and held it to his face... My God, what a sight...! It was terrible! You couldn't see where his eye was supposed to be. Instead there was a lump like a hunk of raw liver, it was sticking to the pillowcase and awful stuff was coming out.

I did the best I could to comfort him and stop the pain and crushed some headache tablets in a glass of warm milk.

'Drink this up, pet. This'll do ye.'

As soon as I took the pillow away it was all he could do to stop himself crying out.

'Try not to cry, son. Don't let the customers hear ye. Ye'll feel a lot better tomorrow. You'll see.'

By the next morning it was worse, so I took him straight to the hospital. They put drops in it and sent us away. By the following day he was nearly going mad with the pains, and it wasn't just the one eye but both of them. There was nothing I could do for him, no place he could sit or lie where he could get any ease at all, you could see the poor little feller was in agony.

'We're goin' to the proper place this time,' I said to him. And we went to the Sunderland Eye Infirmary. 'They'll know what to do. They'll sharp stop the pains when we get there. Just you see. All ye've got to do is hang on and pray to God it won't get any worse till we get there,' I was whispering to him. 'Come on, now. Say "Please God, don't let this pain get any worse till I get to the Infirmary. Just keep is all right till I get there. That's all I'm askin'." Keep sayin' that over and over in your head and He'll do it for ye, son. He'll watch over ye. Him and me together.'

They took Johnny in straightaway and kept him in.

Every day I went up but they wouldn't let me see him, they wouldn't tell me anything about him, and I used to walk around outside hoping I could see him through a window. One day when I got back home there was a postcard waiting for me to tell me they wanted to see me immediately, so I went straight back to the station and got the train back to Sunderland.

207

When I got there, they told me that after giving Johnny a thorough examination, they had decided his eye was so bad they were going to have to operate immediately, otherwise he might lose the other eye. A large abscess had built up behind the eye and not only was it pushing the eye out, it was also threatening his little brain and it had to be drained.

I said 'What d'ye mean... "operate"..? How can you operate on somebody's eye?'

'Well, you can't,' this one said. 'That's why we have to take it out.'

'Take it out..? Well, can ye put it back again after ye've drained the abscess or whatever it is you have to do?'

'No, I'm afraid we cannot. It's gone too far. His right eye is already destroyed, and if we don't take it out immediately, the infection might destroy the other one. It's already affected.'

'My God!' I says. 'But he's only a bairn...he's not ten years old... Can ye not do better than that? Surely there's some ointment or somethin' ye could put on without...'

'Not only will he lose his sight, he'll lose his mind as well, if we don't operate.'

'What..!'

But these people weren't going to argue. What they said went, and they began to usher me out. I supposed they must have had other cases to attend to as well as Johnny, so I said 'If ye must, ye must. I certainly can't do anythin' more for him... But I must see him first...before ye do it... I want to have a last look at him before it happens.'

They said it would only upset Johnny if I did, and I'd best go home and try not to think about it too much, that he was in good hands and they were doing all they could.

'All right,' I said. 'All right. If that's what ye think is best for Johnny, that's what I'll do. But I've got just one thing more to say before I go, and that is: if when ye cut the abscess out, ye find that ye can save the eye after all, will ye do it? Will ye try your very, very best to do it?'

'Course we will!' this 'Sister' one snaps. 'That's what we're here for!'

Nine years old, that's all he was... And to think it had been

208

festering on for nearly two years and he'd kept it to himself all that time. I'd never realised until now what he must have gone through, it was only when the infirmary doctor had been asking him all these questions, that it came out about the months and months of awful headaches, how he'd gradually been going blind and how he'd been seeing these blankets of blood in front of his eyes...terrible things for a little bairn to suffer. And yet he'd never once moaned about it, never told anybody about it, not even Joe; I'd have known if he'd told Joe because Joe would have come straight to me.

By the time I got home I was just about out of my mind thinking about it. I thought 'They say drink will drown out your sorrows, so I'll see if it'll drown mine. There's plenty of it here.' So I went to the cupboard, took out a bottle of O'Callagan's rum, supped a large glass of it, and passed out.

Next day when I went to the infirmary I couldn't stop shaking as I went up the steps and through the door. There was a very strong smell of antiseptic and nurses with very serious faces in starched hats hurrying by, and I thought 'It's Johnny! It's somethin' to do with my little bairn, I know it is!'

I'd brought a nice woollen jumper I'd only ever worn once and had washed and pressed so it looked brand new, to give to the Sister in the hope she'd let me in to see Johnny. I couldn't bear to go back again without seeing him, knowing he was only a few yards away and that he must be needing his mother after all this time; and knowing they'd have it in their minds to say no.

'Look,' I said to her. 'I've fetched ye this lovely present. It'll keep ye warm in the corridor... Now I'll not make a sound. Just a look at him to make sure he's all right.'

'Only a minute, then,' she says. 'He's very weak and won't want to be bothered.'

Her words cut into me like a knife. 'Bother him...?' Me...his Mam...bother my little Johnny..? Who did she think she was? Did she think she was his mother now and I was just somebody off the street?

But I quickly said 'Right. Thank you. Thank you very much,' before she changed her mind or somebody came up and said 'That one's not supposed to go in,' or something.

My feet felt as heavy as lead as I went towards the ward where Johnny was, and I was having to fight back the tears. I've never dreaded meeting anybody in my life more than I did my own son that morning. When I got there, there was another lad in his place and my heart nearly stopped. Then I saw this nurse pointing to another bed further down. Very carefully and slowly I went in so that once I'd seen him, I could prepare myself. I had to see him before he saw me. And then I saw his little body propped up in bed with his head covered in white bandages, only one little eye was peeping out of all that tight white. I wasn't a one that cried easy, I'd learnt early that that doesn't solve anything, but as I was walking towards him I thought my heart was going to burst, and I was saying to myself, 'Come on, now Francie. Get a hold of yourself, woman. You're his mother and that little bairn's goin' to be dependin' on ye. Ye can't afford any tears... Not yet, not now...'

As soon as Johnny saw me, he waved. I knew it, he'd plucked up the courage. Now I must do the same. So I went straight up to him with a big smile on my face, as though nothing at all was wrong, as though he'd just had a tooth out or something.

'Hello, son!' I said with a big beam on my face, at least that's what I hoped it looked like. 'Look what your Mam's brought you to eat.' I started unwrapping this little pie I'd made him, and trying not to look him in the face. 'Made any pals yet, have ye..? Who's that poor little lad over there..? Poor soul, he looks in a bad way.'

'He had an accident. He got run over by a tram horse.'

'Has he? Eeeh! Where? What a shame! I bet he was up to somethin' he shouldn't have been... Wor Joe's been away from school again. The School Board man's been round...you know, that truant master feller. I'll larrup 'im when he comes home tonight. I'll murder him... I'll...'

'Ma, I've got a secret to tell you,' Johnny says. 'It's going to upset you a bit, but it's not for you to worry. If it's for anybody, it's for me.'

'What could you have to worry about at your age?' I said, making on I was going to give him a shove, but scared to touch him in case it hurt him or upset what they'd done to him, in any way.

'Come here, Mam,' he says, getting me to bend right over as though there were loads of people present, even though there was nobody.

'They took my eye out, you know.'

210

'Is that all you've got to tell me..? Is that the secret ye were goin' to tell is..? Huh! That's nowt... I thought it was goin' to be somethin' important...You've still got one, haven't ye? Some people's got none... I know quite a few with none at all. Nobody needs two when they've got one good'un like yours.'

'My left one's not very good either.'

'Who told ye that?'

'I heard the doctor telling somebody.'

'Well, I don't care if they take the two of them. They can take your head off, and it'd make no difference to me. I'd love you just the same. Even if they took your arms and legs as well.'

My own eyes felt as though they were going to explode. I felt so ashamed that I had two perfect eyes at my age, and my poor little bairn only had one bad one. I'd have gladly pulled out both mine and given them to him... But he never once complained, neither then or at any time, and he never once cried about it. I knew that seeing as he hadn't done it in front of me, he'd never do it in front of anybody else.

After a week there was no more they could do for him, so they took the bandages off and let him out. Although I'd gone up to see him every day, I couldn't always get there during visiting hours, and sometimes they wouldn't let me in, no matter how much I begged for just a few minutes. They were very strict and sometimes I had to stand outside the window and wave and wave to try and attract his attention. Sometimes I was lucky and the trip was worth it just for a smile or a wave of his little hand. Other times he'd be facing the other way, or asleep, or maybe they'd taken him somewhere, and I'd have to fight the bitterness all the way back and pray to God he wouldn't think I hadn't bothered to come to see him.

Sitting beside him on the train home with this big pink eye patch he had on, I wondered what I should say when the time came that I looked into that little face with no eye in it.

He must have known what I was thinking because he suddenly said 'Ma, have you ever seen the place where the eye should be when it's not there...the socket place, I mean?'

'Your mother's tough, she can look at anythin'. Nothin' like that ever bothers her. Why, like?'

'Well, you're never going to see mine. You're never going to see the vacancy there.'

He must have heard them using that word, it wasn't a word he'd have made up by himself.

'Don't be daft! I'll have to bathe it and all that... These drops they gave me have to go in. Ye cannot do everythin' yourself. They told me how to do it.'

'No, Ma. You won't... I'm always going to look after it myself. You're never going to see... Not ever!'

And I never ever did, not even to this day.

'As soon as we get back, I'm goin' to the chemists and we're goin' to buy ye the best glass eye money can buy, one of the little thin ones that look really nice, just like the real thing. It'll be as good as a new eye. You'll see. Ye won't know the difference.'

The sticky-out ones they gave you at the hospital were thick and horrible, they bulged right out and stared at you, they'd give anybody a fright. I wasn't going to have my little Johnny going around with one of those things, so I got the best one we could afford and he took care of it all by himself. He would take it out when necessary, the way they had told him at the hospital, and he would clean it and clean the socket, and put it back. But he was just a lad, and as with everything else, accidents happen, especially when you're cleaning anything as fragile as that, and it got broken.

Although Johnny never ever mentioned his eye, he must have been very sensitive about it all the time, because he wouldn't go out the house without it, he said he was too ashamed. I said there was no call to be ashamed of a thing like that, it wasn't his fault. But I learned my lesson and I got him two new ones so that he would always have a spare, and he always kept his spare one in a little egg cup, locked away, and nobody went near it but him. The only way was to get two at the same time, because it was hard to get a match for a broken one, no two had exactly the same pattern.

Even though Johnny was only nine, and I was a grown-up, I left him to see to it himself because he had a right to deal with it in his own way, and nobody was less clumsy or more sensible than he was. Yet you could sit and talk to him, and if after a bit you were looking at his face, he would begin to colour up and go out of the room, he was always ashamed of his eye. And he never wanted his photo taken.

A few weeks after Johnny came out of the Infirmary, the other eye started giving trouble, and a doctor I went to told me it was because they must have used a dirty instrument when they were taking the other one out. I didn't know whether it was true or not, but I didn't go back to the Infirmary, I just went to the doctor in town instead. All he did was put drops in every few days that cost pounds over the course of a few months and did nothing. Johnny bathed it every day and took great care of it and gradually it cleared up by itself, but he never had perfect sight in it, and eventually I had to get him glasses.

16

In 1924 Walter was born and I had a bad time with him, it was a long birth and they thought there was going to be three of them. He was thirteen and three-quarter pounds and he came out all twisted and blue, the midwife said it was caused by all the cold water I used to have my arms in when I was cleaning and gutting the fish for the shop. Whether it really was that, or whether it was because he got strangled up with the cord while he was being born, which is what I think, I'll never know. I had never picked any of the others up when they cried, because I didn't think it was a good idea, but I did it with Walter for quite a while. I'd let him cry for a bit to stretch his lungs, but no more than that, and after a month he was as pink as he should be.

Just like when I'd had Edmund and Francie, O'Callaghan couldn't have cared less. I didn't even know where he was at the time I was having Walter, except that he'd be drinking in one place or another...you wouldn't get any prize for guessing that much. However, the Frederick Street fish shop was still going in spite of his antics, so I wasn't complaining.

I never had much time to spend with my bairns, I was always far too busy; but I loved them as much as any mother loved her bairns. To me, sitting cuddling them in rags when they were starving, and rocking them to sleep on the pavement with your hand out wasn't loving them. Loving them meant looking after them and teaching them to look after themselves and be somebody in life, not just moaning around until somebody put them in the workhouse and took them off you. Sometimes I'd be rushing about here and there like a bluebottle, and I'd hear them singing or talking when they were in their beds, and I'd have a listen outside their bedroom door. One night I was going past when I heard our Joe crying, he was about thirteen at the time and he was saying he was going to run away the next day, and Johnny was trying to tell him not to.

I was really upset and I burst in. 'What have I done to ye that ye'd be runnin' away from is, wor Joe?'

'It's not you, Ma,' Joe says. 'It's him, wor...father. He's horrible to we. He's always liftin' we up by wor lugs and hittin' we for nothin'.'

'He's what!'

'Don't tell him, Ma! Don't tell him I said it, or he'll kill we!'

'I won't tell him, son...don't you worry. You just go to sleep and promise me ye'll never let me hear ye talkin' about runnin' away no more... I'll look after ye. No harm'll come to ye as long as I'm alive. I promise ye that... Will you promise me, now, Joe?'

'Aye. All right, Ma,' he says in his big deep voice, but I could see he wasn't too sure.

When I was saying my prayers that night, I said 'Please God, show me a way to put that man off this earth. I want to kill him!'

A few days after that, an old woman in the next lane who always had a kind word for the bairns, and had lost her own in the war, lost her husband. She was very poor and had nothing to look decent in even for her own man's funeral, the whole family had never been much more than paupers, and she asked me if I'd lend her a black coat and hat. She was the same size as me so I made her up a little parcel of everything, right down to the gloves and stockings.

'Oh, thanks, Mrs O'Callaghan,' she said. 'Thank you very, very much. I'll fetch them back as soon as I get back home.'

'Don't you worry,' I said. 'Keep them till the next day. I'm in no hurry.'

O'Callaghan came in just as she was going out the shop, and he says 'What's she so full of thanks about?'

I told him.

'Hmmh... Ye did, did ye?' He turned around, locked the front door and put the key in his pocket. 'And how much did you hire that little lot out for, may I ask?'

'What've ye locked the door for..? We've customers comin' in shortly.'

'How much!' he yelled.

'Nowt!' I yelled back. 'What d'ye take me for..? She's a poor woman. They're my clothes and I'll do what the hell I like with them. I'll lend them to whoever I please.'

'Will ye now..? Right, my girl..! Right, my little bitch..! Call yourself a business woman, do you..? I'll show you some business.'

He went into the cupboard and had the nerve to put my man's gloves on, my Johnny's gloves. He didn't even know how to wear them properly, for all his brothers were fighting men...real fighting men.

'Do you know who those gloves belong to..? Those are a champion's gloves! You're not fit to wear them!'

He chucked a pair over to me and told me to put them on.

'Prepare to defend yourself,' he said, and squared up in his fashion.

I chucked them back at him. 'I'm not boxin' ye. I wouldn't give ye the satisfaction.'

'Please yourself,' he said, and straight away punched me in the mouth and knocked me against the wall. 'See what ye get for being cheeky? Now put them on.'

I realised I had no choice but to put them on; if I hadn't, he'd have boxed me around anyway. So I put them on and put my mitts up, the way Johnny used to do.

'Right!' he said. 'Let the best one win.'

I'd never seen him in a fight with another man, I'd never seen him in a fight with anybody...except me and the bairns. I was strong and I was tough and I gave him back all I could, but he got me in the corner in the end and he bashed me till I was out for the count. When I came around I was lying on the bed with a stocking of ice on my head. I think he must have got into a panic in case he'd done me serious harm, because they'd have been no end of witnesses for the way he treated me, even though he would generally try to do it so nobody would know.

Edmund, his eldest bairn, was the one O'Callaghan treated the worst. He was forever going into tantrums, and, by God, didn't he get thrashed for it; sometimes I had to go on my hands and knees and beg him to stop. One day he'd done something O'Callaghan hadn't liked and O'Callaghan chased him into the yard. Edmund ran into the lavatory and locked himself in and wouldn't open the door, so O'Callaghan took an axe and chopped the whole door down. I've never been one for telling lies, but I had to with O'Callaghan, I had to about our Edmund or he would have murdered him I don't know how

216

many times. Edmund could be a little bugger when he wanted, but if I was mad with him I'd have to hide it from O'Callaghan.

One day it was a special holiday for something or other, and I'd baked stuff for a picnic and decided to take the bairns to the beach; I never took the bairns anywhere because I never had the time, but this day I'd made up me mind we'd have ourselves a day to remember.

Eventually I got everything ready, packed the basket, dressed them all up, and away we went. It was a lovely summer's afternoon, the sun was shining with all its might, and to make it that bit more of a treat, we got the tram down. As soon as we got there, Edmund and Francie wanted to go on the swings, so we all waited with the hamper and things until they'd had a few shots. But when the time came to go on down to the beach, Edmund wouldn't budge off the roundabout. I pulled and dragged to get him off but he was hanging on to the pole as though his hands were stuck to it, and as I pulled one of his fingers off, the other would go back on, and he was a strong little bugger; and all the while he was yelling and screaming as though he was being murdered. I'd given baby Walter to Johnny to hold in the meantime, and now he started crying. People were looking and shouting and running up, and eventually somebody fetched the police. By this time I was absolutely past myself with Edmund, and the only way to have stopped him yelling, was either to leave him there all day, or strangle him.

It took two big policemen to eventually get him off, and when they did, they took him down to the beach and threw salty water over him to try and shut him up because he still wouldn't stop yelling. One of them filled one of the kids' pails and brought back some for me and chucked it over me as well, because by this time I was practically going out of my mind with him; it wasn't just that he was making a bloody awful racket, what was so terrible was that he was doing it in front of hundreds of people, everybody for miles around was looking at us.

I got the policemen to keep hold of Edmund until I shoved everything back in the baskets and gave them to Johnny and Joe to carry, got Francie to take Johnny's hand, and with Walter still bawling in my left arm, I grabbed Edmund in my right hand, and ran all the way home, yanking Edmund every few yards as he tried to dig in his heels and hang on to lampposts or anything else he could get hold of.

Poor Francie and Joe and Johnny had never even got to sit on the sands, and Edmund was still yelling when we came through the market place and bumped into O'Callaghan.

'What the hell's going on?' O'Callaghan says. 'I thought you were going to the beach for the day?'

I was in such a state, I told him what had happened, I wasn't thinking of the consequences.

'Right!' he said, and picked Edmund up under his arm and went off with him; still the silly little bugger was yelling, and we were all running after him because we were scared of what O'Callaghan was going to do.

'Shut up, ye little sod! Shut up!' O'Callaghan was shouting.

'No, Jack!' I was begging and pleading. 'Don't hurt him on account of that. He just got himself a bit over-excited. He's just stubborn, that's all.'

'Stubborn, is he..! Well, we'll see about that...'

We had a big rain barrel in the yard and I don't know whether O'Callaghan had had it in mind all the time, but as soon as we got back he shoved Edmund straight down into it head first with all his clothes on, and he ducked him and ducked him till I thought he'd drown the poor bairn... But it cured him, he certainly stopped yelling. I'm not saying O'Callaghan was right, but that was the last canary fit Edmund threw for a very long time.

The ducking in the barrel didn't change his personality, if anything he was worse, but there was no more non-stop yelling. About a month after the business at the beach, he was running around the yard with a carving knife in each hand, as though he'd gone completely wild, and neither Joe or Johnny could stop him; he chased the two of them into the house and was jabbing at them and laughing all of the time. I heard all the fuss, came in out of the shop, took the knives off him, thrashed him, and threw him into bed. But no sooner was I back in the shop, than he was at it again. Downstairs in the fish shop the customers were waiting to be served and they must have been wondering what the hell was going on as I ran back up the stairs shouting 'I'll skin ye alive, ye little sod!'

I rushed back in and gave him another hiding and clashed him on to the bed, but still he kept on laughing.

'I'll brain ye!' I says, and I boxed his ears. Suddenly he vomited red stuff all over me. 'Blood..! Oh, my God! I've damaged his little brain..!' I got hold of him and clasped him tightly. 'Oh, me little bairn... What have I done... What's your wicked, cruel mother done to ye..? Say somethin'!'

All of a sudden he struggled free and started laughing all over again, crazier than ever. I looked at him in sheer amazement, he'd gone completely crackers. He got out of bed and went to the cupboard and grabbed an empty bottle.

Then I knew... Wine..! That's what it was. Red wine! The little bugger had been drinking his father's red wine...

'Come here,' I said, 'and give's a look at ye. Oh my godfather..! You've drunk the whole bloody lot! Your father'll murder the two of we when he comes back... You're drunk, ye stupid little fool!'

Just then, Terry, one of O'Callaghan's sisters, came in and saw the mess Edmund was in and I told her all about it.

'There's no time to buy any more now, Francie. The pubs'll all be shut.'

'Can we fill it up with anythin' else that looks like wine?'

'That'd be no use. He'd soon know the difference. You'll just have to own up and tell him the truth.'

As we were talking, in came O'Callaghan straight to the cupboard.

'There's a serious thing happened here tonight, Jack,' I said. 'That little bairn, your own bairn, has been drinkin' your wine. And it's not his fault. Ye can't blame the bairn. He didn't know what he was doin' was wrong. He's seen you doin' it often enough. He's vomitted all over the place.'

I thought 'What's he goin' to do now? Is he goin' to lambaste the two of us in front of his own sister. Or is he goin' to wait until she's gone?'

O'Callaghan looked at little Edmund who had now gone very white, was looking very sick and in an awful mess, and then he turned to his sister and said 'That's it, Terry. That's the finish. I'll never bring another drop into this house as long as I live.' With that he went to bed and didn't say another word. What a relief... I could hardly believe it.

But the next day he had either forgotten his promise or decided it wasn't worth bothering about, because the last thing he said before he went out was 'See you don't forget to get my stuff in...And make sure none of them gets in there while I'm out. I'm holding you responsible.'

The business was now going down and down; not just because he was taking so much from the till, but because he was frightening away the customers. If he wasn't shouting and cursing in the back either at me or at a bottle-opener, he would upset them in the shop by his nasty manner or the lustful way he would grab me in front of them: 'Howay, let's go to bed, Francie.' I'd just smile at the customers and pretend he was only kidding, but I'd be blue with shame; he was just like a stallion but with less manners. He'd always be drunk when he wanted me to go to bed with him...and when he felt like it, that's when it had to be. Some nights it might be as early as nine o'clock, which was the busiest time in the fish-and-chip business, and I'd be in the middle of serving somebody when he would stagger in, slam the fryer lid down and say

'That's it! We're finished for the night. You can all beat it until tomorrow.' He would then rake the fires out and shoo out anybody who still hadn't gone.

Folks would come in during the day for a few fish scraps, and if he was coming in or going out and saw it, he'd knock them out my hand on to the floor, or grab them and toss them in the fire. 'What d'ye think this is..? We sell fish here! We don't give it away..! If you buy it, you can have it. If you don't, that's where it goes...'

Anybody who couldn't pay there and then was turned away whenever O'Callaghan was in the shop. 'What the hell do you think it is..?' he'd say. 'We're here to do business, not to run a bloody charity!'

How awful it is to see the look on somebody's face when you say something like that to them, you completely take away what little bit of pride they might have managed to tack together. They never come back

. He once hit me in the shop just because I gave some kids a bit of batter for nothing.

'It's all right,' I'd whispered to him. 'I'll give them a few chips less to make up for it.'

'Don't lie to me, ye stupid bitch..! The little brats might make a mug out of you, but they're not making one out of me!'

He was so mean, I had to charge for everything down to the last batter when he was there, he'd have sold them the fins off the fish's backs if they'd asked for them. They knew what to expect when they came in and saw him standing.

I knew how far I could go with him, and often the best policy was to put up with it and say nothing; he was such a clevershite, or thought he was, that you could never win an argument with him over anything. But one night I was serving in the shop, and he'd come back when the pubs had closed and was getting stuck into his home supply, and was particularly bad with his cursing and clicking the bottle tops. You could hear it all over the shop, so I made the excuse to my customers that I needed some more chips and went into the back and told him to be quiet, at least until the customers had gone, because it was bad for business. I was coming back out into the shop carrying a pail of chipped potatoes in either hand, when O'Callaghan chucked a bottle of stout all over my face and hair and apron. Then he grabbed my arm and twisted it up my back.

'Don't you ever tell me what I should do and what I shouldn't!' He was shouting at the top of his voice with no regard for anybody. 'What does a slut like you know about manners..! Get out of my sight!' He flung me forwards and I went flying in and bashed into the fryer and just about went into the boiling fat head first.

The customers were all looking and didn't know what to say or do. But I'd had enough now... I pulled the fish-slice out of the scalding fat, and ran straight back into the kitchen where he was just turning to pick up another bottle, and I lashed him with it.

Swish! Swash! Swoosh! into his face it went. I can still remember the look of fear and utter amazement on his face.

'Take that, ye sod! Take that! And that!'

His hand was up reaching for it but before he could take it off me, I saw the big yard shovel and dropped the fish slice. I grabbed the shovel and bashed his legs with it again and again until he fell to the ground. And as he put his arms up to protect himself, I whacked those as well... I didn't care if I broke every bone in his body.

'Take that, ye bugger! And this is for the bairns..!' And I whacked him again and again, and the banging of the shovel echoed around the whole place. 'And this is for Lizzie!'

By God, that fettled him...

When I went back into the shop, nobody had moved and there was dead silence.

I wiped my hands on a tea towel. 'Next, please.'

'A fish and threepenn'orth twice, please, Mrs O'Callaghan,' this woman says in a meek voice.

'Right ye are, Mrs Wallace. Help yourself to vinegar and salt. Like a bit of batter as well?'

'Yes please, if ye've got any to spare.'

'There's plenty tonight... Nice out still, is it?'

I was champion, I felt great. It was the best day's work I did in all my life.

After that night O'Callaghan stole from me just like he always did, from my till and from my hidey places, and he abused me in many ways, and he was a rotten husband and a rotten father. But he never raised a hand to me or the bairns ever again; not in the shop, not in the house, not anywhere. And every year after, for as long as I knew him, his legs would break out in sores; just about the same time as well, like an anniversary.

I didn't have any help in the shop or with looking after the bairns now, so when my sister Lily in Hull asked if I'd take her daughter Gertie and feed and clothe her in exchange for her helping out, because Lily was very hard up, I was only too glad to say yes. Gertie was just turned fifteen and a lovely girl with such a gentle nature, yet big in front for her age, and like a grown woman around the hips. She was bright and willing to do anything and was a great help in the house and in the shop, and everybody liked her.

One morning I was doing the fish in the yard when I heard a scream: 'Aunty! Aunty!' just the twice but in a queer sort of way, not the way girls normally shriek when they're funning. I ran across the yard, wiping my hands on my apron as I went, and very concerned in case she'd had an accident or one of the bairns had. But when I got to the bottom of the stairs that led up to our house, Gertie was standing there, halfway down, looking as though she'd had a terrible fright.

'Gertie! Was that you? Are ye all right? What happened?'

'Yes, Aunty. But I'm all right now. Don't worry. It was nothing.'

'Are ye sure? Ye gave me quite a start...'

'I know... I'm sorry, Aunty.' She put her arms around me and gave me a kiss. I said all right and came away, but it left me wondering; the boys would never tease her or anything because Johnny thought the world of her and wouldn't let any of them bother her.

Three weeks to the day, the same thing happened. This time I ran across the yard and up the stairs in my fish clogs and found Gertie draped over the bannister, white as death.

'Whatever's the matter with ye, pet? Come on! Tell me quickly! What is it?'

She could hardly get the words out.

'It's Uncle Jack again.'

'It's what..? What about your Uncle Jack..? What about him, Gertie? Come on, now. Don't be frightened. Tell me... Nobody's goin' to hurt ye.'

She had apparently been scrubbing the stairs and O'Callaghan had crept up behind her and put his hand right up her skirt.

'Oh, me bairn... I knew he was... But I never, never thought he'd stoop so low as to do a thing like that to a little girl... God forgive him for doin' such a thing!' I gave her a hug and then said 'You wait here hinny. I'll fix him!'

I wasn't afraid of O'Callaghan any more now... I ran down the back stairs, the way she said he'd gone, and down the main street as fast as my legs would carry me, clogs clacking and all, still with my fish apron on and fish scales all over me, until I came to the Buffs Club. I knew where I'd find him, I knew where he'd be...pretending he'd been all along; and sure enough, there he was with his cronies, sitting around a big iron table with a glass of beer in front of him. I thought 'I'll show ye up in front of all your mates, ye swine! I'll let them see what kind of a beast they're drinkin' with! Ye'll have no pals left when they hear what I've got to say.'

But when I started into him, his mates just laughed, they obviously thought the randy sod was a hero; no wonder he drank with them, no wonder he came home a bloody swine if this was the lot he spent his days with.

'You bloody child raper, ye!' I yelled at him. 'I'm workin' in the yard right next to ye practically. And ye'd sneak up behind me back and do a thing like that to a little bairn. Your own neice! Ye should be ashamed of yourself, Jack O'Callaghan.'

All of them were laughing at me. It meant nothing to them.

'Haddaway out o' here! Ne fishwives allowed!' one of them shouted.

'Then how come they allow rats in if it's a buffaloes club!'

I was so mad I got hold of the table by the legs and threw it over, and their beer spilt all over their trousers and on the floor. I didn't wait for them to come at me. I ran straight out and went hurrying back home, feeling I'd made a fool of myself, and half expecting O'Callaghan to come after me and murder me right there in the street. But he didn't, he didn't come home until very late that night, and when he eventually did, he just went to bed and never said a word. I thought he'd maybe learned his lesson and realised he'd done a very bad thing, and was too ashamed to look any of us in the eye.

If our Lily had known, she'd never have spoken to me again for letting such a thing happen to her daughter in my house; so after I'd turned it over and over in my mind, because there was nobody in the world I could go to about something like this, I told Gertie I thought she'd better go back home.

'Oh no, Aunty,' she said. 'Please don't send me away. It's not my fault and I love living here. I know what you're thinking but I won't tell anybody. I know you do everything you can to protect me. I'm sure he won't do it again. Not after what you said to him... I know I shouldn't say it, but I love you the same as I do my own mother.'

Maybe O'Callaghan had learnt his lesson, so I said all right. But from then on Gertie and I slept in the same bed and O'Callaghan slept on his own.

O'Callaghan didn't give up at all; if anything, he got bolder, he even tried to do it to her while I was away at church getting Walter christened and she was at home minding the others. He didn't take the slightest notice of my pleading or scolding, and obviously had no consideration whatsoever for the tender feelings of Gertie and the fact that she was still a bairn, so I decided I'd try a different tack with him... I asked the Catholic priest to call. But when he came he turned out to be little more than a lad and I soon realised I'd made a big mistake. First off, he told me I was exaggerating things, even though he wasn't in a position to know whether I was exaggerating or not...how could he have the faintest idea what my life was like? Then he said that when I'd married O'Callaghan I'd promised at the altar to love, honour and obey him, and that I must abide by those promises. He said I should go to Mass every morning and take all the bairns and ask for Our Lady's help. He said I should go out of my way to please my husband and I could start by giving him a treat for his supper, 'such as a nice piece of gammon, well cooked and nicely presented, or a pair of kippers'.

'What about him, Father?' I said. 'What about what he promised..? Are ye goin' to say anythin' to O'Callaghan, I want to know... Or are ye goin' to let him get away with it scot-free?'

'Look now, Frances...and remember who you're talking to... "Let he who is without stain of sin, cast the first stone"... Can you put your hand to your heart and say you are without stain of sin, Frances..? Eh..? No, I'm sure you cannot... And when were you last at Confession, I should like to know? I cannot remember seeing you there. You'll have to come to Confession at least once a week from now on. Converts must always work that little bit extra hard to make sure they don't slip back. It's only a very little time out of your week, and the Lord will not accept idle excuses.'

'You have the nerve to tell me, Father...to talk to me about love and obey...and confession and everythin'... And yet you're goin' to let that randy sod get away with it... I'm sorry, Father, I didn't mean to say that. But that's what I think, and I have to say it... Serve and obey that womaniser..? Not on your life! Not any more... So I don't want any more of you and your talk. You're no use to me if that's the way ye think.'

'I came at your request to help you and - '

'I invited ye in, and now I'm invitin' ye out.'

'Your soul's headed straight for Hell, my girl. You'd better get yourself to Confession as soon as possible.'

'What about him goin' to Confession..? That's what I fetched ye for... Why should I be the one to go to Hell? What have I done that's wrong...except speak my mind? I'm not the one ill treating her bairns. I'm not the one taking the food out of their mouths to drink meself into a stupor every day that God sends. I'm not the one forcing myself in the filthiest way on somebody else's bairn.'

'Now, now, Frances. You - '

'I'd have been better off never becomin' a Catholic, if that's the price I have to pay.'

'You're one of us now, Frances. You belong to the One, True, Holy and Apostolic Church.'

'I don't know anythin' about that... I joined your church because of my husband...not this one... My real husband... I didn't join because I thought there was anythin' wrong with the one I was brought up in... But if this is what ye get, I might as well get meself back out. At least the vicar wouldn't have taken the man's part just because he was a man, the way yous do.'

After he'd gone I was very sorry for speaking the way I had because I knew you could go to Hell for talking to a Father like that. The bairns were going to a Catholic school and I didn't want them to get into trouble because of it... And if I tried to go back to being a Protestant, they mightn't want me now... They might turn round and said I could go to Hell for changing to a Catholic... So I made up my mind to start going to church again, at least with the Catholic Church you could do nigh on anything and still get forgiven as long as you went to Confession afterwards. But it was a while before I could bring myself to go to Mass when I knew that young priest would be on the altar; and if ever I saw from the nameplate on the Confession box, that he was the one on, I'd leave it till another time, or go somewhere else.

I don't know how much good it does you going to church and not liking the priest, and this one might have been a holy man, or thought himself to be; but I didn't like him and I couldn't help myself, and whenever he was saying the prayers I couldn't take them in. I think he was too young for the job. It's hard when you're used to an old man old enough to be your grandfather, and then all of a sudden you have somebody younger than you are to take his place. He might have learnt the Mass and all the prayers off by heart and be able to speak in Latin, but how can a slip of a lad scarcely in his twenties, who's probably had a very protected upbringing, know anything at all about the ways of the world, especially the way husbands and wives go on?

Every week I'd send Edmund and Francie over to see their Grandma Callaghan, and Johnny and Joe to see their Grandma Robinson. At one time Johnny's grandma was proud of him because he was so bright, and she used to roar and laugh when he would get up on a cracket and start preaching. 'I don't know where that lad gets his brains from,' she'd say. But then when Johnny didn't grow into the big strong-looking lad that she liked to see, she changed her tune and made a fuss of Joe instead. If you weren't a big tough feller, you were no use at all as far as she was concerned, character and brains were far less important.

One Sunday afternoon I was taking baby Walter over to see his Grandma Callaghan, and O'Callaghan said 'I won't be going up to see my mother today, Francie. I was round there last night. You go on up with the kids. You can call in for me at the club on the way back.'

So off we went, and Gertie came with us part of the way before she went to meet a girlfriend for a walk in the park. After we'd visited Mrs Callaghan and the bairns had had their teas, we came back and stopped at O'Callaghan's club and waited outside until closing time... women weren't allowed in. A quarter of an hour after we got there the doors opened and they started coming out, and we had to stand right back out of the way to avoid the drunks. But after the place had emptied and the windows had been shuttered and the lights put out, and only a few drunks were left peeing up against a wall and laughing when they saw us, there was still no sign of O'Callaghan and I thought we must have missed him, so we all went home.

When we got there it was pitch black and straightaway I felt something was wrong. There wasn't a light on anywhere and everything was locked up, even the back-door. I wrapped little Walter up in my coat and put him in a tatey box in the wash-house and told Edmund and Francie to stay and watch him, and then I crawled through the coal-house hatch and up the stairs into the house. There he was in the bedroom...my husband Jack O'Callaghan... And there was poor little Gertie quietly sobbing her heart out. He was lying on the bed beside her with his arms folded behind his head, muffler still tied around his neck, and fast asleep.

Without stopping to think, I grabbed the ends of his muffler and pulled them around the bed-head and wound them round and around and would have choked him to death if he hadn't woke up.

He was brazen now, he didn't give a damn. First thing next morning I marched up to Mrs Callaghan's and spilt all the beans; I told her about the business with Gertie, about the priest, everything.

I thought 'Right, ye bloody swine! Let your mother know what you're like. Nobody else seems to care.'

When I told her, I could see she was really shook up. She was a crafty one though, a good mother and very loyal to her sons; some of them had got themselves into some funny business at times, but no matter what they did she always defended them, and she'd never have a word said against her beloved Jack.

'It must be your fault, Francie, that's all I can say. He's only a normal healthy man with normal healthy appetites. What can you expect if you don't satisfy him yourself..? He's as good looking as any young man you'd find anywhere, and you're lucky to have him. No wonder women chase after him.'

'He's the one doin' the chasin'! And you've no right to put any blame on my niece. If my sister heard you say a thing like that, she'd have her man come up here and ring your neck.'

'Nobody's blaming Gertie. But you know what young girls are... They misinterpret things. He was probably just kissing her goodnight.'

'Do you think I'd be round here, when I've got piles of work to do, if that's all he was doin'..? D'ye think there's no difference between kissin' somebody goodnight, and puttin' your hand up their skirt...especially if she's your own neice!'

'Have you seen it with your own eyes?'

'Seen what?'

'What you just said.'

'He's hardly goin' to do it when I'm there, is he!'

'There you are... So you only have a fifteen-year-old girl's word against that of a grown man... Don't you think you should be rather ashamed of yourself for taking a child's word against that of your own husband? That nearly amounts to slander!'

She was much cleverer with words than I was; she knew it and I knew it, she could twist anything round to suit herself.

'And where do you think you would you be without our Jack to help you bring up all those children..? You need a husband, and they need a father. They're his bairns as well. And don't forget that!'

She was telling me off... I'd come to tell her that her own son was doing something terrible to an innocent little girl, and here she was blaming me.

'You couldn't manage your shop...which you came by in such an underhanded way that left me absolutely stranded...without him getting the fish in for you. It's a hard and thankless task going out every morning, come hail or shine, arguing and bandying down there. And then having to hump cold and slimy fish all the way back. What man worth his salt doesn't deserve a drink after that? Just because you don't like a drink, doesn't mean he shouldn't... I think you're a bit selfish. That's what I think's the matter with you. Jack's a good man. He went and did his duty for his country, like all his brothers. And he did it for you and those children... You should stick by him and not always be running him down the way you do. I know, he's told me.'

'I can't be peelin' tateys, cleanin' fish, lookin' after five bairns, fryin' and servin' in the shop, and be upstairs lyin' under him at the same time. It's late by the time I've finished. And more often than not, I'm dead beat. Yet if I cannot give him what he wants when he wants it, he'll rip me nightie to shreds and chase me out into the street at dead of night. If ye don't give that man what he wants, he rapes ye!'

'Just be careful what you say, Francie! Watch your fishwife language with me, my girl! My upbringing was a lot different to yours! You're a vulgar - '

'Look, Mrs Callaghan. I'm not listenin' to any more of your flannel or your insults. I can see I'm gettin' nowhere talkin' to you. I came because I thought ye might have understood and helped... But I'm goin' to sort this out on my own from now on. I'm goin' straight from here to the solicitor's. I'm goin' to have him up. I'm goin' to get the police on him. We'll see if that'll puts a stop to his shenanigans.'

I knew she was a lot older than me, that she was my mother-in-law and an educated woman and all that, but I'd had enough. I'd listened to her sufficient to know what side she was on, and I wasn't goin' to listen long enough for her to persuade me I was the one at fault. I knew that threat would shut her up, and it did that all right. She knew I was really mad and that if I said I'd do something, I'd more than likely do it. So she took a different tack, speaking more quietly and pleading with me. She said I had to think about the bairns and what a court case would do to them, that they could very well be taken off me if I made out their home was unsatisfactory. She would speak to

229

Jack herself, he would listen to her and take notice of what she said, and she would make sure that he never did anything again that might give the wrong impression. So I said all right we'd leave it at that.

Whether his mother said anything to him at all or not, I don't know, but in less than a week he was at it again. This time I heard Gertie screaming in the washhouse, and when I went down I actually caught him in the middle of it.

I had no other choice but to send poor Gertie back to her mother. Fortunately Lily and her man had by now bought a fish-and-chip shop themselves in Hull, and Lily had written to ask if I could spare Gertie because she'd be very useful to them; they knew she'd learned a lot about the fish-and-chip business from me, and it would be cheaper than getting somebody they'd have to pay wages to. When I told Gertie she'd have to go, she begged me to let her stay, but I told her it was for her own good and I showed her the letter from her mother asking me to let her go. And so she went, and we were all sorry, she really was a lovely lass.

About a month later, I was finding things very hard without Gertie because O'Callaghan had refused to let me get anybody else in her place, when this feller came to the shop demanding the first instalment on a loan repayment for a house. I said 'You've got the wrong place, mister. Nobody here has taken any loans out.' He handed me this form with a moneylender's name on top which showed that O'Callaghan had mortgaged everything in the shop down to the last pan. He'd taken out a loan of £60 for his mother and hadn't said a word to me; why he did it and what she wanted it for, I never got to know. All I needed to know was that every week I had to have the money ready or they'd take the fish-and-chip shop off us.

By the time I'd paid off Mrs Callaghan's debt, the fish-and-chip shop was on its last legs, so when a little fish-and-chip shop in Edith Street come up for rent, I talked O'Callaghan into taking it for himself; I'd look after the Frederick Street business and that would be for our keep, he could have the Edith Street and what profit he made he could have for drinking. The arrangement appealed to him so I set up the Edith Street shop and away we went.

With O'Callaghan out of the way, the Frederick Street business picked up again and sometimes I sat in the yard and cleaned thirteen bags of tateys in a day, apart from two or more boxes of fish. It was good business but no joke when it was snowing and so cold you could have cut a finger off and never felt it. Fish wounds, which you couldn't help getting, were hard to heal...they're funny things, fish. Neighbours would see me in the yard, and if the weather was very bad they would sometimes shout down, 'Howay up and have a cuppa tea, Francie! Afore ye freeze to death out there!'

'I'm too busy,' I'd shout back. 'Wait till I get these done.' I knew if I got up and went into the warm, it would be very hard to go back out again. Old Mrs White would sometimes come down with a cup of hot water and a teaspoon of whiskey in it.

'I don't drink, Mrs White.'

'Here. Get it doon ye, and don't be se daft! Tak it afore ye keel ower. Nebody's ganna knaa.'

The Edith Street shop on the other hand was hardly doing any business at all and we were losing money on it. O'Callaghan said I had the easy shop and he'd been stuck with the hard one, and he wanted to swap. But I wasn't having that, so I said to him, 'I'll tell ye what... I'll do Edith Street one week and see if I can build it up, and you do Frederick Street. The next week we'll swap over. That way we'll know what's wrong, if anythin' is wrong.'

He was contented with that and away we went. But in a matter of weeks both shops went down; O'Callaghan was bad for business wherever he went. So I had to go back and stay in Frederick Street because that was our livelihood, and he half-heartedly went back to Edith Street. Another month or so and Edith Street was completely snookered and we had to get rid of it. Then he came back to Frederick Street and that went down again. Yet still he would sit in the pub opposite watching all the customers going in and out, which they didn't like, and every so often come into the shop, take money out of the till and go back into the pub with it, swearing at anybody who got in his way. Eventually the goodwill I'd built up over all the years was lost, and by the end of 1925 we had to give up what had once been a smashing shop that could have lasted us the rest of our lives, that could have kept us going while our kids got a proper education and a start in life; and we had to give up our home as well,

A little place in Walpole Street then came up for rent, and we took it. We were desperate now, and O'Callaghan agreed we had to make a go of this one.

17

Johnny had been going to St. Bede's grammar school and doing very well, but things were such hard-going at Walpole Street that he had to leave when he was fifteen and try to find a job. He left without complaining, the way he did with everything, because he knew we couldn't manage otherwise. Johnny was like a little father to the others, and they all looked up to him...O'Callaghan's bairns, Edmund, Francie and Walter, just the same.

Although Johnny was dead keen and would have had a go at anything, things were hard everywhere and he couldn't get a job. One day without telling me, he went to see his Uncle Peter Callaghan who was in the merchant navy, and fixed up to go to sea. When he came back that night and told me, I did everything I could to persuade him against it, but he'd made up his mind and there was no budging him. I knew he was doing it for my sake so that he wouldn't be a burden to me, but he'd never say it. 'I thought it would be nice to see a bit of the world,' was all he'd say.

Although I didn't want him to go, he was fourteen and growing into a man and he hadn't had much of a life uptil now, and going to sea would broaden his shoulders as well as his mind...he was a strong and tough little feller but he was still on the small side.

On the day he went, brave as anything, his bright little face was full of smiles. I'd only had a few days to get him ready and fit him out with the things he needed...a white apron, long trousers, a blue jersey and things like that. He had to join the ship at Hull so I made him wear his school cap and shorts to go on the train and get there for half price, and he was so little and young-looking, he looked just like a school bairn when he went off, his little arm going like a windmill out of the train window. I don't know what broke my heart the most...then, or when he finally sailed away from Shields a couple of days later. The ship called to Shields to pick up its cargo and the whole lot of us went down to see Johnny off; there was me and our

Joe, Edmund, Francie and little Walter in my arms. It was a Sunday afternoon and we were standing on the Groyne. Johnny wasn't allowed to leave the ship because he was part of the crew now, so we were all shouting across to him.

Although he was glad we were there, he was pretending he hadn't seen us so that none of the crew would think he was soft...he wrote and told us that afterwards. He had his apron on and his long trousers, and he was pulling on this great big rope with all these huge sailors in front of him. Poor little soul... I couldn't stop myself from shouting 'Come back, son! Don't go! Come on home..!' But he didn't hear me, or at least he didn't seem to, and maybe it was just as well. I felt they should have let a lad like that come off for a while to see his mother, but I suppose he had to obey his orders like everybody else, certainly he didn't look as though he had any intention of coming off. When the ship finally sailed away we stood and waved till Johnny and his ship were just a little speck on the ocean, and I thought to myself, 'There he goes...my little Johnny. Gone away to foreign lands. He's in God's hands now.'

I couldn't help crying as we all humped back home, he had left as big a hole in my life as anybody since his father. He was so canny and such a wise sensible little lad and he was afraid of nothing and nobody. They say that what makes a good boxer is his nature more than his size, and if that was the case, my little Johnny would have made a champion.

Six months later Johnny was back, and there was such a change in him; he was a good bit bigger and older looking, at least we all thought there was. He'd brought back a little metal box he called a 'ditty box' and it was full of coppers that the other seamen had put in when they knew he was coming home, by now they'd have known what a cheerful, tough and hard-working little feller he was and they'd have wanted to show their appreciation. The ship people wanted him to sign on for another voyage but this time I said no, I needed him at home with me, I needed his brains and his backing. And although he'd have gladly gone away again, given half the chance, I think he was contented he'd at least seen something of the world. I said 'You're still young yet, son. Ye've plenty time to see life. However much they want ye, we want ye twice as much.'

The day after he came off the ship he went looking for work and got himself a job on the roads making the navvies' tea and running up and down the line with messages. It wasn't much of a job, especially for a lad with Johnny's brains, but it was honest work and it was better than lounging about. I told all of my bairns the same: 'I don't care what kind of a job ye get, as long as it's honest and it's not blackleggin'.'

Whilst Johnny was working on the roads, he was writing letters for jobs all over the place. By, I don't half wish I could have written letters like that...all neat and clever and no spelling mistakes... Anyway, one morning a letter came through the door addressed to 'Mr John Robinson'. I ran out after the postman and said 'Hey, there's no Mr John Robinson lives here.' So he took it back. Just then there was a shout behind me, and up runs our Johnny.

'Who was it for, Mother?'

'Nothin' for you, son. It was for "Mr John Robinson".'

All excited, he says 'That's me, Ma! That's me..! I'm Mr John Robinson.'

'You, Johnny?' I says. 'You..? Eeeh, yes... I suppose ye are... Why of course ye are, son.'

So I flew up the street after the postman, told him what had happened and got the letter back and fetched it as quickly as I could to let Johnny open it up for himself. He was right! It was for him! It was from the Board of Guardians, the people that used to run the Workhouse. They were offering him a fortnight's work writing out food vouchers for the strike, they must have been impressed by his lovely neat handwriting. Some of the vouchers were worth ten bob each, maybe even more, so it was a really important job and he was so pleased with himself. And I was so proud to think of my little Johnny sending proper letters to people all over, telling them how much money they could have. He understood all the legal words and his writing was very important looking and every bit as good as the Town Clerk's that used to be on the papers when I had the lodging house.

When the fortnight was up, the boss called him into the office and said 'Well, John, I'm afraid your work with us is finished now. You do understand that the job was only for two weeks, don't you?'

'Yes, gentlemen, I do,' Johnny says. 'And I wish to thank you very much for it.'

'However, we are proposing to enter you for an examination for a post with the National Assistance Board...as a relieving officer... Would you be interested?'

'I certainly would, sir,' Johnny said.

The exam lasted for two days and then on the third day there was a long interview. Two of them, including our Johnny..."candidates" they called them...went right through to the end, but the other feller got it, a great big feller by the name of John Brindle. Johnny was very upset and so was I, he'd tried his best and I couldn't believe anybody could have done better. I didn't say anything to Johnny but in my mind I thought it must be because John Brindle was bigger than he was, and that if whoever won was going to have to go to people's houses to do 'Means Tests', which people hated, they might have thought it safer to give the job to John Brindle because of his size.

'Never mind, Johnny,' I said. 'They're bound to be lookin' for more people in a while. Then it'll be your turn. You'll see.' I put a few coppers in his hand. 'Here. Had yoursel' to the pictures tonight and forget all about it. Ye've done all ye could. There'll be another time, I know there will.' I was thinking to myself, 'With him out the way, I'm goin' to see if I can find out what really happened so we'll know for the next time'.

When he went off to the pictures he had his usual cheery smile on his face. 'Don't worry, Ma. I'll do better next time.'

'I know you will, son,' I says, and I gave him a hug and let him go.

Mr Campbell was a lodging-house keeper I'd known for a long time and always got on very well with, and I knew that he was a business friend of the head man at the Guardians. As soon as Johnny had gone, I put my hat and coat on and went to see this Mr Campbell and told him everything, and said I'd be more than grateful for anything he could find out about why our Johnny hadn't got the job.

A couple of days later Mr Campbell sent for me. 'His papers were brilliant, Francie. He got top marks. He's a real scholar...' Then he took my hand and lowered his head and said 'I'm afraid it was only having one eye, that did it.'

I couldn't believe it. I wouldn't believe it... If it was his eye with this job, was this the way it would be all his life? Through no fault of his own? What difference should that make? He wrote their vouchers for them, didn't he? He'd passed their exams with his lovely handwriting, hadn't he? He was even boxing with one eye.

I could never tell Johnny the real reason but I'd already told him Mr Campbell was going to find out, so I was going to have to tell him something. So what I told him was that they thought John Brindle was more able for it because of the district he'd be working in and the rough people he'd be having to deal with. I knew this wouldn't bother him so much because he realised that some kids sprouted away earlier than others, and that he was growing all the time. Mind, never in a thousand years would he be as big as John Brindle; of all the lads to be up against, he had to get John Brindle who was probably the biggest lad in Shields.

From then on Johnny worked harder than ever at his skipping and boxing training, and he never let a day go by without a workout. He bought himself a pair of Indian Clubs to juggle with and he would twist them this way and that, as quick as anything. People used to think that if you were small, you were no good for anything but being a jockey. 'Look at the size of your Joe! He'll make two of your Johnny,' they'd say. But I'd tell them, 'No, he wouldn't. Nobody would. Johnny's as tough and as good as any of them. You only have to shake hands with him to know what's in him.'

Joe was the opposite of our Johnny. Where Johnny was little and clever and responsible, Joe was big and daft and you couldn't trust him to do anything right. At school he was a dud compared to Johnny....what they would call a 'dunce', and you never came to expect any better; I cannot remember once in all the years he was there...and half the time he wasn't...when he come home with good marks for anything. Joe was going to have to get a job based on his muscles, because he would never have got anything if they went by brains.

When Joe left school he got a job as a joiner's apprentice at Readheads in the shipyards, and in no time he was getting himself into trouble acting the daft lad. One night I'd made a big meal and finished up with spice pudding, Joe was a big eater but he'd eaten so much the sweat was coming off him.

'Mother, I cannot eat another bite,' he says. 'But I'll tell ye what. So it isn't wasted, wrap it up and I'll share it out with me mates at the yard tomorrow.'

236

So I did, and the next day he took it to the yard and when they stopped for their break, he sliced it up and handed it around. The thing about spice pudding was that you always put in a button and a thruppence, and Joe had got the button and another feller, Alfie Brennan, had got the thruppence. When Joe came home he was as glum as anything. 'Mother, I squeezed the bits of the puddin' and felt something hard and thought I was givin' meself the one with the thruppenny bit in. I ate all that puddin' last night and a great big piece of it today, and I've ended up with nowt but a pain in the belly.'

'Ye got your share of the puddin', didn't ye?' I said to him.

'Aye, but I only ate it for the thruppence. It feels like a bucket o' lead in me belly. I can hardly walk.'

It was all I could do to keep a straight face, to look at him you'd think it was the end of the world. 'I'll tell ye what... You bring Alfie round tonight before it's too late. You hold him down and I'll slit his belly open with the gully. Then you can put your hand in and pull the thruppenny bit out.'

'Ah, mother...' he says. 'I'm serious.'

'Well, so am I.'

One day the apprentices had been messing about with a fire extinguisher and broke the end off, and when the stuff started shooting out they couldn't stop it. The foreman heard the commotion and came to see what was the matter. Joe had seen him coming, clasped the fire extinguisher to himself and jumped into a bin with it, and somebody had then put the lid on. But Joe couldn't stop it squirting out, and it blasted the lid off, the bin rolled over and Joe fell out of it with the thing still in his hands. It sprayed all over the foreman, Joe was already drenched to the skin with the stuff, and they both had to go home to get cleaned up. That fettled Joe with Readheads and it was a long time before he could get another job.

O'Callaghan used to go on about Johnny and Joe not working even when they were out every day looking for work, and I could have strangled him for it. Both Johnny and Joe and even our little Edmund had more sense of responsibility in their little finger, than he had in his whole body.

There was a public house right next door to the Walpole Street shop and we had thought it would have been good for business. It was

237

a big mistake, a very big mistake. I should have known by now that all the promises a drunken man makes, drunk or sober, aren't worth a light. The pub got all the business, ours as well. We struggled on with it until 1929, but the more I poured in of myself, the more O'Callaghan took out in drink, and in the finish he laid that one out the way he'd laid out all the others.

When we were put out of it, that was the end as far as I was concerned, there'd be no more fish-and-chip shop businesses for me. We were left without a penny to our names and we had to move out and look for somewhere else to live, yet still I had O'Callaghan like a useless millstone around my neck, grinding me down, grinding all of us down. I was forty now and I had old bairns and I had young bairns, but they were still bairns and still had to be looked after, and I still felt a responsibility to my father and those of my sisters who had come to depend on me.

After searching and searching and dragging the bairns around everywhere with me, I found a house with cheap rent in Hudson Street and we all moved in. It wasn't a very nice area but it was only going to cost us thirteen shillings a week. Straightaway I got a job cleaning Mr Campbell's lodging house in Tyne Dock, and because Mr Campbell himself was an old man on his own and didn't have anybody to do for him, I did his washing and cleaned his house for an extra half a crown. But it still wasn't enough to keep a family of seven, not when there's a drinking man in the house, so I asked Mrs Barnett if there was any chance of Mr Barnett finding O'Callaghan a job.

'To tell the truth, Francie,' she said, 'we'd find it hard to recommend him. It could rebound back on Mr Barnett. But I'll ask him for your sake, even if it's just something to keep that man off your back a bit.'

In a couple of weeks Mr Barnett sent word that he'd got O'Callaghan a job as a fitter's labourer. 'But if he messes it up, I cannot do it again,' Mr Barnett said. 'I've my own reputation to think of as well.' I thanked him and Mrs Barnett very much for being so kind to me over all these years, and I promised I wouldn't cause them any more embarrassment after this.

O'Callaghan went for the job and the firm took him on. I didn't know how much they were paying him but he only gave me a pound a week.

'Surely to God you're gettin' more than this?' I said to him after he'd been at it a few weeks and I knew his lying-on period would be over.

'I'm only getting twenty-eight shillings, and I have to have something for myself or what's the point in working.'

One day I was at my wits' end, I had fourpence in my purse and it was all I had in the world. I wasn't a gambler and I'd never used a slot machine in my life, but I saw this machine and I thought to myself, 'Kill or cure, I've nowt to lose.' So I put it in, penny by penny, determined to lose the lot or make my fortune. On the very last penny, twelve shillings and eight pence came shooting out. Bang, clatter, bang-bang! Just like that... I thought all my Christmases had come at once. 'Who says God frowns on a gambling man..? If he does, he doesn't on a woman,' I was saying to myself as I was picking it all up. Before anything could happen to it, before the man could come out of his little box and say the machine wasn't working properly and he had to have his money back, and before O'Callaghan could get his hands on it, I spent every penny on groceries and two bob's worth of coal so we could have hot meals again. I'd never again be able to say l was an unlucky woman.

On top of the lodging house work, I got some painting and decorating jobs through Mr Campbell, and that brought in a few extra shillings. Ceilings were high and dirty and painters would get out of doing them if they could. But they didn't bother me, I'd wash down walls ready for the painters and wash and paint the ceilings as well if they'd let me. I'd turn my nose up at nothing.

Mr Campbell was good to me and got me little bits of jobs whenever he could, he knew I had a family and an idle scrounger to support. 'Could I cook for the lodgers?' I'd ask. 'D'ye have any more laundry needs doin'? Were ye satisfied with the last lot I did for ye..? What about your shirts? I hand-wring every one, ye know. I'd never put a good shirt through a mangle.' Poor man, I was always on to him, he must have got fed up with me at times.

One night after doing the lodging house ceilings I had a terrible attack of lumbago, and when I got home I could neither sit nor stand; and when I lay down, every time I moved, pains shot through my arms and legs like daggers.

'You'll have to help with the bairns and that tonight, Jack,' I said. 'It feels as though somebody's twisting gullys in me back.'

'It's no use you complaining... My own's killing me. Too much hard work, that's what mine's caused by. Outside in all weathers, lifting and shovelling. I've been having to do the work of two men because they're too mean to take on extra labour... What you get wouldn't keep a canary... My back's gradually giving way under the strain, I can feel it. Not that a little thing like that would matter to you with your little bits of twinges. A touch of rheumatism's all you've got. But you have to make such a song and dance about it... If I don't get right, I might never be able to work again. Nobody can rely on you. You're always having kids. Whatever pain you've got, mine's ten times as bad. So don't expect me to go running around after you!'

God, how I hated this man. And may God forgive me for it, but I made up my mind to get rid of him once and for all. Mr Campbell had once bought some weed-killer to finish his dog off with because it was getting to be a nuisance, and it did the job very well, it was stone cold the next day and it was a pretty big dog, a mastiff or something, one of those with strings of slaver always hanging from their mouths. And I thought to myself, 'If that stuff's good enough to do in a big strong dog like that, it should do fine for O'Callaghan.'

I was very nervous when I went into the hardware shop and I nearly bought something else instead, but at the last minute I plucked up the courage and got it. I'd been thinking for days how to do it and I remembered Mr Campbell saying he had to mix his well in with minced meat so the dog wouldn't taste it, and I'd been thinking the same would probably apply to O'Callaghan. So what I did was to make a very savoury dinner, sprinkle the poison all over it, and then cover it with thick gravy.

He didn't come in till very late that night and I'd had to keep heating his meal up and then it would get cold and I'd have to heat it up again; but I was determined not to waste either the meal or the poison, I wasn't sure I'd have the nerve to go back for another lot. At last he came in and sat down at the table; I'd put the kids to bed very early on because I didn't want them to see what was going to happen, for all I knew it might take effect straightaway. I put out his dinner and checked he had plenty salt and vinegar and pepper to make everything nice for him. He took one look at it and said 'What the hell's that?'

I said 'What the hell does it look like..? It's your dinner, isn't it?'

'It looks like a plate of overcooked cat shit to me!'

'If ye'd come in at the proper time, it'd've been fit to eat. I've nowt to make any more. So you'll just have to get on with it.'

He got up, took the plate, clashed the lot in the fireplace, and went out. I ran straight upstairs and fell on my knees to thank God. And I never tried anything like that again.

A couple of weeks after, though it couldn't have had anything to do with it, at least that's what I kept telling myself, an anonymous letter printed in big block letters was sent to Mr Campbell accusing him of me being his mistress. He was raving mad about it and showed it to me. I didn't know what to say, I was beside myself with embarrassment.

'Do you know who's writing this is, Francie?'

'I've no idea, Mr Campbell. Honestly I don't. I couldn't tell ye.'

I had my suspicions though, and obviously so did he. He swore he'd find out who it was and that he'd take them to court for slander; but I think he just wanted to make sure the message got back to the proper quarter, because I knew as well as he did that nobody was going to own up to it, and there wasn't much chance of the police finding out. The result of it all was that Mr Campbell said it would be for the best if I didn't work for him anymore, so that nobody would have any cause to point a finger at him. He must have seen the look on my face because straight after he said he wasn't blaming me; all the same he knew I'd be the one who'd suffer most; I think he felt he had to punish somebody so he punished me because I was handiest.

About a month later I bumped into him when I was coming out of a lodging house where I'd been enquiring about work.

'Ah, Francie. Just the person I wanted to see... Francie, I've a bit of property in Leighton Street and I think it might suit you down to the ground. It has six big bedrooms, stables and all kinds of outbuildings. The house itself is in good condition. It wants doing up a bit, but you could have it fit to live in in no time. It would make a lovely home for you all. The children would have plenty room to play, and there's a big garden where Jack could raise his poultry and keep himself occupied... Eventually you could take in boarders or whatever you like... What do you think..?'

'I've got no money, Mr Campbell. We're broke. Where would I get the money to buy a great big house like that? It's out of the question.' I thought 'Why is he sayin' all this? Is it to ease his conscience? Hasn't he the faintest idea what it's like to have nothin' at all? People like him say they're broke when they mean they're down to their last thousand pounds.'

'By "doing it up", I only mean elbow grease... There'd be very little to spend. It's perfectly sound. You'd get a full mortgage on it. It wouldn't cost you much if you paid in instalments. The land's big enough to build a public house on if you wanted. You could do the garages up and let them off...same with the stables. It would pay for itself in no time.'

'Mr Campbell...'

'All you'd have to find, is the money for the solicitor's fees. And they won't be much. You can take your time to pay them. They're never in too much of a hurry to press their bills. Not in cases like yours.'

'Well, thank ye, Mr Campbell. I'll think about it. I'll talk it over with O'Callaghan.'

I'd never considered anything like this before, but when I got back I put Mr Campbell's proposal to O'Callaghan; I'd nothing to lose, and I was beginning to warm to the idea, I'd been having a think about the possibilities on the way home.

'Look, Jack. We've got to put our brains in steep over this and see what we can come up with. Johnny's bringin' in seven and six a week regular. You're getting a quid or so on the buildin's. And I think if I asked Mr Campbell, he might take me back on...' I'd heard that Mr Campbell couldn't get anybody else to take my place and that he'd be only too glad to have me back, even though he hadn't said anything to me... 'It'd be our own property. That's what ye always wanted, wasn't it? Ye could have your ducks and hens...and goats and horses... Anythin' ye wanted... The sheds would be grand for them. And there's lots of good grass, Mr Campbell says.'

'I'll have to think about it... Give me a day or two.'

'We cannot take too long. He's waitin' for wor answer.'

'Don't be so impulsive, woman. It's a big step to take. I'll have to weigh it up.'

The next day he came home saying he'd had to give up his job because his back was giving him too much trouble; whether he'd been given the sack or what, I never found out, but what I did find out was that it didn't affect his drinking, he was out that night celebrating the fact that he'd lost his job.

'That's it,' I said. 'I'll go and tell Mr Campbell it's all off.'

So I went to see Mr Campbell and thanked him for his offer but told him we couldn't afford to buy the place after all.

'The bank will lend you it.'

'I can't do anythin' like that, Mr Campbell. I don't know how to go on with those people. They'd run rings round somebody like me. And if anythin' happened and I couldn't pay, we'd be bankrupt and they'd take my bairns.'

'Oh, Francie,' he says, shaking his head. 'Come on, I'll go down with you. We'll go to the bank and arrange a loan right now. Don't worry, I'll make sure you won't be paying any more than you can afford. It won't cost you any more than whatever rent you're paying now, I promise.'

And he did as he said, and we all moved in, and it was a wonderful place.

Johnny had now got into the Guardians...'Public Assistance', it was called. I knew he would, they had to let him in, they'd never find a better harder worker anywhere and they must have realised it. He'd taken the exams again and passed with flying colours, just like he did before. He was well liked at the office where he worked, they would have appreciated his honesty and his respectfulness, and he was willing to work any amount of overtime to get a few extra coppers for his mother; that would have gone down well as well, I bet. One week he came in with £3 bonus money and I used it to buy O'Callaghan a new suit and his first batch of hens. What with those and whatever he could get for his drink, he wouldn't bother us so much, I reckoned, and we'd be left free to get on with things.

I think O'Callaghan loved animals, he was certainly very interested in them and he'd always had a pair of canaries breeding in a cage in the washhouse, or a rabbit hutch in the backyard, and for the first few weeks he was rolling out yards of wire netting and nailing it up all over the place. Like a busy workman he was, carrying timber here, and tarpaulin there, and I thought 'This is it. At last I've found the answer, somethin' to keep his mind off the drink and the other business. Let him get what he wants and encourage him to look after his pet animals and things, and he might make a bit of money out of them as well as keeping himself occupied.'

As soon as the hens settled in they started to lay, and in no time he was getting half a dozen eggs every day. He said he was making a business out of it so he would have to charge me the same way he charged everybody else, and when his brother Peter Callaghan, who I liked the best of all the Callaghans, once came and I boiled him one of the eggs, I had to pay for that as well. O'Callaghan had come in and seen his brother tucking into the egg. 'Lovely egg this, Francie', Peter had said. 'One of Jack's produce, is it?'

As soon as his brother had left, before the seat of the chair he'd been sitting on had had a chance to have got cold, O'Callaghan asked me if I'd put the money for the egg in his little box.

'What..?'

'Did ye put the money in the box..? They're part of our livelihood.'

'I haven't yet, but I will... God forgive me if ever I should give your own brother a tuppeny ha'penny egg for nowt.'

He also had some lovely ducks which he let swim in a big kit he kept filled with water. Then he got himself a couple of pigs to fatten up, and a goat, and he would go around with his pony and cart collecting old vegetable scraps for them. Even when we gave up the fish-and-chip shops he'd still hung on to Darkie, the pony, I think he loved it more than he ever loved anything in his life. The only animals I ever saw him ill-use were cats, and he hated them. They were always at his canaries, and at the fish when we had the shop, and he would throw the shovel, the mallet or a gully, whatever he could lay his hands on, at them. One day he caught a cat in a barrel of fish and he took it by the tail and started swinging it over his head; I think it was his intention to get a good swing on it so he could throw it a long way, the way kids do with a sling; but the tail came clean off in his hand and the poor cat went flying; I don't know what happened to it but it never came back, we would have recognised it if it had.

Johnny's wages were enough to pay for the mortgage payments and I always put that aside for that purpose. Every Friday, before setting out for the lodging houses where I worked, including Mr

Campbell's again now, I'd divide the money up into portions; so much went in the pewter for the gas bill, so much under the clock for the coal, so much here for this and so much there for that, ready for when the various collectors came. The mortgage had to be paid at the big office downtown and this was O'Callaghan's responsibility.

We'd been at Leighton Street for about nine or ten months, by which time the novelty of cleaning out the animals every week had worn off, and O'Callaghan had started drinking heavily again, and every night when I came in from work, he'd be speechless drunk. When I asked him where all the money was coming from, he'd say 'The sailors down the market. If you carry their bags for them or find them a place to kip, they'll always tip you a bob or two. They go daft when they get paid. They cannot get rid of it fast enough, heh-heh.'

I thought 'Well, if it's honestly come by and it keeps him out of our hair, there's no point me complainin',' because otherwise things were going grand.

One night after a particularly wearying day at the lodging house, I'd come home aching all over. I was so glad to open the gate, it had been a lousy day right from the start and I'd be glad to see the back of it. I'd had such a job getting Walter off to school that morning, he'd been in one of his moods and had kicked up such a fuss; another place Joe had been working at had shut down and they'd all been given the sack so he'd been out of work for two months; Francie had the measles and was in bed crying when I'd left to go to work; Johnny was looking a bit peaky around the gills these days, he was taking on far too much studying for one so young, they'd got him on studying about Poor Law for some exams; it had been the day for scrubbing the floors and big yard at the lodging house and my knees were full of grit and what a mess I looked; it was wet and windy and the garden was full of papers and rubbish that had blown in.

When I opened the door of the house, there was a great pile of papers all over the floor, all of them bills and demanding letters; gas was three months overdue and they were threatening to close it off, coal unpaid for a month and no more deliveries to be made until all bills were paid in full, a solicitor's letter from the grocer, another gas bill, and another, and another, another threatening letter from somebody else, and here was one saying they were coming to shut the gas off on Thursday. Thursday..? That was tomorrow..! And the best of the lot was four letters from the building society... they were going to take the house off us. After a whole year of effort getting it put right just the way we wanted it, they were going to take our house and sheds and garden and everything else off us... I couldn't believe it.

O'Callaghan was asleep in an armchair. I grabbed hold of him and shook him.

'Jack..! Oh my God, Jack...! Say it isn't true! Tell me there's been a mistake. What's the meanin' of it!' I screamed at him. I could have torn the face of him with my bare hands.

'You've read them, haven't you..? You can see as well as me... What are you going to do about it..? You're the one who thinks they're so bloody clever.'

'How long has this been goin' on for..? Just tell me that, will ye?'

'Don't ask me... I saved them all up so you could deal with them all at the same time. It's easier that way. So don't start shouting at me with your foul mouth, you stupid fuckin' bitch.'

'I've never asked ye once all this time because I trusted ye, trusted ye with all our hard-earned money. I never thought that even you were this bad.'

'Shut up! Stop your whingeing, for Christ's sake! What's done's done. And that's all there is to it.'

'Well, I'm going straight out tomorrow mornin' to find out if all this is true. And if it is, and they're really goin' to do all these things to us, I'm leavin' ye. And the bairns are comin' with me.'

'Three of them are mine.'

I just looked at him. I didn't feel afraid of him any more. There was nothing he could do to us now, not worse than this. If I'd been the kind of person who spat, I'd have spat on him sitting there with his stupid grin on his face.

The next morning I only had to make two calls to find that everything was true, there was no point traipsing around them all and being humiliated. When I came back from work that night I put all of the bills in my purse, they'd all get their money in due course. O'Callaghan was sitting in the chair and had this cocky look on his face.

'Happy now?'

'We're off as soon as I can find a place. You can do what ye like.'

I tossed him all the letters to do with the house and property.

'Here. You keep them. I won't be needin' them any more.'

'Haddaway and shite!'

I felt absolutely exhausted, as though all the blood had been drained out of my body, and I flopped down in a chair. He just got up and went out and I heard him talking sweet nothings to his pony. 'And how's my little lover, today, eh? How's my sweet little Darkie? Shall Jackie get you some hay? Is that what you want..? Come on, then.'

I buried my head in the chair and I wept and I sobbed till I thought my heart would break. Then I heard whistling and Johnny came in. When he saw me, he said 'Whatever's the matter, Mother..? I've never seen you so upset-looking.'

I gripped his little white hand in my big red one.

'I'm sorry, but there's no tea nor nothin' ready for ye, son. I'm just about past meself this time.'

I told him what had happened.

'I'm leavin' him for good this time, Johnny. I'm goin' to look for another place for us. Will you come with is, son? I don't know what I'd do without you. I've got to do it now while the iron's hot...or tomorrow I'll forgive him and we'll be back where we started. I want to go now before I calm down.'

'Course I will. Come on, try and pull yourself together... Where shall we look first?'

He never said 'I'm glad', 'You're doing the right thing', or anything like that. He would never interfere, neither would Joe. They respected O'Callaghan because he was my husband and because he was their stepfather, and now they were growing up, not even Joe would ever say a word to make things any worse than they were already. They put up with him because of me, but I knew they'd never allow him to hit me again.

'Let's go and see your cousin Harry in Ford Street first. He might know of somethin' that would suit.' Mrs Robinson had given the grandson she'd adopted, a lot of her property, and his wife was in the estate business.

I hadn't seen much of Harry for a long time, with him living at the Robinsons, but he was a nice feller and he was keen enough to help. Unfortunately the only thing on their books was a two-roomed place at the back of the Robin Hood Inn in Primrose which was miles away along the Newcastle Road.

'It wouldn't be much use to you, Francie,' he said. 'The rent's cheap but it's a terrible place.'

'We'll take it,' I said straightaway. I couldn't take a chance in case he let it to somebody else. 'I don't care what it's like. I don't even need to see it... When can we move in?'

He just shrugged.

'Tonight..? Right. Thank you very much, Harry... Er, things are a bit tight seein' as it's a Thursday. Need we not pay in advance, till the end of the week? Till my money comes in..? I've got a good job and I'll be able to pay all right. It's just that I'm a bit short at the moment.'

Harry said that was all right so Johnny and me went straight up. When we got there, you never saw anything like it. Johnny had run up ahead and was chasing the pigeons out when I came up the stairs. The rooms were small and they were scruffy; there was nothing on the floor and nothing on the walls, even the plaster was peeling off; there were loose boards and mouse holes all over; there were big gaps around the windows; the window panes were broken and the legs of the bed were sticking down through a hole in the floorboards; the table only had three and a half legs and when we put our things on it, the whole thing fell over. But at least it had no O'Callaghan in it, and Johnny and me went back for the rest of the bairns.

The next day before I went to work I had to barricade Walter in his bed so he wouldn't fall out, and tell Edmund and Francie to look after him, it was too far for them to go to their school so I'd have to keep both of them off till I found a nearer one. When I came back from work and Johnny came in from his, I took him and Joe...and a barrow Joe had got lend of...and we went to Leighton Street to get our things. At the moment we had nothing but the clothes we were wearing. When we got there O'Callaghan was sitting, large as life, I think he thought we'd come back for him; I'd left him before but always had to go back because of the bairns, even the times he'd chased me out into the street in my nighty and locked the door and I'd had to stay with the poor old lady across the street when we were in Frederick Street, I'd always gone back in time to make breakfast. I think he thought I couldn't get by without him.

I had a piece of notepaper and a pencil in my hand and I handed it to him and said 'Right, Jack. I want you to write on that piece of paper that I can keep the bairns.'

He just laughed. 'Give's it here. Where do you want me to write? You can have the whole bloody lot of them, and good riddance.' He scribbled something on the paper and shoved it aside. I didn't know whether it would have had any legal value or not but I picked it up and put it in my purse.

When Johnny and Joe were out of the way getting things to put in the cart, and I was going through the drawers in the kitchen, O'Callaghan came up to me and said 'I know what'll happen to you. You'll end up a whore down on the docks. And when you do, I'll be the first one to give you your two bob... See that piano..? Wait a minute.' He then went out and came back with the big chopping axe he used for cutting logs. 'This is all this is fit for... Firewood.' With that he took the axe and chopped the piano to pieces. 'Maybe that'll teach you to hide money in it. This is supposed to be a musical instrument.' Johnny and Joe came running in.

'Stay back! Stay back!' I shouted to them, frightened in case he'd turn on them next.

'Are you all right, Ma?' they both asked. The two of them would have rushed at him and broken it over his neck if I'd asked them to. O'Callaghan was laughing like a maniac.

'Yes, I'm all right. Don't worry. Just get on with what you're doin'. He'll swing for somebody one day.'

It was true I'd used the piano to hide money in the past, but not for a long time, there'd been nowt to hide. What was a piano to me now? I'd a lot more on my mind than a piano. He was a fool, he could have got something for it, it would have kept him in drink for a month.

The next day I went back on my own for the rest of the stuff, I'd show him I wasn't scared of him any more and that I wasn't hiding behind my two sons. I knew if he went on the way he'd done the day before, they'd have gone for him and I wouldn't have been able to stop them. I also knew that if I didn't get the rest of the stuff now, he'd only get rid of it or smash it up like he'd done the piano. I didn't know what to expect when I went this time, not even whether he'd be there or not, and I got a real surprise.

When I went in, all the wood from the piano had been cleared away and the place was all tidy and the table set for tea. In one corner sat Mrs Callaghan, and in the other was O'Callaghan all smiles with his wavy hair combed and smartened up and looking as though butter wouldn't melt in his mouth. I could tell they were waiting for me, but I just nodded and got on with what I had to do, getting some pans and towels and other things together; I wasn't taking everything, just what I needed, I'd leave him enough for himself.

Mrs Callaghan was first to speak. 'Francie, you don't know what you're doing to those poor bairns.'

I just answered as I was going around gathering things up, a teatowel here, packet of flakes there; I wasn't going to come to attention for her anymore.

'Mrs Callaghan, the time when I would listen to you has been over for a long time. If you've anythin' worthwhile to say, say it to your son over there. He's the one who could do with some advice.'

She already had her hat and coat on, and without another word she quickly got up and went out. Not quarter of an hour later she came back with a priest. He came in and smiled to O'Callaghan and then to me and then sat himself down.

'I'll just put the kettle on, Father,' she said.

'Good evening, Father,' O'Callaghan says, getting his own oar in straight away.

I just smiled to be polite, I knew what was coming.

'Would you sit down a minute, Francie. We'd all like a friendly word with you,' the priest says to me.

'I'm sorry but I haven't the time, Father. I've got to be gettin' back to my children.'

'But I want to have a little chat with you. It won't take much time. And it's very important for your soul and for the souls of all your little ones.'

I didn't want to be rude. 'All right then, Father. But ye'll have to make it quick. I've a lot to do.'

As soon as he started on about the vows of marriage and obeying your husband and all that, I got up.

'Will you please sit down, Francie,' he said like a schoolmaster and looking very stern.

'Are you here to hear Jack O'Callaghan's side of the story? Or are ye here to hear mine..? Because if ye want to hear his side, and haven't already heard it, ye don't need me to be here... And if ye want

250

to hear my side, I'm goin' to set aside your cloth and talk to ye as though ye were an ordinary human bein'.'

'That's all right, my dear girl,' he said, smiling again. 'Just sit yourself down. You shall have your say, I promise you.'

So I sat down and I told him. I told him everything. But when I'd finished, I knew I was no further forward. I knew he had his job to do like everybody else and that he had to try and get O'Callaghan and me back together again. He kept asking me to think again if only for the sake of the children, and I told him it was for the sake of the children as much as anything else that I was going. I told him they'd end up as bad as he was if that was the only example of a father or a man they were getting...and I could see I'd struck home with that one.

'So don't tell me I'm goin' to Hell, because I'm sick of bein' told that. They're queuin' up to put me there... But I'll tell ye this: wherever I'm goin', I'm takin' my bairns with me...every one of them. I had them, and I'm keepin' them.'

As soon as I'd said it, I thought 'I'm invitin' it. I'm puttin' meself there. Things are bad enough as it is without any bad words or curses from him.' So I dropped on my knees and said 'Look, Father. I'm goin' now, no matter what you or anybody says. I've made me mind up about that... But I'll make a bargain with ye. I'll stay away six months. Durin' that time I'll make sure me bairns all go to Mass and Holy Communion and everythin'. Me as well. If at the end of it, I find I've made a mistake, I'll apologise and come back. If not, I won't, and I'll stop away forever.'

To my surprise he said 'All right, my child. I'll pray for you.' And that was that. Neither O'Callaghan or his mother said a word, I think they were too shocked.

I don't know about the Robin Hood Inn, but the rooms behind it that we lived in was just like living in Sherwood Forest or whatever it was. The wind and rain always came in and nothing we did would keep it out. We'd put up cardboard and bits of lath around the window but if it didn't blow off, the draughts were worse than they were before. And there was nothing we could do about the roof leaking, except put a pail or basin under it that was always getting knocked over.

Everything was tin pot, and the ramshackle beds which had me,

251

Francie and Walter in one, and Johnny, Joe and Edmund in the other, were so overloaded they were always collapsing during the night, and we were forever trying to sort out blankets and bodies in the dark. I was terrified in case it would happen one night without me waking up and the little bairns would be suffocated, so I put Johnny and Joe on the floor, kept Francie with me, and put Walter in with Edmund. There was now more room in the beds but less on the floor, and you couldn't get moved for bodies if you got up in the middle of the night.

I had to get into Tyne Dock for my first lodging house, that was the beginning of Shields but it was a very long way to walk, and after I'd cleaned that place I had to get down to the market to do the rest. Getting to work in the morning wasn't so bad because I could put my thumb up when the wagons came along, and most of them would give you a lift. It was coming back at night that was hard, because I'd never take a lift off anybody if I didn't know them, and I'd be walking back tired after a hard day's work, with the meal and the bairns and the washing to see to when I got back.

One night I was walking home when who should I bump into but Jim Kilcaddy.

'What are you doin' out here, Francie?' he says. 'Everybody's been wonderin' where ye'd got to. Jinny was just sayin', we haven't seen ye for ages.'

When I left O'Callaghan I didn't want anybody else involved, I didn't want any of them to know...not my family nor the Robinsons...although the Callaghans would all know by now. I hadn't even told Harry when we went to him about the house, and he'd had sense enough not to ask. No woman could ever expect any sympathy if she left her husband, even though she took all her children with her. When a woman was deserted by her husband, it was different, people would always find excuses for him: 'She must have been a poor housekeeper' or 'She never pleased him enough in bed' and things like that; though you never heard of him taking all the kids with him. When it was the woman that went, she was always a sloven or a slut, and 'worse than muck'; it didn't matter that she hadn't off gone with another man and that that had nothing at all to do with her leaving.

'Oh, hello Jimmy.'

'Where ye goin'?'

'I'm just lookin' for a house.'

'Ye must be mad..! What are ye lookin' for a house right out here for?'

'Oh...just because.'

'Because what..? Stop still a minute, will ye.' He grabbed a hold of my arm and turned me around. He was a canny feller and I was sorry for being so short with him but I didn't want him poking his nose around.

'Where are ye livin'?'

'Not far.'

'I'll see ye home, then. I'll have a cuppa tea with ye, an' ye can tell is how ye've been. Your Jinny'd gan mad if I told her I'd seen ye, and not found out how ye were or where ye were livin'.'

'Some other time, Jimmy.'

'Howay, lass. It's gettin' dark. You shouldn't be walkin' the road on your own. There's all sorts comes along here. From Newcastle an' all ower.'

'I'm all right, Jimmy. I'm not a little girl any more now, ye know.'

'Why I know that. But this is your brother-in-law speakin'. I insist... Look, wherever you're goin', I'm follerin', so you might as well make a straight line for home. We haven't seen ye in a long time and we've been worried about ye.'

No matter what I said I couldn't get rid of him, so in the end I said all right and he came home with me and I told him everything.

'Thank God for that,' he said when I'd finished. 'Ye couldn't be doin' a better thing than leavin' the swine. Me and Jinny'll certainly back ye up. Ye can be sure of that.'

'But it's very hard with the bairns. The three little'uns are his as well.'

'Have ye got nowt at all left? Nothin' from all your years in the shop? Where's it all gone?'

Like everybody else, he thought it impossible that anybody could manage to drink a thriving business into the ground. They all thought that I'd be bound to have something left.

'Nobody could have drunk all that away.'

'No..? Don't kid yoursel'. Ye can do anythin' if ye try hard enough. And he certainly did. Body and soul... I'm practically down to the bones of me bum.'

He put a coin in my hand and closed it. 'There's half a dollar for ye. It isn't much, but I'll come through the week and see ye again.'

And he did. He was a big daft feller, Jim Kilcaddy, he was always telling you daft stories to make you laugh, no matter how depressed you were. That's what I used to like about him, he could always make you laugh.

Joe had been out of work so long and he had nagged on and on about wanting to go to sea like Johnny had done, that in the finish I let him go. I thought he might learn a trade that might stand him in good stead when he came back, because he hadn't been able to get taken on as an apprentice in Shields or anywhere hereabouts. Even though I knew Johnny would miss him more than anybody, he'd said Joe wouldn't come to any harm, so we'd scratted together to set him up with his own tool chest, and off he went, happy as Larry.

I did my best to teach my bairns not to be ashamed of being poor, but not to moan about it either; it's a funny thing but if people think you have nothing, they'll never give you very much, and it's for sure respect won't be amongst it. So when I went out, even when I was looking for work, I always tried to look as though I had more than I really did, that way at least they'd give me the time of day. I'd stuff my handbag with paper to make it bulge and stick some spoons in the bottom with a few coppers to make them jingle so people would think I could back up whatever I said. And at night I used to keep a piece of wood that would flare up, so that if I heard anybody outside, I could put it on and they'd see the light through the tuppenny paper blinds we had up at the window, and they'd think 'Eeeh, they must be doin' very canny for themselves. They've got their light on this time of night.'

It was so important to me that people thought I could pay my own way, that if we were having our dinner and the bairns had next to nothing to eat, I'd lock the door so nobody could come in and see what they were getting. I suppose more than anything I wanted the Robinsons to think I could pay my own way and wouldn't come begging to them for help. I'd rather wash the sheets off the beds and take them to the pawnshop for a week, than go to the Robinsons, and I did so many a time.

I don't know what poor people would have done without the pawnshop, it was both a friend and an enemy at the same time. Some used it to get money to buy food, some because they needed to buy or redeem something for a wedding or a funeral, and others because they needed to pay off a debt or lend somebody. They were everywhere and practically everybody used them at one time or another. Some always had their most treasured belongings in them...wedding dresses, rings, pocket watches... They would take almost anything if it had some value. But like many of the people that used them, it always made me feel ashamed to go in and I'd go to great lengths to make sure there was nobody I knew hanging about; and I'd always peep inside first before I went in.

18

Every day I did five other lodging houses apart from Campbell's lodging house, and I worked it so that I did the big weekly scrubbing in one lodgings on the Monday, and then did only the sweeping, cleaning and washing up in the five others; then on the Tuesday I'd do the weekly scrubbing in another one and so on, always doing the hardest job first when I was freshest. After I'd finished I'd go around the property dealers seeking a better place for us to live in, and at the same time keeping my eye open for better paid work. Often I didn't get back till very late, depending on whether I'd been lucky enough to get a lift back or not, because it was a long and wearying trail back uphill, especially after traipsing around looking for something to better our situation, on top of a full day's hard labour. All in all it would be about nine or ten miles and I'd be so relieved if I caught the likes of Bobby Robson, the canny feller who drove the tatey wagons in every Monday and Wednesday; sometimes I'd be too tired to stop and stick my thumb up because it was so hard to get started again, and so I'd just keep going, but Bobby would always keep a look-out for me and what a lovely sight it was to see his lorry slow down and halt just a few yards in front of me, and his friendly face poking out the window. He was one of those rough and ready but really kind people, the best kind of human being on this earth.

It was after eight o'clock when I got back one Thursday night and straightaway I started getting the bairns ready for bed and making them their meals. The backdoor was open to let the steam out and let some fresh air in because it was stinking after the bairns had been in it all day, and you could see down into the alley that led to a small grocer's shop across the road. As I was kneeling down holding up the bleezer at the fire to get it going, I could hear the voices of some of the neighbours coming out of the shop.

'She's no good. There's no man there. All those bairns, and no man. She's on the streets from morn till night, the brazen bitch.'

'The only time she cleans the stairs is on a Sunday. Down on her hands and knees like God knows what. Ye'll never see her doin' it on any decent day o' the week.'

'You're not tellin' me owt I don't know... Have ye not seen her on the road puttin' her thumb up to those dirty wagon drivers..? She'd get in with anybody...it doesn't matter who they are. Ye wouldn't need anybody to spell out what goes on in there. Then they'll be takin' her into the pubs so she can do her business in there.'

'Wor Tom said he was certain it was her he saw walkin' along the docks t'other night.'

'It's those poor little bairns I feel sorry for. Somebody should get the Cruelty man. They should be taken off her. Not one of them's as much as seen their own father, I'll bet.'

'What gets me, is the way she walks about like Lady Muck. Always with her head stuck right up as though she owned the place. And those rooms not fit to keep a dog in.'

'She keeps that little one in bed all day. Goes out galavantin' and doesn't give a ha'penny toss about him, poor little soul.'

All of a sudden I realised they were talking about me! My stomach heaved and I thought I was going to be sick, only there was nothing to fetch up, I'd had nothing to eat all day. I sat down on the edge of the bed and a queer feeling came over me. I felt sick and dizzy at the same time and little lights were dancing in front of my eyes. I lost the feeling in my arms and my legs went all weak. My whole body went cold and clammy. My heart was beating like a drum and I thought I'd have to do something or I'd go into a fit.

I took a deep breath, put my hand against the wall, and pushed myself to my feet...

'By God,' I thought, 'it's right that listeners hear no good of themselves.' And I kept repeating it while I went around turning every pocket out, emptying out every little tin with pins and things in, and poking my fingers in the lining of my purse. Round and round I went, more quickly and clumsily, muttering away to myself like somebody not right. 'I'll finish it this time, Lord. I've had enough. I'm not puttin' my bairns through any more of this. This world's no good. Your family...your neighbours...nobody cares whether ye live or die. I want no more of it. Not one another day of this...'

Then I heard Johnny carrying his bike up the stairs. He was

working at the Guardians in Jarrow.

I rushed to the door and opened it. 'Johnny! Give's your tea money! Quick..! Ye haven't spent it, have ye..? Where is it..? I need it!'

'I'm sorry, Mother,' he says, 'but they went away and forgot it. They'll give it to me tomorrow, though. Don't upset yourself over that.'

'I need it now! I need it right now!'

'You don't need to pay the rent or anything tonight, do you?' He had his arm around my shoulder and was smiling.

'Oh, Johnny. Oh, Johnny...' And I started to cry.

'Come on, Ma. We'll get the bairns their tea and then you and me are going out. I'm going to take you for a nice walk.'

'Son, I couldn't walk another yard today. I'm just about all in.'

'Let's see your face, Ma.'

He took my face in his hands and turned it towards him and he said 'Mother, whatever's the matter..? Are you all right..? Sit down a while and I'll put a cup of tea on. We'll just stay in instead.'

'No, Johnny, no... I want to go out, like ye said. I want to go for that walk. I think I need it.'

'All right, Ma. Come on now, don't worry. Everything's going to be all right.'

Going for a walk with Johnny was always a treat, it didn't have to be anywhere special, he was what made it. If the weather was fine, the five of us would go out together on a weekend, Johnny carrying Walter on his back as we walked through the fields at the back of the Robin Hood, just walking and talking amongst ourselves. We would follow the rows of hedges all the way round and back, and while the kids were playing on the grass Johnny would be telling me how Joe and him had planned to save up enough money to buy me a business and a huge house, already set up and waiting for me to go in and take the reins and be the big boss, just like Mrs Robinson. He'd say they were saving right now to buy me all kinds of gowns and jewels as well, I only had to be patient for a few more years and it would all come true. I'd laugh and take a swipe at him. 'Get out of it, ye daftie..! Who d'ye think you're kiddin'..? You're not the Prime Minister yet. You're still only an office boy... But ye will be one day, son. Stick in and I know ye will. You'll be somebody important for your mother to be proud of and look up to.' But the truth was, I couldn't be any more proud of him, no matter what he did in the future, than I was right now... And so we would go on, talking about dreams and how wonderful the future was going to be and how we were all going to look after each other and live happily ever after. And by the time we got back, I'd always be cheered and we'd be laughing at all the talk.

This particular night I really needed that kind of walk, and although it was dark, we went for half an hour after we'd tucked up the bairns. As we were coming across the last field and I'd been listening to him talking about this and that, I stopped him and told him what was troubling me.

'Johnny, I'm glad ye didn't have the tea money tonight. I'm really glad of it. God sent those fellers away without payin' ye tonight, on purpose. I know he did. I was nearly goin' to do a very bad thing tonight, son. A very bad thing. I was goin' to wait till we were all abed and then I was goin' to put the money in the meter and gas we all.'

'What..? I don't believe it! I'd never believe a thing like that. You've got far too much spirit to do a thing like that, Ma. I've seen them bend your back but they'll never break it. None of them! Nobody! You're tougher and better than any of them... You must never say a thing like that again, or even let it enter your head... He hasn't been bothering you again, has he..? If he has, I'll kill him. Now! Tonight..! Was it him, Ma? I want to know... Tell me!'

'It's got nothin' to do with O'Callaghan this time, son. It's the people downstairs.'

'Which people? Who?'

I told him everything that had happened from the time I'd come back from work that night, everything that had been said except the really bad words, I couldn't bear to say them in front of my own son.

'Come on, Ma. We're going to see them.'

'No, Johnny. No! We cannot afford to make any trouble. It'll all bound back on us.'

'Never mind. Come on.'

He still wasn't very big but he was such a smart feller in his navy blue suit that he went to work in. He took my hand and we went down the stairs and out into the alley and along to where one of the ones I'd told him about lived, and without any hesitation he knocked on the door. Mrs McArdle, the one who'd had most to say, opened it and came out on to the step so she could see who it was. As soon as she saw me, she slammed the door; not so fast however, that Johnny hadn't managed to get his foot in.

She pushed and shoved that door against Johnny's poor boot, shouting 'Gettaway! Gettaway or I'll fetch the pollis!'

But Johnny wouldn't budge.

'You'll not shut this door, Mrs McArdle, until you hear what I've got to say,' he says in this quiet strong little voice that he had, all the Robinsons had very deep voices.'

It stopped her and she put her face right up to the crack but she wouldn't open the door any further.

'You've been calling my mother today, haven't you..? Well I'm going to tell you something... My mother is as good a woman as you or anybody. And if you were half as good as she is, you'd have nothing to fear from anybody. Yet you and your friends nearly made her put her head in the gas oven tonight.. Nobody knows what my mother has gone through in her life. You people know nothing about my mother... But I'll tell you this and you'd better take heed... If you ever say things like that again, you'll be in big trouble. Neighbours are supposed to help one another and be kind to each other. You sound like the kind of people who would kick anybody they saw on their hands and knees.'

With that, he got tight hold of my arm and marched me back up the stairs to our room.

'Thanks, son,' I said. 'I'll get down and thank God for havin' a son like you. And I promise I'll never think that way again. I don't care what they say.' And I hugged him and I hugged him.

Scarcely three quarters of an hour went by, and we'd just cleared away the dishes, when there was a knock on the door. It was Mrs McArdle with Mr McArdle standing a little way down the stairs behind her. Whether he'd made her come, whether she'd made him come, or what, I didn't know, but she started apologising and she couldn't stop.

From then on all three of the women who'd done the gossiping couldn't do enough for us, though Johnny would take nothing from them; if you hurt Johnny, and especially if anybody hurt any of his family, he wouldn't easily forget it. However, I wasn't one to hold a grudge and I forgave them because I realised that although they were wrong, they'd probably been thinking of the bairns, and you couldn't blame them for that. They must have told all of the other neighbours about us because they all mucked in together to bring cast-offs, food and even coal...two of the families were pitfolk and you couldn't find better than those people. But this couldn't go on, it got to be too much and Johnny didn't like it at all; I only wanted good neighbours, not charity. Apart from that, the room was getting worse; we'd known from the start it was condemned, that's why we got it so cheap, and that's why the landlord wouldn't lift a hammer to knock a single nail in.

Out of courtesy I told the neighbours we were leaving, and they begged us to stay.

'You don't need to worry about a thing, Mrs O'Callaghan. We'll help ye with your rent and everythin'. Ye need never want for anythin'. If only ye'll stay here, we'll keep an eye on ye all. We'll look after little Walter for ye when ye go to work, and help ye wherever we can. Just say the word.'

'Thank ye very much for bein' so kind to me and the bairns. But I can't bring them up here. They need somethin' better than this. Me and my son have made up our minds.'

From there we went to Eleanor Street which was a bit better; but once you'd said that, you'd said everything, and so I kept on searching every night after work. There were places all right, nice places that would have suited us right down to the ground, but you needed good money to rent them, and we didn't have it. But at last I found a canny place in Chichester consisting of four little boxrooms, which was very handy because children weren't supposed to be allowed and it meant I'd be able to hide them whenever the landlady came, which she did every Monday. But hiding three healthy bairns and keeping them quiet as mice and stopping them from suddenly bursting in, is something nobody can do forever, especially when one of them was our Edmund, and one day she came unexpectedly when they were all sitting around the table having their dinners.

'What's all this!' she says.

It was a bit late in the day then, I know, but I says 'I've got somethin' to confess to ye. They're my bairns, and I've got nowhere else to go. As ye can see, I'm lookin' after your place very well and keepin' it clean and - '

'I'm sorry, Francie, but I told you before ever you came in that I'd have no children living here. No animals, no children. I think I made that very clear. I don't like having to do it but I'm going to have to give you notice to leave.'

'Isn't it a shame that little bairns have to be shoved out in a stable or somewhere. They haven't a right to live. Only us. Anybody'd think they were dogs or somethin'. Instead of little human bein's.'

'It's the regulations, Francie. The house isn't big enough. I'd only get myself into trouble.'

I didn't know whether that was the truth or not, or whether it was just her, but I knew it was her place and she could give any reason she liked. I just looked at her, I wasn't going to go down on my knees but surely to God she could see it in my face, I was so fed up. Uptil now I'd been as friendly as I could to her and every time she'd come for her rent I'd always give her a cup of tea and an oven-bottom cake to take away with her.

It was easy for her to say 'Pack up and go', but it was a lot harder to do. Pack up and go where? Back to Eleanor Street if it was still vacant, which it wasn't? Back to the Robin Hood which I'd heard they were knocking down..? I had three bairns and a lad as well as myself, I was sick of putting all our belongings on a horse and cart or in wheelbarrows where everybody could see all we had, and traipsing back and forward, back and forward, Johnny pushing one and me pushing the other.

She stood there for a couple of minutes but I could see she was going to stand firm and not even a cocker spaniel would have moved her. 'But I'm not going to put you out. Not straightaway. What I'm doing is asking you to look for somewhere else as soon as possible. I don't want you to take just anything, but I want it clear that I want you out sooner rather than later.'

Four or five days later I was scrubbing out one of the lodging houses, when one of the inspectors I knew from years back when I had the lodging house in Thrift Street, came in. He was delighted to see me.

'Francie..! Francie Robinson..! I don't believe it after all this time... How are you, pet? Where've you been? What've you been doing with yourself?'

He was a nice feller and had always been good to me, and I knew he was genuinely interested in me, so I told him so much but not everything; he knew about Johnny dying and heard I'd got married again but he didn't know who to, so I just filled him in without going into too much detail. You could never be too sure with men, even ones you'd known for a long time, when it came to telling them you were widowed or separated; often the ones you'd least expect, would be the first to take liberties.

It came out that I was looking for a better place to live, and I was so glad it did. Straightaway he said he knew whoever it was at the Town Hall that was in charge of council housing, and he'd see what he could do. I thought he was just being polite but two days later I called into his office, as he'd told me to do, and he'd got us a council flat in Thames Lane. It was the best place we'd ever had. Joe came back from sea a few weeks later, and some of the happiest days of my life were spent in it.

Ever since I'd left O'Callaghan, I'd encouraged young Edmund and Francie to go and see him on a Sunday and be respectful to him whenever they saw him in the street; as far as I was concerned, that was their duty and that was his right. But one night when I'd decided to take the bairns for a treat to the Penny Paragon Pictures...bairns could get in for a jam jar each...O'Callaghan jumped out of a back lane and grabbed hold of Francie. It wasn't the first time either.

'How come she didn't come to see me on Sunday?' he says.

'She sprained her ankle playin', and she couldn't get her clogs on all day. That's why she didn't. Because she couldn't.'

'You're a bloody liar!'

'She did... Didn't ye, pet? Tell your dad.'

'If she was properly looked after, she'd never have got her ankle sprained. You're not fit to be in charge of children. Somebody should come along and take them off you. I'm going to see the Cruelty Inspector pays a visit to your door, missus. You just see if I don't.'

'Is that so? Well make sure ye tell him that you're on the dole and that you're gettin' four shillin's a week allowance for these bairns. And that I'm not gettin' a farthin' out of it... Now, if you jump round one more street corner at me, or out of one more back lane or alley,

I'll take the matter to the dole office. They'll sharp sort you out.'

He cursed and swore and called me all the 'f's' and 'c's' right there in the street in front of the bairns. A feller was walking up behind him and heard everything.

'By gum, I think you want to wash your mouth out with something,' he says to O'Callaghan.

Plucked up by this feller being there, I says to O'Callaghan, 'If you say that word once more to me, I'll take me shoe off and bray ye with it.'

'You wouldn't know any better, fetched up in a common lodging house. Swear words wouldn't bother the likes of you. That's the only language you know.'

So I took my shoe off and I went to whack him with it, and this feller says 'Go on, hinny! I'm right behind ye. Give him one for me while you're at it!'

But O'Callaghan was always a coward, and because there was a man there, he slunk off.

'You haven't heard the last of this!' he shouted as he went off. 'Don't you worry!'

'What you need is to get yoursel' a court order from a solicitor,' the feller says. 'He's a bad'un, that one. If he bothers ye when you've got that, they'll lock him up in jail.'

So I went to the solicitor's, it seemed like a good idea, but I told him I didn't want to go to court; so he said he would send O'Callaghan a letter first, to see how that went. I don't know what he put in it, but whatever it was must have scared the living daylights out of O'Callaghan, because he never again came up to me in the street after that, not ever, not so much as to say hello or goodbye.

I was forty-three when I left O'Callaghan, and he'd had the best years of my life, or what should have been the best years of my life; I was only with my real husband Johnny for a few years, and then all those years with that sod.

Young Edmund had lovely wavy hair like his father and was a good looking and strong lad, but he was every bit as much a handful as Joe, and he could be a right contrary little bugger. I think part of his trouble was that his name was 'O'Callaghan', when what he always wanted was to be called 'Robinson' like his two big brothers.

Whatever they did, sooner or later he did and he always tried to do it better, and often enough he won medals for it; they were good swimmers, so he became a good swimmer; they went to sea, so he went to sea; they were good boxers, so he became a good boxer; he was always trying to draw attention to himself, always trying to outdo the other two.

When he was twelve he got a job as an errand boy at a greengrocer's, and one day the boss came to tell me Edmund had pinched a few shillings; he was very polite and called it a 'mistake', but it wasn't a mistake as far as I was concerned. I told him I'd punish him as soon as he came home and that I'd pay the money back as soon as I got it. The feller wouldn't take it, but said he wouldn't take Edmund back either. I was really upset about it and when I happened to see O'Callaghan later that afternoon, I told him what his shenanigans had done to his son. Instead of bowing his head in shame, he said he'd skin him alive when he got his hands on him.

When I got back home that night after work, I found a message from Edmund. It said:

Dear Mum,
    By the time you get this, I'll
    be out of existence.'
        Your loving son, Edmund. x x x

I didn't pay too much attention to it because I knew what Edmund was, he'd deliberately play on your feelings just like our Joe would. But as soon as Johnny came home, seeing as Edmund still hadn't come back, we went out looking for him and we looked everywhere. We didn't find him but weren't all that worried because we were sure he'd have gone to stay with one of his Callaghan aunts, and we weren't going to go there. However, when he hadn't come back by dinnertime the next day, I went to the police and gave them a photograph, I knew the Callaghans wouldn't have kept him that long, they'd have made him come home long before now.

O'Callaghan came to the house to see if he was back yet, and I said no, but that when he did, no matter what he'd done, I didn't want him given a hiding that would only drive him away again.

It was Johnny who found him eventually, he'd been all over on his bike asking people questions, which was the only way to do it really; and when he brought him back, he was stinking of turnips and horse muck, apparently he'd slept in a farmer's byre all night. He was so sorry for himself when he came back, what with bits of straw sticking in his hair and cow muck dried on his face and clothes, I didn't know whether to laugh or cry.

Cleaning the lodging houses was becoming very hard for me now, some of them were practically falling down and two of them had been closed, so I was always on the lookout for other work, and when somebody put me on to a couple who were opening a fish-and-chip shop, I was very interested. The couple were called Smith and they'd emigrated to Canada in 1921 after Mr Smith had been laid off at the pit, and now they'd come back with a bit of money and wanted to start a business. They hadn't the first idea about the fish-and-chip business, how or where to buy fish or tateys or anything, so they asked me if I'd show them. I said I'd show them if they gave me a job; I didn't care whether it was buying fish, peeling tateys, serving, or anything else, as long as it was something, but I wasn't going to tell them all about it for nothing. They said they'd be glad to have me, so I gave up the lodging house work altogether and set to work in their shop, and in no time it was going like a house on fire and they were thrilled to bits.

One night I was putting chips in the fryer, when a bloke with too much drink inside him came in and shouted to the whole shop, 'Aye, he's won again!'

I didn't know what he was on about so I carried on with my work and didn't even bother turning around, you get a lot of daft buggers coming into fish-and-chip shops when the pubs close.

'Hey..! I'm talkin' to you,' he yells. 'Francie..! Your lad's won again.'

'Won what..? Who d'ye mean?'

'Won the fight..! Your Joe, man..! Ye should be out celebratin', not messin' about in here!'

'What fight..?' I didn't know what he was talking about.

'Come on..! Has he not told ye?'

'I don't know what you're talkin' about.'

The feller just looked, realised he must have put his foot in it, and went out without getting anything.

'Our Joe fightin'?' I said to myself. 'If he is, he's been deceivin' me... I'll have this out with him as soon as he comes home.' I was really mad because the lads knew I didn't want them to have anything to do with boxing, not the fight game. That's what had killed their father. I didn't mind them learning how to defend themselves down at the gym, but not going in for contests or anything like that.

When young Edmund came to meet me after I finished at the shop, as one of them always did, I said to him, 'Is wor Joe in the house?'

'Aye, he is. He's gettin' his supper and goin' to bed. Why like..?'

'Never you mind why,' I says. 'I'm askin' the questions, not you... It's a funny him goin' to his bed already, isn't it? I've never known him to be in bed this early. He's usually out enjoyin' hesel' this time o' night.'

Edmund never said another word but I should have known better, because he was just as keen on boxing as the other two.

When we got back, Joe was still up, it took Joe ages to do anything except fall asleep.

I was hanging my hat and coat up and he was messing about at the sink doing something with his hair.

'What's this I hear about you, wor Joe?'

'What's that, Mother?'

'You know very well what... Are you fightin'? And ye'd better tell me the truth because I'm goin' to find out one way or another. I'll ask our Johnny. He won't tell me a lie.'

'Fightin'? Who told ye I was fightin'?'

'Never you mind.'

'Willy Neil,' Edmund blurted out.

'Willy Neil..! That stupid bugger..! He wouldn't know his arse from his elbow.'

'Don't you start swearin' in here, wor Joe. Ye won't get out of it that way.'

But Joe couldn't kid anybody, everything he ever did was written all over his face.

'Don't play funny games with me, lad! Come on! Tell me..! Ye've been boxin', haven't ye? I know ye have.'

'Aye, but it's nowt much. Just messin' about, that's all.'

'It's nothin' of the sort! I lost your Dad like that and I'm not losin'

267

you an' all. It's got to stop.'

'I cannot, Ma.'

'What d'ye mean, ye "cannot"?'

'It's not that simple. I've got to fight a feller in Leith up in Scotland.'

'Who says ye've got to fight some feller up in Scotland?'

'I beat him in Sunderland a couple of weeks ago and I've got to give him a return.'

When I got the whole story, it turned out he'd been fighting all over the place and everybody had been covering up for him so I wouldn't find out, he was being billed as the 'Knockout Specialist' so that even if I'd seen the posters I wouldn't have been any the wiser. I knew he must have had plenty of fights to earn that title, and when he told me his uncle Stoker Allen was training him, I knew it was the real stuff all right. And I knew enough about boxing to know that once you were matched to fight somebody, you had to turn up or you'd lose face.

'Ye wouldn't want people to go round sayin' I was a coward, would ye?'

'No. Course not. But ye shouldn't have got yourself into the fix in the first place.'

Just then Johnny came in and I turned on him before he had a chance to get the door closed. 'I'm surprised at you, our Johnny.'

'What do you mean, Mother?'

'You know what I mean! You're in on it as well. You're the one who steps into the corner of the ring and wipes him down. Aren't you?'

He looked at Joe and Joe looked at him and then it dawned on me what had been in the bags I'd been seeing on the landing all these months, that's what they'd had their bloodstained towels and shorts and boots and things in, they'd been sneaking them out to get them washed somewhere so I wouldn't know.

Then the whole story came out... Joe and his pal Alfie and a few others had been to the fairground one time and had been standing outside the boxing booth, when the barker had been calling for anybody in the crowd to go three rounds with his man, an ugly feller with ginger hair who was bouncing about with his kit on, punching the air and blowing hard like he could flatten anybody and anything.

'Gan on, Joe,' his mates had said to him. 'Ye could easy sort that bugger out. He's oulder than me dad.'

Nobody else was volunteering, so when the barker heard Joe's pals urging him to have a go, he turned to Joe and invited him up.

'Come on, son. You're a fine strapping lad. Ye don't have to knock him out. Ye've only got to still be on your feet at the end of three rounds. There's ten shillings for ye if ye manage it.'

So Joe had gone into the tent and they'd fitted him with shorts and gloves and all that, and Joe had beat the feller in the second round by knocking him out for the count. When Joe had put his clothes back on and was leaving the tent with his winnings, the barker had said to him, 'Listen, young feller. I'll give ye four pounds a week if ye come with me and let me take care of ye.'

'Na,' says Joe. 'Me mother doesn't want it, so I won't.' Or so he told me he'd said.

He did carry on though, but not with the circus. Later on that night a smartly dressed feller had come up to Joe and said 'I saw you beat that pug, and you were good. You were right not to go with the likes of that lot. Otherwise you'd end up like the man you beat. What you need is somebody who knows what they're talking about. Somebody with good connections. Somebody like me. I'd look after you. Let me make matches for you, Joe. I know who you are. You're Johnny Robinson's son... By, your father was a great boxer. I knew him well. Curley's my name. I'll find you good men, Joe. Worthy men. Men with a reputation.'

Egged on by his mates, Joe, who never weighed up anything properly, had said yes, and Stoker Allen, ex-champion of the navy, became his trainer. From then on Joe had fought at all the local venues like the variety halls, skating rinks, stadiums and the place they called the 'Blood Kit'. He called himself 'Spike Robinson, the Knockout Specialist'. I realised that a lot of lads did things like that if they didn't want their parents to know; the Callaghans did the same thing. Walter Callaghan had called himself 'Young Walters' when he fought people like Jimmy Wilde, and his brother Tom was known as 'Stoker Callaghan, the Iron Man of Jarrow'.

Anyway Joe went to fight the feller in Leith and beat him there on his own home ground, but the feller still wasn't satisfied so Joe had to give him another fight, this time in Shields. When he came and told me, I said 'All right, Joe. But this is his last chance. When you get into the ring, before you get started I want you to announce to everybody that win lose or draw, this is your last fight. I don't mind ye boxin' amongst your pals but I don't want ye gettin' in a ring and fightin' for prize money any more.'

'All right, Mother. If that's what you want, that's what I'll do.'

And that's what he did. Mind, not that you'd notice the difference, because all the time he'd been at it, he'd never once come home with a black eye or even so much as a scratch. Although I never wanted any of them to fight, I think if Johnny had had his two eyes and gone in for it, he'd have been the better of the two. He was more like his father...very quick with his hands and very light on his feet, and he had a hardness to his body that Joe never had. Joe was always softer in every way than Johnny.

Now that I'd put a stop to Joe's making any money out of boxing, he had to look harder than ever for work because every week it was getting harder to get, and now Edmund had left school and he was looking for a job as well.

One morning Joe and Edmund had gone to the dole office and the man behind the desk had said 'Sorry, boys. Nothing doing. But I could send you to Canada to work on the farms, if you like. It's the land of opportunity.' And he had filled their heads with wonderful ideas about Canada, so the two of them had said 'Right. If there's work, we'll go.' But when they came home and told me, I wasn't happy about it at all. It was all in the papers and I had it from our Nellie as well, that a lot of young lads were going out and being treated like animals when they got there, and then they had no way of getting back.

I said 'Well you two aren't goin' to Canada. But I'll tell ye what I'll do. I'll put my hat and coat on and come down to the dole office with ye and have a word with them. They've no right to keep sendin' young lads and lasses to these places when they know they're not bein' properly looked after.' So all three of us went back to the dole office, though the two lads weren't too happy about it at all. 'Ye'll make we look like a couple of pansies bringin' their mammy,' Joe says. 'I don't care,' I says. 'I'm goin' to see about this. And yous two are comin' as well.'

'Excuse me,' I said to the man when we got there. 'I believe ye've been tellin' my lads ye can send them to Canada..? Well, I don't want ye tellin' my lads anythin' of the sort in future. Ye've no right to be doin' it to anybody else's either... How many of your own have ye sent out..? None, I'll bet... Some people might want their bairns away so they can pass the Means Test, but I'm not one of them. I want mine here where I can keep an eye on them. So don't you ever mention Canada or Australia or anywhere else when they come into your shop... Have ye nothin' else on your books? Nothin' at all? Surely ye have somethin'. Things are hard but the world hasn't stopped turnin' altogether, has it?'

He never said a word, he just looked and looked in his book, turning page after page; and then he said 'I've one at the shipyard but it doesn't pay very much. And I don't know how long it's for, the way things are.'

'Right,' I said. 'Wor Edmund'll have that one. When has he to start?'

'What about me?' Joe said when we were coming away. 'Wor Edmund's just a kid.'

'They kicked ye out when you were there because ye messed about too much. Ye should've got on with your job like everybody else... One look at you, and they'll say "Hoppit!"'

'Ah man, Ma. I wasn't doin' much wrong. Anyway, that was ages ago. D'ye think every shipyard on the Tyne has got me picture up? "Wanted. Joe Robinson. Dead or Alive".'

'Howay, ye useless bugger.' I gave him a thump on his daft back and the two of us went back home. But what I'd said must have got through to him because the next thing is he's trying to grow himself a tash; but all he got was just a few stray hairs, and he gave it up after a couple of weeks.

One day he said 'This is ne good Mother. Ye won't let is fight, and I cannot get a job. I'm goin' back to sea.'

I couldn't stop him any more, he was old enough to make up his own mind, and off he went. After he'd gone, I wondered whether I'd done the right thing or not, whether I should have tried to stop him. 'Course you have, Ma,' Johnny says one night when I'd got myself upset thinking about our Joe. 'A bit of discipline won't do him any harm, and things might be better when he comes back. It must be hard for him when I'm working and Edmund's working and he's not.'

271

I was still working in Smith's fish-and-chip shop and one day, I don't know whether I'd pricked my hands with a piece of fishbone or what, but my hands swelled up to nearly twice their normal size and went bright blue and shiny; it just happened in a matter of hours but my hands were so painful and my fingers so thick, that I couldn't do anything with them and had to come home. They still hadn't healed by the next day so I went to the chemist's to see if he could give me something, because I knew Mr and Mrs Smith depended on me and I didn't want to let them down. He gave me some ointment to put on but said I'd have to keep my hands covered with it for three days and stay away from all fish. I went to the shop and told the Smiths and they were very sorry for me, they could see the state of my hands, but it was obvious they were worried about their business.

By the end of three days, by which time my hands were a lot better, I had developed such a pain in my back that I couldn't move. My mother used to get bad backs from working in the tatey fields and bending over the fish all day, and so did I, and she always used to say 'Whatever ye do, Francie, never stop workin' for very long. That's what causes it. If ye don't rest for too long, it won't get to you.' Now it had happened to me. My back had been stiff in the mornings for years, but once I got up and got moving it usually went away, or at least it was manageable. But now that I'd been off for three days, it had hit me, and when I got out of bed it was worse, not better. I tried every day to get up and walk around, but in the finish I had to go back to bed. It was a week before I was able to go back to the fish-and-chip shop, and when I did I could see the Smiths weren't very pleased; they had seen for themselves how bad my hands were, but of course nobody can see a pain in the back.

The shop was down to three days a week and they wanted it built back up as soon as possible, and I wanted the work so I worked to all hours day after day, long before they came in in the morning and sometimes till long after they'd gone home at night. They weren't all that quick themselves, they were older and I don't think a pit was much preparation for a fish-and-chip shop, but they weren't keen on the idea of taking on anybody else. In my opinion, a good woman like Lizzie Flood would have been worth her weight in gold, but I think they were beginning to have second thoughts about the whole thing now that they'd realised how dependant they were.

All the extra work with the fish brought my hands up worse than before, and this time I carried on, but in the end I couldn't even hold a knife and I had to take a couple more days off. This brought the lumbago back as bad as before, and by the time I was over it and went back to the shop, which was nearly nine days this time, the shop was already closed.

Johnny still had his job with the Public Assistance, Joe was away at sea and there'd be nothing from him until he came back, Edmund was just an apprentice getting less than it took to keep him, and Francie and Walter were still at school; and all this time O'Callaghan was getting an allowance for them and not giving me a penny of it, so I was forced to go and see about dole. When I got there they took a dim view of the fact that I had left my husband, and said I wasn't entitled to anything because I wasn't legally separated; O'Callaghan had lost Leighton Street long ago and was just living with one or other of his family. I was so desperate I went to see Mr Campbell to see if he could do anything; he'd always been helpful and he knew all kinds of people.

It so happened that Mr Campbell knew somebody at the dole office, so he went and told them not to take O'Callaghan into consideration, but that meant I had to say I was getting the children's allowance even though I wasn't, and the only way he would give me anything was if I took him back. It meant the dole would be less than it ought to be, but at least I'd get something, so I thanked Mr Campbell and went back to the dole office. But when I got there, the one who'd turned me down before was really vexed because somebody had gone over her head, you could see it in her face.

'You understand you have to be available for work, to claim benefit,' she says in this hoity-toity voice.

'Oh yes, madam,' I says. 'I'm prepared to do anythin' ye give is.'

'Right,' she says. 'There's a fish-and-chip shop on Fowler street needing somebody. I see you've had plenty of experience with fish and chips. You can start there first thing on Monday morning.'

'Oh, I'm very sorry,' I says. 'But that's the one thing I can't do any more. It affects my hands.'

'Give me a look.'

I showed her.

'They look all right to me.'

273

'Well they are now. It's only when they come in contact with fish that they get bad.'

'When you work, you mean?'

'Yes, but... Not any work. Just fish and cold water.'

'They didn't seem to bother you when you had your own business.'

'They didn't then...no.'

'They only started bothering you since you started working for somebody else. Is that it?'

'Yes...but not the way you mean.'

'Don't waste any more of our time, Mrs O'Callaghan. When you are prepared to take work that's offered to you, then and only then can your claim be considered. Good day.'

So much for the dole...

The employment situation was no better when Joe came back from sea, if anything it was worse, and we'd been getting these letters from him telling about the great fights he and his sailor mates had had, so I pretty much knew what to expect when he came back. I knew I couldn't hold him back from boxing any more; his uncle Stoker Allen, who he called 'Uncle Ned', was always at him, and so was his Uncle Geordie Robinson. The only one who might have been able to stop him was Johnny, and he wouldn't either; Johnny loved boxing every bit as much as Joe, and he loved being his second, the one in the corner that towelled him down and chivvied him to do this and that, and Joe wouldn't have anybody else.

How our Joe could ever be a boxer, I'll never know. I'll grant he was very well built and very strong and loved a scrap, especially with a crowd behind him, he loved all that. But compared with his dad and what he used to do...getting up early and going for long runs, lifting weights and skipping and all that, eating and drinking only what was good for him and going to bed at the proper time... All the training Joe seemed to do was singing, dancing and drinking; some nights he never went to bed at all. He always had a huge gang of friends who would follow him anywhere, not just because of the boxing, but because of the kind of feller he was. They were a rough lot and used to go around yelling and singing at the tops of their voices as though they weren't right in the head, it was a wonder the whole lot of them weren't locked up.

But Joe never took the boxing seriously and he'd get fed up with Stoker who was a real disciplinarian and followed him all over punching the air and blowing hard. Stoker loved fighting more than anything, he never talked about anything else, he certainly didn't have much of a life with Lily.

'Quick, Joe! There, look! Catch-a-pigeon! Catchapigeon!' he'd be shouting every time they went down a back lane.

After a while Joe'd get the wanderlust again and back he'd go to sea.

19

One Sunday I'd gone over to JaneAnne's to see my father because I'd heard he was poorly, and he started ranting on about none of us ever doing a thing for him, and like with all old people when they are getting a bit past themselves, some of what he said made sense and some of it didn't. When he couldn't find something, even one of his holey socks, he'd blame anybody for pinching it, and then when he realised he was getting things mixed up, he'd get very frustrated. I'd always sent him food and baccy whenever I could, and even when I hadn't the money to pay for it myself, I'd buy it with the postal order Nellie sent me for him, so there was rarely a week went by without I sent something. But every time I went it was the same thing.

'Wor Jinny! Come here..! D'ye hear what wor Francie says..? She says she never stopped sendin' is me baccy money. So, what have ye got to say about that eh?'

'Ye've had it, man. Ye forget things, Dad,' JaneAnne would say.

'Not as much as yous'd like to think..!' he'd shout. 'I'm not allowed to have a gill. I'm not allowed to have a pipe. I'm not allowed to bloody breathe nearly... I don't know why somebody doesn't just stick a knife in me when I'm asleep, an' that'll be an end of it. Then yous can all go out and spend me money... As for Francie, she thinks because she sends ye somebody's oul' shart an' their bloody oul' singlet, that's her duty satisfied... Well, it's not... She's the youngest and the worst of the whole damned lot of ye.'

This particular morning he was worse than usual. I knew he wasn't responsible for everything he said, but he was responsible for a whole lot of other things he'd done in his life, and I just couldn't help the bitterness coming out.

'What did ye ever do for me?' I shouted at him.

He lowered his head and waved his hand as much as to say 'Go on, bugger off.'

Three days later he was dead, he was eighty-three. He always used to say he intended to live to a ripe old age, and he'd have felt himself cheated if he'd known; one of his brothers had lived to ninety-three, and another one, Uncle Billy, till he was ninety-seven. I think he knocked himself up too much with all the drinking and everything. There was no doubt he had a hard life, but a lot of it was of his own making; he had a lovely wife if only he'd appreciated her, they could have weathered things together and made a shot of it if only he hadn't been so selfish and fond of the bottle.

Johnny was doing well at his job and bringing a little bit more in now, Joe was sending a pound a month from sea, Edmund had started working as a labourer to his cousin Harry Robinson who did all his own repairs to his various properties, and I'd got myself a few cleaning jobs. With what little we'd been able to save, I'd opened a savings account in young Francie's name, just a little something put aside because she was the only girl in the family, so she was the one who'd need it most. I'd been doing it for quite a while and there was nearly four pounds in it when O'Callaghan heard about it.

I think O'Callaghan was fonder of Francie than either of his two lads, and he was always trying to get her to go and live with him even though he had no fit place; whether it was to try and spite me or because he really cared about her, I don't know, but I wouldn't have given him credit either way. I sent Francie to see him on a Sunday and he'd do things like tell her I was dying and that she'd have to go and live with him soon, and she'd come home crying. Edmund and Walter didn't like going to see him, and only went if I made them; they'd tell him nothing; but he used to quiz Francie about everything...what we were doing, what we had in the house and who'd been calling...and she must have told him about the savings.

One day he got her out of school by telling the teacher she was wanted at home because her mother had taken ill, and then took her to the bank, got her to sign on the dotted line, and took the whole four pounds out; he gave Francie a shilling and a pat on the head and sent her on her way.

For all he could do a thing like that, he still had the neck to get on to the bairns to ask me to have him back, mainly our soft Joe and little Francie that was; not Johnny, I think he was scared of Johnny. But it wouldn't have mattered to me if he'd got at the whole lot of them, it was a matter between him and me, and nobody else, and I wouldn't dream of having him back and going through all that again. People would come up to me and say he really loved me, people who knew nothing of the life he'd led me, people who had no idea what living with a man like that was. I wouldn't wish O'Callaghan on anybody, I'd done my stint with him and they were welcome to him if they thought he was such a fine feller. For me there was no turning back.

Life was hard but we were happy in Thames Lane, and I never had to sit down at a table and take stock to realise it. I wasn't earning good money and got nothing from the dole, and I wouldn't have even asked now in case it embarrassed Johnny, but Joe and Edmund were earning their keep when they managed to get work, and all of them were healthy in mind and body. Not only were Joe and Johnny strong young men who would never hear a word said against me even in fun, but Edmund also, and I think Edmund would have put his fists up to his father quicker than any if it ever came to it.

Edmund was full of swagger and self confidence. He had now gone to sea as well, but there was a time when Joe and him had been looking for work in Shields, and Edmund said he could get both of them a job; Edmund didn't even have a job himself at the time but he'd once worked as a joiner's apprentice, and to hear him you'd think he knew everything. This particular day the two of them went to a building site looking for work and Edmund says 'Leave everythin' to me, Joe. Don't say a word.'

When our Joe opened his mouth he was as blunt as a yard of tripe, and if anybody asked if he'd done this, that or t'other, and he hadn't, he'd say so. Edmund would be just the opposite.

Edmund steps over the foundations of a house these men were digging, and he says to this feller with a shovel, 'Hey mate, is the gaffer about?'

'Ower there. With the baldy head.'

'Right... Howay, Joe. Follow me.'

The two of them then walked over to the foreman.

'Canny weather,' Edmund says.

'Aye.'

'Fine lookin' buildin' this is ganna be, if what we've seen so far is anythin' to go by... I was just sayin' to our kid here, this is the place for us. They're obviously only employin' top class craftsmen here.'

'I don't know so much about that... Why like? What d'ye want?'

'We'd like to join ye. Bricklayin', joinery...we can do owt.'

'Can ye build chimneys?'

'Can we build chimneys..? Why aye, man!' says Edmund. 'We've been buildin' them all wor lives.'

'Right, clevershite,' says the foreman. 'Be here at seven o'clock on Monday and get started on that roof over there.'

'What did I tell ye?' says Edmund as he and Joe are going back home. 'Leave it to your Uncle Edmund... He's the man. He knows what he's doin'.'

When the two of them came back home, Edmund waltzes in, full of himself. What he was going to do and what he wasn't going to do, was nobody's business. According to Edmund this was going to be the start of something big for both of them, they were going to be chimney specialists and have their own business, and on the Saturday morning I had to give him the money for a full set of tools and a few for Joe as well...all in all it cost me nearly two pound.

On the way to the building site on the Monday morning, Edmund says to Joe, 'Ye realise you're goin' to have to be my labourer, don't ye..? I'm the one who knows what to do.'

'Haddaway and loss yoursel'!' says Joe. 'Afore I black both your eyes for ye.'

'I'm serious, man.'

'So am I.'

'I'm the one they'll be holding responsible for this chimney.'

'You're the one who's full o' shit, more like it.'

When they got there Edmund says 'Right, Joe. Shake your tools and make plenty of noise. We've got to work fast to show them we're no mugs. That way we'll make plenty money and they'll have to keep us on.'

'I know bugger-all about chimneys,' says Joe. 'And neither do you.'

'Just watch me. I've seen them puttin' them up many a time. There's nowt to it. Nowt at all. Pass that.'

The two of them built three chimneys before the day was out, and not one was still up when they went back next morning; the whole lot had fallen off and smashed to pieces on the ground. Of course they were sacked straight away, got no pay, and I'd thrown away two pounds on tools for building chimneys.

He was a plucky lad though, Edmund, and always looking for a fight. Two things made him tough... One was that his own father had given him hidings like no man ever gave a son, and the other was Joe and Johnny. When he was a kid at school he was always sending for Johnny or Joe whenever he got into trouble. In the finish they said 'Ye'll have to stand up for yourself, Edmund. If they plug ye, plug them back.' They taught him how to look after himself with his fists and after that he came on a main. He hated anybody telling him what to do, and one time Johnny was telling him off for something he'd said or done, and Edmund comes out with 'Who the hell d'ye think you are, Johnny..? You're not me father. I'm as much a Robinson as you are, any time. Put them up!'

'Oh, shut up, Edmund, before you get yourself hurt,' Johnny says to him.

'C'mon big man! Let's see how good ye really are!' says Edmund, cheeky as you like.

'Go away, sonny boy. I've warned you once. I won't warn you again.'

Joe then steps in between them, turns his back on Edmund, and faces Johnny and winks at him. Then he and Johnny burst out laughing. Edmund quickly picks up the carving knife and jabs it into Joe's backside. Joe turns round with his eyes staring and grabs a hold of Edmund as though he's going to lay him out. And then they all start laughing and that was the end of it.

Little Walter wasn't like Johnny, Joe or Edmund, you could see he'd never make a boxer, it would have showed when he was just a few years old if he had. He wanted nothing at all to do with fighting and none of the other lads could push him into it, and I was glad of it. But it wasn't because he was soft... When he was only eight he slashed his arm on a barrel brace, and the metal spring made a gash six inches long, gaping to the bone, and I had to take a spoon and scrape out umpteen little bits of rusty metal that had got right down into it. All the time I was doing it and putting antiseptic on, he never said a word; he just stood near the window with his arm on the table reading his Dandy comic. He was an awful one for his comics, he got a job delivering papers and the man in the shop would give him last week's leftovers. Even when he started work, he spent all his pocket money on them. If only he'd set his mind to read some of Johnny's knowledge books instead, they'd have done him a lot more good. But like Johnny, Edmund and Francie, he was stubborn as a mule. Joe could be determined if he'd really made up his mind about something, but he was never stubborn for the sake of it, not like the rest of them.

In 1934, with the money Johnny had been saving from his job, he bought himself a sports bike and joined the Belle Vue Cycling Club. There was a feller in the club called George Armstrong who was an all-round athlete and well known down at the beach where all the boxing and sporting fellers used to go, and he used to get right under our Johnny's skin; Johnny took after his father, he hated boasters and he hated people who made a big fuss, and George Armstrong was both. He was always jogging and puffing and punching the air, even though he wasn't a boxer, and according to our Johnny had never won anything worth winning in his life. He would take his Indian clubs down on the sands and strip down to the waist to show off his muscles in front of the girls, dive off the pier in front of a big crowd, and things like that. He also had a very fancy bike, and one day he said to Johnny, 'The club's too slow for me. They never go far enough because there's too many bints in it. I'm goin' for a tour around the whole country... Land's End to John O'Groats.'

'Are you?' says Johnny in his matter-of-fact way. 'I wish you luck.'

As Johnny's getting on his bike ready to ride away, Armstrong says to him, 'The trouble is, I cannot get anybody to go with.'

'Why not go by yourself, then?' Johnny says.

'What! Ye cannot go on a trip like that on your own! Ye've got to have somebody else.'

'Why's that?'

'Nobody could do it on their own. It's too far. Ye need somebody else in case anythin' goes wrong. Ye might have an accident or somethin' and need somebody to get help.'

'Well, find somebody. I'm sure people would be queuing up for the chance if they knew.'

'What! They're too bloody soft, man. There's nobody in Shields with the stamina for a trip like that. No spunk, that's their trouble.'

'Just you, you mean?'

'Aye, me... Why..? You're not sayin' you have?'

'I don't know. All I know is that if you could do it, I could do it.'

'Right then! You're on! Let's see what you're made of, Robin-son.'

'I don't fancy it.'

'There ye are! I knew it!'

'Two weeks with somebody like you wouldn't be my idea of a holiday. That's all I'm saying.'

'Ahht! Ye don't kid me, Johnny Robinson. You couldn't bloody do it.'

'Right. When do you want to go?'

There and then the two of them arranged to go on this trip around England on their next holiday, and in between times they worked out what way they'd go and what they'd need to take with them and all that sort of thing, even though Johnny couldn't stick him.

When the time and day came that they were to meet at the Lifeboat memorial, only Johnny turned up, with his bike all packed with pans and things; Armstrong was the one who was supposed to be bringing the tent, and he didn't turn up at all. Johnny waited an hour and a half and then took off on his own. He did the whole trip that they were supposed to do together, all by himself, and just slept out in the open because he didn't have a tent... That's the sort of young man Johnny was. Joe would never have done that, he'd have just said 'Bugger it,' and come home; but then, Joe wouldn't have arranged anything like that in the first place.

When a nice shy lass from Tyne Dock called Evelyn Smithwhite joined the club, Johnny was daft about her, and because she hadn't a proper bike and couldn't even ride properly, he bought her one; a 'Ladies Hercules' was what it was called, and he was really pleased with himself when he got it, even though Evelyn didn't even know how to work the pedals. The club went to Barnard Castle for its Easter meet, and Johnny had to keep one hand on his handlebars and the other one on Evelyn's saddle, and steer her all the way there. When they got there, a telegram was waiting for Johnny from our Joe, saying he'd just got back from sea. Evelyn couldn't ride back herself, and Johnny wanted to get home as fast as he could, so he left her there with the rest of the camp, telling her he'd be back on the Monday for her, and pedalled all the way back to Shields to see Joe. As good as his word, he went back for Evelyn on the Monday and brought her back to Shields, by then she'd just about got the hang of the pedals.

We'd all been worried about Joe on that trip because so much had happened to him. First he'd picked up dysentery and had to go into hospital in Durban, and by the time he'd got over it, he'd missed his ship and had to get one that was going to Russia, the SS Goodwood, I think it was. The ship called at a place called Vladivostock and Joe and a couple of his mates had gone to a dance and got into an argument. This turned into a big fight and a gang of Russians jumped on Joe and were kicking hell's bells out of him, when this Welsh crew from the sister ship came in; he reckoned they saved his life. On the way back to England the Goodwood crashed into an iceberg and got stuck, part of the front of the ship had caved in and the only way they could get on their way again was for some of the crew to climb overboard and repair the damage. Joe had been amongst them and it was so cold that bottles of rum had to be lowered over the side to keep them going. We read about it in the papers, it had been big news. So Johnny wasn't being thoughtless when he left Evelyn in Barnard Castle over the weekend, and she did have the rest of the club members to keep her company.

20

In 1935 Johnny and Evelyn got engaged, and now that all the others had just about grown up, Johnny was set on me having something to occupy my mind with, something that would provide for the future; there was still a lot of unemployment around, and talk of war, and nobody knew what was going to happen. Johnny was being sent to work in Cockfield shortly and he wanted to get married first, but he was worried about what would happen to me.

'What about getting a little business of your own, Mother..? Something that will keep you busy and bring in a steady income...but where you wouldn't have to work too hard... I was thinking of a little retail shop maybe...something you can easily handle. We'll give you all the help we can. I'll see that everybody pulls their weight to help you get started.'

I thought it was a wonderful idea, something like that was what I'd yearned for, and I told Johnny I'd keep an eye out for a place; and I certainly did, I looked all over for one. Every day as soon as I'd finished work, I'd set off to do the rounds of property agents and follow up any tips I'd had from this one and that, and before very long a little shop in William Street came up for sale.

As soon as Johnny came in from work I said 'Johnny! I think I've seen just the place! Will ye come with is straightaway and have a look at it?'

He could see I was all excited and he smiled. 'Take it easy, Ma. It isn't going to disappear before we've had our tea, is it?'

'It might, Johnny. It might. I couldn't eat anythin' anyhow, not till I've seen about it. Somebody might come and get it while we're havin' wor tea.'

'Howay, then,' he said, putting his coat back on. 'Let's have a look... You won't be too hasty, will you?' he said as we were walking along the street.

'Don't worry... What I want you to do, Johnny, is to say nothin' till afterwards. Listen to all they have to say and read any books they bring out for us to look at. Leave the rest to me.'

When we got to the shop, which was practically on the corner of William Street, we went in and I told the owners, who looked as though they were husband and wife, that my son and I were interested in buying.

'Is it all right if we have a look around?'

'Help yourselves,' the man said.

So we went behind the counters and had a look in all the bins and on all the shelves and in the drawers.

'Does the upstairs go with it..? We'd prefer a place where we can live in.'

'Oh, yes. I'll take ye up,' says the woman. And she took us upstairs and showed us the bedrooms and the kitchen downstairs and the backyard which was quite big. There were less rooms than Thames Street where we were living, but I wouldn't be needing so much space now the family were nearly grown up.

The shop was small and dark, with the serving counter on the right as you went in; this is where the scales and till were. The woodwork seemed to be fairly sound although the shop was probably several hundred hears old, and the door was solid enough; the bell had a good catchy ring to it. On the shelves behind the counter were jars of sweets, cigarettes, baccy, matches, pins and other things that were most called for; on the other two sides were bread, sugar, tea, and bins of flour, rice and corn.

I whispered to Johnny, 'I could make a grand place of this. You'll see if I couldn't.'

'Well, what d'ye think?' the man asked when we'd had a good look around.

'Before we go any further, I'll need to know how much you're askin'...to make sure we're not wastin' our time.'

He hummed and hawed a bit and then she blurted out, 'Forty-five pound...and that's a real bargain.'

'Forty-five pound..! That's an awful lot, isn't it? Ye haven't got much stock so ye can't have that much business... Some of your bins are goin' mouldy. Ye cannot sell flour in that state, surely.'

'Which bins are mouldy?' the woman says in this aggrieved voice. 'Show me which bins are goin' mouldy!'

'That one there, for a start.'

'Where?'

'That one there with the flour in it.'

'That's not mould! That's just the colour of the tin!'

'This is, though... Look... It comes off with your finger... See... Smell that.'

'Ye always get that! That's nowt. That'd never do anybody any harm.'

'Can I see your books..?' I says to the man.

'If you're serious about buyin' the shop, ye can,' the woman says.

'Oh, I'm serious all right.'

'Here y'are then.'

There were two books and I put them on the counter so Johnny and I could both look at them. 'Mmmm... Aha.... Hmmh...' I still couldn't read some words very well but I was perfect with numbers. After a while I said 'I'm offerin' thirty-two pound, and not a penny more.'

'Oh,' the feller says, trying it on. 'Well, we've got this young couple interested and they said they're willin' to pay the full price. Isn't that right, Nora?'

'Yes it is. They said it was just what they wanted, and that they were very happy with the price.'

'When are they comin' back?'

'Er, er...tonight I think. Isn't that right, Eddie?'

'That's what they said.'

I thought to myself, 'Two can play that game.'

'Fair enough,' I said. 'Ye must take the best price ye can get. But there's my offer... I'll be back tomorrow mornin'. If nobody's taken it by then, and you're prepared to take my offer, I'll take it. If not, I've got my eye on another place just as good.'

The next morning they hadn't sold it, but the two of them argued and argued about the price; he was prepared to come down but she wasn't. However I decided I'd stick to my offer. Johnny was going to give me £40 towards it because I was going to need to have it painted, and I'd need to do a fair bit of work, and get quite a few things, to have it the way I wanted. Eventually it changed hands for £35 and they agreed to move out straightaway and take our place in Thames Lane.

By nine o'clock Monday morning all the girls were at it...Evelyn, our Edmund's girl, Nellie, and our Francie; and as soon as we got started, we saw what we were in for. Things might look all right from the outside, but when you see beneath the surface it's amazing what you find. At one time there'd be a bakery next door, and when we pulled off the wallpaper in the living room, the beetles poured out like a waterfall...black ones and brown ones, big ones and little ones...cockroaches, spiders and all sorts; you couldn't step on the floor without squashing dozens of them with a horrible crackling and squelching. On top of that there were signs of rats and mice everywhere, and we had to try and block the holes up wherever we could find them.

First we chucked out all the old stock; foodstuffs we put in sacks to sell to somebody with hens, the rest we dumped. Then we washed all the bins out, cleaned and polished all the fittings, and scrubbed the whole place from top to bottom. Scarcely was it dry, before we painted it. Now it looked lovely and bright and clean.

I knew exactly what kind of shop it should be for this area. Poor people make good customers; they can't always pay on the dot but they're honest if you trust them, and they can never be bothered to shop around; if they know where they can get all they want handy, that's where they'll go. They like a place they can come in even though they're a bit under the weather, or old and doddery, and know you'll give them what they want, even if they've forgotten what they've come for. They want a place they can come into on their crutches, in their curlers and slippers and sometimes their dressing gowns, and they want to be able to buy a penn'orth or a ha'porth of anything in the shop. They want to know you aren't going to diddle them by bamboozling their little bairns if they send them in with a message. They like to know that when you say you haven't got so-and-so, you really haven't got it; and if you say 'I'll get it by such and such a time or day,' that you'll get it.

I'd made up my mind that I was going to sell a little bit of everything from a pinch of snuff to a big potato; I'd sell a Woodbine and a match for a ha'penny, I'd sell a little cornet with a teaspoonful of tea and a teaspoon of sugar, I'd sell half a loaf of bread and an ounce of margarine.

I was sufficiently well known around the market to get credit, and by the end of the week my little shop was fully stocked. I told the lasses not to put anything in any drawer or on any shelf without asking me; I'd be the one selling it and I wanted to be able to put my hands on everything straight away, I wanted to be able to put my hands on it even if the light went out. I knew which things had to be at the front, and which had to be away under the counter. I knew what would attract customers by its appearance, like fresh fruit and vegetables, bread, teacakes and sweets; and which things...like baccy and snuff...you never need put out because they'd always ask for it, and if they didn't, shoving it under their faces would only annoy them.

Things like seasonings, such as nutmeg, peppers and spice, you could afford to keep out of sight because their smell would do the trick, and in any case, they weren't much to look at.

I had all the usual groceries including bacon, ham and corned beef, and all the common minerals like Tizer and Crawford's ginger beer; I had cough drops, liver pills and lipstick, soap, toothbrushes and TCP; hairnets, stockings, combs and hankies; kettles and pans, cheap knives and spoons, waterbottles, bait tins, bait hankies and bootlaces, candles, mothballs, pencils and pins, brushes and shovels; practically anything, in other words. There wasn't an inch of empty space anywhere, and nothing in the shop was going to cost more than a few coppers.

A business run on these lines in this area couldn't fail. And it didn't. Before the first week was out, I was taking three pounds a day. Folks saw the boxes of biscuits, jars of sweets and boxes of clay pipes and whatever was going into the shop from the vans that were rolling up, and they were coming in to buy before we'd even got it unloaded and on to the shelves. I was open all hours and they would knock on the door at yon time at night when other shops had shut long since.

'Mrs O'Callaghan, ha' ye got some more o' that belly-ache powder? For heartburn? He's bad again. He says it's the water, but I think it's more likely the beer.'

'Can ye spare is half a pound o' lentils? I'm makin' a sup of broth, and I forgot to get any when I was in this afternoon.'

'Just give's five tabs will ye, hinny? I'm reet out on 'em and I'm dyin' for a smoke.'

'I've got to put wor lad's bait up and I haven't a crust of bread in the hoose.'

'Ha' ye got a packet of Aspro's, Mrs Callaghan..? I'm gannin' mad wi' this pain in me head.'

Soon I was changing my sweet windows three times a week, and that's a good sign; I sold an awful lot of sweets, especially ha'penny gob-stoppers, liquorice root, cinnamon, smarties and dolly mixtures. I really knew very little about the kind of business I had now, but I trusted my instincts and I'd tackle anything. People would say to me, 'Francie, if ye put muck in your window, ye'd sell it.'

When the various commercial travellers came in, maybe just for a packet of tabs or an ounce of St Bruno for themselves, I'd say 'Hey, you're from the paper company, aren't ye..? I'll tell ye what... Give's a few packets of pens and some envelopes and pads. I bet ye I can sell them.' And I would. And the next time he came he'd bring a few more and I'd sell them as well, and so it would go on.

I'd do anything to keep my customers happy and make them want to come back to my little shop, and I made it into a lovely friendly place packed with good things; I'd be singing when they came in and the last thing they'd hear when they went out would be my cheery voice or laugh at some joke we'd had together. They were miserable times for ordinary working folk because there was so much unemployment everywhere and the threat of war was always in the air; one day there was going to be one, the next there wasn't, and people didn't know where they were. Either way, they had to scratch for a living so they were glad of anything that gave them a bit of pleasure and cost them nothing, and having a bit of fun with somebody cost nothing.

I soon found out the very poor ones and I'd help them all I could, I wouldn't push them to buy anything they didn't want and couldn't afford. But ones that had a bit of money in their purse, I'd say to them, 'Look at my lovely wavy hair... I bet ye don't know how I got that..? Well, it was them curlers that did it. They're only tuppence a packet and they'll last ye forever if ye look after them...'

Or I'd say, 'How about a new teapot, Mrs Nicholson..? They make a lovely cup of tea. I use the very same meself. Look at the design on the side. It'd brighten any kitchen up, wouldn't it.'

'Well, I would, but I haven't got the money... Smashin' though, aren't they..? I could just see meself with one.'

'Look... Take it, before they all go. I don't know whether I'll be gettin' any more in. It'll only cost ye a tanner a week. You couldn't get a better offer than that, could ye?'

A feller with a short thick stick who was a bit heavy on his feet came in one day and asked for a flitch of ham, he said it was for a funeral reception. He pointed to the best one hanging up in the shop. 'That 'un,' he says. He knew what he wanted all right.

'All of it?'

'Aye.'

'It'll cost ye nineteen shillings.'

'I haven't that much on is, but I'll pay ye next weekend when me son gets paid.'

'When your son gets paid?'

'Aye.'

'Why when your son gets paid?'

'Because he's the only one workin' in the house. But he'll definitely give is the money and I'll come straight in with it.'

'Nineteen shillings is a lot of money, ye know... And I've never seen ye before, have I?'

'Ye can trust is, can't ye?'

'Next weekend, ye say?'

'Aye... You can wait but the funeral won't.'

'How much have ye got on ye?'

'Five bob.'

'I could give ye five bob's worth... Why not take that. It'll get ye a canny bit ham.'

'Na. I need the lot. It's me brother who's died and we're holdin' the reception at our place. Five bob's worth'll gan nowhere with all the friends and relations he has. Me and the wife wouldn't want to appear mean. He wouldn't have stinted himself if it had been me instead of him.'

'Wouldn't ye need the five bob for bread and butter for the sandwiches?'

'Aye, the ham wouldn't be much good on its own.'

'How much bread do you want then?'

'Half a dozen or a dozen, I suppose...dependin' on how big they are.'

I really wanted to help him if I could but he wasn't making it easy.

'Have ye got no surety..? Nothin' at all..?' His clothes were little better than rags; even if he showed me he had something of value, a pocket watch or something... I wouldn't have necessarily taken it but it would have been nice to know.

'Right,' he said, and he swung his leg up on the counter and it landed with such a thump. I thought 'God almighty! What's he goin' to do next?'

He then pulled his trouser leg up and unstrapped this wooden leg which was attached at the knee, and before I could say anything, he'd shoved it towards me, worn greasy leather straps and all.

'That do ye?' he says.

'I don't want it..! What am I goin' to do with that?'

'Hang it up beside your hams. I'll have it back when I bring the money.'

I was going to say something but couldn't think what, and he must have seen by the look on my face that I was flummoxed, and he laughed.

'Don't worry. It's off as much as it's on. You keep it and maybe then ye'll give is what I come for.'

'How are ye goin' to carry it?'

'The bread I'll carry on me back. The flitch I'll wear instead of the leg if ye'll pass is the straps back.'

He was a funny bugger, I'll say that for him. He hobbled to the door and whistled, and two raggy-arsed little kids came in.

'There y'are. Wheelbarrers.'

I gave him everything he wanted, I couldn't do much else, and the leg hung up in the shop for more than two months. Eventually he came with the money. 'Sorry, missus. Wor lad got laid off.' He counted out fifteen shillings and it took him ages. 'It was a bit more than that, I know. But I've got nowt else and I need me leg back.'

Sometimes a gentlemanly sort of feller might come in for a special brand of baccy I'd never heard of, and I'd tell him I'd just sold the last ounce not twenty minutes ago. 'If ye can wait, I can have it for ye this afternoon. But if you're in a hurry, ye might like to try this. It's just as good.' He might be standing wondering what to do, so I'd say 'D'ye smoke much of it?' And he might say 'A canny bit.' 'Do ye..? How much a week would ye say..?' 'About four ounces.' 'Right. Come back tomorrow morning and I'll have all ye want. I'll put a regular order in so it'll be waitin' here for ye every week. You won't need to go lookin' anywhere else for it, because I'll always have it put by for ye.'

None of my stock was wasted, nothing thrown away; I'd a man come around for all the broken biscuits and I got a shilling for those, a pig feller came for any fruit and vegetables that were left over and I got something for those, a dog man came for any meat that had gone off, and if you opened your cardboard boxes carefully you could sell them back for a penny or tuppence. And if you'd had something in the shop a long time and couldn't get rid of it, like an expensive box of chocolates, you'd give it for a Christmas raffle or something like that.

I sold tons of snuff; that and clay pipes I could nearly have made a living out of. Women were the worst for it. I had a little silver ladle like a deep teaspoon and I'd give them as many measures as they wanted, heaped or level, depending on how much they could afford. You learned to give a special little tap against the side so they got just the right amount. It cost fourpence ha'penny for a level scoop, and a tanner for a heaped, so you couldn't afford to spill any. One well-to-do woman came in for three bob's worth a day, 'to clear her brain', she said.

21

Young Francie was fifteen and had been helping me in the shop until it got going but now she wanted to work somewhere else and make her own way. I didn't mind, I could manage on my own now, and they all had to be independent sooner or later. The trouble with Francie was that she was such a smashing looking lass that all the lads were after her and she was a terrible one for them. Because she was the only girl in the family, her brothers were very protective, all of us were, and she didn't like it. I used to look at her shoes every night when she'd gone to bed to make sure there was no soil or sand on them, and the time she got her hair cut our Johnny wouldn't speak to her for a month.

She probably thought what we didn't know about we wouldn't worry about, so when a chambermaid's job at a hotel in Bayswater in London came up and she begged me to let her go, I said 'All right, but see you take care of yourself... And write home every week.'

She was only at the job for three months before she and this Irish lass she'd got pally with left, because the two of them didn't like living at the hotel with all the rules and regulations, and they got a room between them in Camden. Then they got a job at the Cumberland Hotel where they didn't have to live in, and the two of them were having a grand old time.

Although she wrote home the first few weeks she was away, that soon stopped and we didn't hear a word for her for a long time and we were getting worried, so I went to the police station and asked them if they could find her and bring her back. They said they'd do what they could but London was a very big place and they couldn't promise anything. Meanwhile Francie and her pal were having such a great time staying out to all hours, that they kept sleeping in in the mornings and had been told that if they were late once more they were for the high jump. But Francie had made a friend of the chef at the hotel and he had lent her an alarm clock, and when they were bringing it home it had gone off, and neither Francie or her pal knew how to stop it. Right in the middle of Oxford Street it was ringing and ringing like all the bells in hell and everybody was looking at them, so Francie had put it under her coat to try and muffle it and the two of them had started running to get away from all the fuss they were creating. In no time they ran into two big coppers.

'What's goin' on here?' they said. 'What have ye got under there? Where are you goin'? What's your names? How old are you? Where've you come from? Where do you live?'

The coppers weren't entirely satisfied with the answers they were getting so they took Francie and her friend to the station and questioned them some more and found out everything.

'Do you realise we could put you on the next train and send you back to South Shields?' they said to Francie. 'Does your mother know where you are?'

'Oh yes,' says Francie. 'She said I could come. There's no work in the north.'

'Do you keep in touch with her regular?'

Then it came out that she'd been too busy, supposedly having to work all hours at the hotel, and hadn't had the time.

'You should be ashamed of yourselves, the two of you. Your poor mothers must be worried out of their minds.'

Both Francie and the other girl said they were very sorry and would write to their mothers as soon as they got the chance.

'You bet you will!' the sergeant in charge says. You can just sit down at that table, the two of you. And you can pick up a pen, and take a sheet of this each, and write a letter to your parents right now. Otherwise I'm goin' to keep you in here all night.' He then tore two pages off his pad and gave them one each. 'When you've finished, give them to me back. I'll see they get posted first thing in the morning.'

I got the letter a few days later, told the police in Shields, and a couple of days after that two 'tecs came to the shop to say they'd checked on Francie in London and that she was all right, the Cumberland Hotel had a good name apparently.

A few weeks after that, Francie fell out with her friend, left the hotel and went to work as a barmaid in Battersea, and stopped writing again. I was fed up with her antics by now so I got Edmund to telephone her at the pub she was working at, and tell her I was very poorly and she had to come home at once; I knew that was the only thing that would have made her come back. When she got off the train at Newcastle Central Station, I was waiting for her.

'Right, my girl! You're home for good now. You're not goin' anywhere no more, I don't care how good the job is. I've had enough of your malarky.'

Johnny had Evelyn, Edmund had a lovely colleen called Nellie Curran, but no lass could tie our Joe down, he couldn't care less about girls; as long as he had all his mates around, he was happy. The only girl Joe cared about was Francie, and at some time every night he would make it his business to call in at the bar where she was working; she worked in umpteen different places, she was always wanting to try something new and could never hold a job down for very long. Joe would go in, have a beer and have a few words with her, and be off somewhere else; but most nights, and always on Saturday nights, he'd end up at Francie's bar to see her home. If she told him to go home himself because she had a feller that was going to see her home, Joe would say 'Oh, aye. And who's this then?' And then he'd go over and look the feller over. 'Watch yoursel' when you're with my sister, mate. Or you'll be sorry.'

One night Joe was getting himself spruced up to go out when Francie says to him, 'I don't know what to do with myself, Joe... I've got so many boyfriends, I don't know which one to go out with.' This wasn't good news to Joe, he was more lenient with her than I was, and much more than Johnny and Edmund were, but he had his limits, and Francie would deliberately torment him.

'What d'ye mean?'

'Well, take tonight... I've got three separate dates with three different lads.'

'What'll ye do if they all come at once?'

'They're not comin' to the house, daftie... I've arranged to meet them at different places.'

'Where..?'

'Oh, not far.'

'Where though?'

'One outside Ropper's fish-and-chip shop, another one under the big lamp, and the other outside St Bede's... I'm not trampin' all over to meet any feller.'

'When are ye supposed to be meetin' them?'

'Eight o'clock.'

'Somebody's ganna be disappointed, aren't they?' Joe says as he carries on polishing his shoes.

While all this was going on, I'm not saying a word, I'm just getting on with whatever I had to do and pretending I'm paying no attention.

Joe then finishes polishing his shoes, tosses the rag at the shoe box, combs his hair with his hands, and goes out whistling.

'T'ta, Ma,' he says. 'See ye later on, Francie.'

'T'ta, son.'

'T'ta, Joe, ye big daft bugger,' yells Francie.

Twenty minutes later there's a knock on the door and Joe pushes these three fellers in, they're so frightened and embarrassed they don't know what to do with themselves.

'Here y'are, Francie,' he says, and he lines these three poor fellers up under the light. 'Take a good look at them and take your pick.'

He then goes out and you could hear him laughing to himself all the way up the street. Poor Francie... She ran upstairs crying her eyes out and stayed there all night. I made the three fellers a cup of tea and then sent them on their way, I couldn't do much else.

Whenever Joe was short of a few shillings for a beer, he'd walk up and down the shop, all dressed up, picking this up and putting it down, and then picking something else up and fiddling with that.

'I know what you're after, Joe,' I'd say. But you're not gettin' a penny out of me. Ye should make your money last, instead of spendin' it as though ye thought every night was your last.'

'I never had nowt in the first place, so how can I make it last?' he'd grumble.

I'd shut up the shop, say no more, and go into the kitchen and sit myself down to do a bit of darning. A few minutes later he'd come in. Poor bugger, he was right, he hardly ever had any money except when he came back from sea. But it wouldn't stop him getting himself ready as though he was going to a party, there was never a night he'd stay in, not if you'd tied him to a chair and put lead in his boots.

He'd come and sit opposite and start making daft faces.

'Haddaway Joe, afore I clout ye.'

'I've only come to sit and look at the most beautiful girl in the world. There's nothing wrong with that, is there?'

'You're interruptin' is. Ye'll make me stick the needle in me finger.'

'I never said a word. You're the one who's doin' the interruptin'. I'm just sittin' not doin' any harm to anybody.'

He'd start again with his faces, almost stretching the nose off his face, until I could stand it no more.

'Ye'll stay like that if ye don't stop it, ye silly bugger. Then ye'll be sorry.'

'Who cares what I look like..? I'm not goin' anywhere.'

He'd sit there a bit longer and then get up.

'Well, I might as well take me coat off and go to bed. I've nowt else to do.'

'Aye, ye might. And mebbes ye might get it into your head that money doesn't grow on trees.'

Then he'd start doing a bit of shadow boxing and knock the flypaper all over the room till the flies were coming off, and it got on your nerves.

'Stoppit, wor Joe!' I'd raise my fist. 'I'll let ye have it, mind...'

'I've changed me mind about goin' to bed. It's too early. I think I'll stay down and tease you instead. It's more fun.'

He'd try to make me laugh with his daft faces again, and when he saw he was getting nowhere, he'd go out and I'd hear him clattering around in the shop.

'Why don't ye sell beer, Ma?' he'd shout. 'Who wants snuff and nutmegs and stuff.'

Then all would go very quiet and I'd have to get up to see what he was up to. Most of the shop would be pitch black except from where a bit light came in from the street light, and I wouldn't be able to see him. Suddenly he'd jump out and grab me from behind.

'Got ya!'

I'd shriek, even though I was expecting it. 'Get off, ye daft bugger! If I catch ye at that till, mind, Joe, I'll nail your hand to the counter.' I'd pick up the hammer I used to crack the toffee with, and wave it at him. 'I'll rive your liver out by the roots!'

'One day they'll have ye up for the way you've treated me, Ma... And ye know what I'll say..? I'll say "Forgive that poor woman, judge. I was only testin' her." And he'll say "Saint or sinner, there goes a real gentleman."'

I wouldn't be able to take any more of his nonsense.

'Come here. Here's five bob... Go and loss yourself.'

'Ta, Mother.' He'd put his arms around me and be giving me sloppy kisses on the cheek and I'd be trying to push him away. 'There's nobody like ye.'

'There's nobody like you either...thank God!'

Whenever Johnny was in, Joe would get around him much easier than he'd get round me; if I gave him anything I'd always make him sweat first. He hadn't to think money came easy.

Johnny would never ask anybody for anything, let alone drink; if he didn't have it, he'd do without; but it wouldn't stop him giving to somebody else, it embarrassed him seeing people having to ask for things. Johnny always liked to say and do the right things, he always dressed the part and there was nothing he hated more than making a fool of himself. But there was nothing our Joe liked better; he wouldn't let anybody else make a fool of him, but he didn't care what lengths he went to himself.

Johnny took great care of his clothes, always hung them up on the hanger and things like that, where Joe's were always over a chair. Joe was twice the size of Johnny, and he knew how careful Johnny was with his clothes, so he would go upstairs and put on Johnny's' jacket, which only came halfway up his arms, blacken his face with soot, and come down in his underpants. With a dead straight face he'd say 'Right, Johnny. If you lend is anythin' less than two bob, I'm walkin' round the block like this. And tomorrow I'm walkin' into that office of yours with nowt on.'

'Don't be so daft, Joe,' Johnny would plead with him. 'It'll affect Mam's business if ye keep on doing things like this... Howay, man. Act your age.'

'Why should it affect Mam's business..?'

'Because it will... What's she going to say if some customer comes in and says "Was that your crazy son I saw running around the market in his underwear the other night?"'

'Righto then, Johnny. If somebody doesn't give me half a crown by the time I count to ten, I'm goin' outside and I'm shoutin' that Mrs O'Callaghan's got rats in her shop.'

Either Johnny would give him a few bob if he had it, or I would, and then Joe would be upstairs in a jiffy, get changed, and come bouncing back down.

'Had ye there, didn't I..? The two of yous are as daft as a brush.' He'd be nipping our cheeks. 'I wouldn't have really done it, ye know, Johnny...not unless I had no other choice.' He mightn't have shouted about the rats, but he'd certainly have gone round the block dressed like an idiot, he'd done it many a time just for the hell of it.

After a voyage, if the ship had docked in the Tyne, Joe would come home with a dozen or more of his shipmates.

'Howay, lads! In to see me Ma! She's been dyin' to meet yous... Go on! Everybody in!'

'No, Joe,' I'd say. 'Not again... Why can't ye just come by yourself?'

'They're orphans, Ma. Every last one of them. They've no homes to go to.'

'Haddaway! Ye'd say owt but your prayers, wor Joe.'

They'd see I was only having a bit fun with him and they'd be laughing and sitting down and making themselves at home.

'Didn't I tell yous ye'd get a great welcome..? This is Matty, Ma. And this is Tug... Billy, Titch, Freddy, Ginge... There's little Willy over there, the one with the big gob... And of course that waster, Whitfield - Put those crates over there, lads... Where's the glasses, Ma..? I've somethin' special all the way from Istanbul for ye... There now... Drink that.'

'Stout from Istanbul..? Ye must think I'm as daft as you are!'

'That's no ordinary stout, Ma. That's export stuff. That's what the harem girls drink. Puts fire in their bellies for the dancin' and all that... Howay Ma, give's a dance... Me mother's a marvellous dancer, lads. Watch this...' He'd have me by the waist and be pulling and shoving me and lifting me off the floor and singing at the same time.

'Gan on wi' ye! Ye cannot dance at all. Ye never could, ye big flat-footed fool.'

'Howay Mother, I'm ganna learn ye the polka.' He'd still have a tight hold of me and wouldn't let me go.

'Watch carefully, Ma. Just follow my dainty steps... De de de-da-da... That's good... You're gettin' the knack... See that..? What did I tell you boys..? Ye could go round the world a thousand times and ye'd never find one like me ould Ma. Will they, Ma..? Right..! Who's next for a dance with me Ma..? Somebody..? Anybody..? Howay, don't be scared of her... Ah, good lad, Titch... Gan on, son... Tra-la-la, tra-la-la-la.'

Night after night would be the same thing, he knew he could get away with murder when he only had a few days shore leave, and as soon as the pubs closed they'd all troop in, singing and laughing, banging and falling about. Joe thought there was nothing I liked better.

'Into the shop, Dick, and pull down the biggest ham ye can find. Me mother'll show ye how to slice it...'

The feller would come in with one of my hams and give it to Joe.

'Back ye get for some bread and butter... Ma, how d'ye work this thing? It's bust again.. Never mind. Give's that knife, Mick.' He had such a big voice on him and would get himself so excited. 'Right Dick, cut those loaves up and Scotty can make the sandwiches... This'll be really good business for ye, Ma, you'll see. We're goin' to have a real feed tonight, lads. And then me mother's goin' to give us a song. Wait till ye hear her sing "Kathleen"... Howay, Ma. Just a couple of verses to give them some idea of what to expect... "I'll take you home again..."' Howay, Ma..! She used to be on the stage, ye know.'

'Joe! God forgive ye for tellin' such fibs!'

'These buggers wouldn't know the difference,' he would laugh, and the rest of them would all be laughing as well.

When the party was over, which would never be before three or four o'clock in the morning, and there'd always be at least three of them asleep in the chairs or on the floor, I'd tell Joe enough was enough and I wanted no more of it.

'And I mean it this time, d'ye hear..? No more..! I'm sick of the mess and I'm sick of all the carry-on. It was like bedlam in here last night. The neighbours'll have the police one of these nights, I can see it comin'. They say things like "Your Joe back, is he?" I know what they mean.'

'Ah, Ma. It's just a bit fun and - '

'Don't "Ah, Ma" me any more. If you bring one more of your boozy pals to this house, I'll flatten ye. I'm not kiddin' this time. I mean it.'

'All right, Ma. Last night was the finish, I promise ye. Just you and me tonight, eh? A quiet chat between ourselves.''

'That's what I want. You're my son, it's you I want to see.'

He'd give me a hug and a kiss and off he'd go, waving and grinning. But I might as well have saved my breath.

Later that night after I'd closed the shop and bolted the doors, there'd be a tap on the shop door which led into the street, and a voice would come through the letterbox: 'It's me, Ma. Joe. Your favourite son...the one who loves his Ma and never makes any noise.'

'Is there anybody with ye, wor Joe..? Because I'm not lettin' ye in if there is. I can hear somebody laughin'.'

'That's just some drunken fool down the street. Nowt to do with me, Ma. Honest.'

'Are ye sure there's nobody else?'

'Howay man, Ma! It's freezin' out here. Open up and ye'll see if I'm tellin' the truth or not.'

As soon as he heard the bolt being drawn back, all his pals would gather at the door, and the minute I opened it, they'd all rush in led by Joe.'

'Into the back, lads!'

'Get out! Get out, ye waster! I told ye not to fetch anybody back here again! I'm too tired. I want to go to bed.'

'We won't make any noise, Ma. We'll just sing quietly... No dancin' tonight, lads. Any man tries to dance will get both his legs broken.'

'Right ye are, Joe,' somebody would shout.

'How's that for service, Ma?'

'I don't want any singin' either. And I want every one of ye out of here by midnight.'

'We'll be away long before that, Ma... Right, lads?'

'Right ye are, Joe.'

'What'll ye be doin'?'

'We'll probably just have a few hands of cards. We've all got sore throats from last night.'

I wouldn't be in my bed five minutes before they'd start up

singing. Sometimes I'd be so mad, I'd come down and bray him with anything I could lay my hands on...a broom, a picture frame, the breadboard...but it didn't make a ha'porth of difference. Every time I walloped him, the whole lot of them would cheer; and the louder I yelled at him, the louder he'd sing, and sometimes he'd drown me out by cupping his mouth with his hand and whooping like a Red Indian. The more vexed I became, the dafter he got.

'Howay, Paddy. Sing me mother an Irish song to melt her hard heart... Only kiddin', Ma... You'll love this one. It's your favourite.'

'I don't want any more bloody songs..! Irish, Scotch or anythin' else!'

'Please don't shout at him, Ma. He's very sensitive and won't sing till he gets absolute quiet... Give the lad a chance, over there! Let we hear a pin drop.'

Somewhere a bottle would smash on the stone floor.

'Right. Away ye go, Paddy'

The lad would start and they'd all be quiet for a while.

'Now, isn't that lovely, Ma? Are ye enjoyin' yoursel'..? Course ye are.'

If I wasn't up when Joe came in, he would climb over the backyard wall to get in. Then I'd hear him downstairs in the shop and in the kitchen, creeping about. He'd call up the stairs in a loud whisper, 'Ma..! Mother..! Where are ye..? Are ye hidin' somewhere..? Ye've got a brush or somethin', haven't ye..? I know ye have.' He'd be dead scared I was going to brain him in the dark, and I'd be listening to it all in bed and thinking 'By, I must have knocked against somethin' when I was carryin' him. He's a bloody lunatic.'

After he'd satisfied himself I wasn't hiding downstairs, he'd start coming up one step at a time. 'I'm warnin' ye, I've got a gun here, Mother... If ye jump out, and I don't know who it is, it might go off... I'll have to shoot ye in self defence... I won't know it's you in the dark. It's loaded. Don't do anythin' silly, Ma... Ma, I know you're hidin' there somewhere. Say somethin'.'

'For God's sake, shut up and come to bed, ye stupid bugger!' I'd yell from my bed.

Now that he knew he was safe, he'd bound up the stairs, miss a few, and scramble back up; a horse coming up would have made less noise. He'd open the door very slowly and come over to the bed and put his hand on my face.

'Here ye are...all the time pretendin' to be asleep, eh? Stay right where ye are. Your supper's comin' straight up.'

'No, Joe. I don't want anythin'. I just want to be left in peace.'

He'd clatter down the stairs, out through the shop and away to knock up the fish-and-chip shop to see if they had any left-overs. If he had no luck there, he'd come back and hack up some bread and ham from the shop, and make these terrible sandwiches of his; then he'd heat up the teapot and pour out some tea. The whole lot would go on the oven shelf as a tray, and by the time it got to me, cold chips would be floating in stewed tea, or his huge sandwiches would have sprung apart and be soaked.

He'd light the oil lamp and bring it, and black smoke would be pouring out the top. He'd put it down, haul me up so I was sitting, and plonk the tray on the bed.

'There y'are... How's that!'

I'd take one look. 'What the hell's that? I can't eat that..!'

He'd have a hurt look on his face. 'What's wrong with it?'

'Look at it, man... It's nowt but soggy slops.'

'It's lovely, man. Howay, I'll help ye to eat it. I came home especially early to make it for ye. Ye weren't lookin' too good before I went out, I could tell. See..? I miss nowt, Mother. I'm goin' to lie down on the floor beside ye to make sure you're all right. And to make sure ye eat your supper.'

'Ye'll not, ye know! Get out, you silly bugger. Go on! Go to your own bed before I crown ye with it!'

As often as not he would just lie there on the floor and go to sleep, and he'd still be there when I got up in the morning.

One time he came home from sea and told me he'd come into the big money.

'Just say where you want to go, Ma, and I'm takin' ye.'

'Save your money, Joe. I don't want ye spendin' it on me.'

But no, he insisted he give me this big treat, so the two of us got all dressed up and out we went. First of all we into the posh end of the pictures, then we went for something to eat, and to finish up we went to a hotel for a drink. All the while he had me paying because he said he'd forgotten to bring his wallet out with him. On the way back he told me it was all a big joke and he had no money at all. I was so

303

mad I said 'I've a good mind to call the police and have ye arrested. You're nowt but a fraud, and I want nowt more to do with ye..! Now get away from me. I don't want you walkin' along the street beside me.'

When he saw how mad I was, he wouldn't let me alone. 'Ah, don't spoil it, Ma. Ye enjoyed yoursel', didn't ye..? We both enjoyed worselves, didn't we..? Don't be like that, Ma. I'll see ye all right. You know that. I'll never let ye down.'

He could be as thick-skinned as a rhinoceros and no matter what ye said it wouldn't matter; but in some ways you could very easily upset him... Every Sunday night I'd fry up the scraps from the dinner for when Joe and Francie came home from Francie's job at the pub, but this particular Sunday when he'd gone to fetch her, he found she'd been asked to a party where this young bloke that Francie fancied was going to be, and Joe would only allow her to go if he went along as well. Francie had agreed, so off they'd went and clean forgot that I was waiting at home with their fry-up.

The night went on into the early hours of the morning and there wasn't a sign of them, and by now all kinds of fears were running through my mind. I was sitting in the kitchen when I heard a noise upstairs, so I picked up the poker and went to see what it was. It seemed to come from the cupboard where the shoes were kept, and I thought I might have a burglar, or O'Callaghan even, so I flung open the door and chucked everything out, including all the boots and shoes, and I was yelling 'Come out, ye bugger whoever ye are! Come out, ye swine!'

Just then, Francie and Joe came in through the back, and Joe, thinking I was being attacked, flew up the stairs and was behind me in a flash. But I hadn't heard them come in for all the noise I was making. There was no light and I got an awful shock when I saw this big feller behind me, so I jumped up and clobbered him hard with a boot.

'It's me, Ma..! Joe... What's the matter..? Howay, down. You're all right. There's nobody here but Francie and me.'

He brought me downstairs into the kitchen, but I'd had a hell of a fright and I was in no mood for any more of his carry-on, and I turned on him.

'You, ye bloody great fool! You're the cause of all my troubles!

I'm sick of ye..! Sick! Sick! Sick!'

He had his mouth open, not knowing what to say, and I smashed my fist into his face with all my might.

He stood there, big tears rolling down his cheeks. 'What d'ye do that for?' he says.

'I'm fed up with ye, that's why. Ye make me so vexed. Ye never take any notice of what anybody says to ye.'

He never said a word, he just sat in a chair and cried, and I left him to it, I thought maybe he'd learn his lesson this time.

At weekends Johnny, Joe and all the boxing lads, used to go down to the beach with their girlfriends, and their banjos and fiddles, make a bonfire, cook some grub, have a few bottles of beer and a singsong, and have a whale of a time. One weekend Joe met a lass there called Renee Parker, and he brought her home for tea one Sunday to see what I thought of her, and she was a really nice girl. After a while the two of them decided to get engaged so I told Joe he'd have to go and see Renee's mother to ask her if it was all right, so he did. But Renee's mother wasn't any too pleased about it. 'Our Renee's a Protestant, and you're a Catholic, aren't you?' she says to Joe.

'Aye, that's right but it makes no difference to me. I'll marry her in any church she wants.'

'Well she's not getting married in a Catholic church, I'll tell you that. And I'm not having her changing to any Catholic religion... When Renee gets married, it'll be at her own church.'

'Well all right. But there's no "have to be" about it,' says Joe. 'The fairest thing to me seems to split the difference and get married in a registry office.'

'What..! No daughter of mine is getting married in any registry office..! Renee wants a proper wedding... Anyway, before you start, how much money have you coming in every week...? How do we know you'll be able to give her a comfortable home and look after her the way she's accustomed to?'

'That depends on what she's accustomed to, I suppose.'

'"You suppose"..! Well I can tell you that's not a good enough answer for our Renee... Look at your own mother... She's parted from her husband, isn't she? Look at the life they've had.'

'I came here to talk about your daughter, not my mother. So ye

305

can shut up about that, because ye know nothin' about my mother! And if that's the way you feel, ye can keep your daughter. As far as I'm concerned, it's finished... That's it, Renee,' he says, and off Joe went, leaving the two of them behind in the house, one mad as hell, the other bubbling her heart out.

'It's all off, Mother,' Joe says when he came back. 'Me and Renee's finished. Kaput.'

'Ah no, Joe... She's such a canny lass.'

But he wasn't willing to talk about it any more so I let it drop.

First thing next morning, who should come into the shop but Mrs Parker asking to see Joe. He was still in bed so I told her to wait until I'd seen to the customers and then I'd fetch him.

'Tell her to go and loss herself,' he says when I went up. 'I couldn't care less about her or her daughter.'

'I'll do no such thing! You're not treatin' anybody who comes to my house like that. Get yoursel' up, this minute! Or I'll fetch her up and she can see what a big soft lump ye are.'

Joe wasn't a stubborn lad but on the odd occasion when he was, nothing would shift him. He just put his hands behind his head.

'Right, ye big bairn,' I said to him, 'I'll learn ye!' and I went down and told Mrs Parker she could go on up. And she did, and she was up there for quite a while. But when she came back down you could see she was very upset. She bought one or two things in the shop, just to be polite I think, and then she went.

Night after night after that, Renee would come to the house and Joe would ignore her and go out without saying where he was going, and just leave her sitting there.

One night I said to her, 'Renee, have ye got no guts..? If a lad did that to me, I'd never look at him again.'

'It's not Joe's fault. It's what my mother said.'

'Aye, I know. But that's over and done with. She never said anythin' that bad that I can make out. I'd be the same if I was in her shoes. You've done nothing wrong to him, and he's got no right treatin' you as though ye had... If I was you, as soon as he comes back I'd give him a choice... Either he shows ye that he loves ye, if he really does. Or he goes his way and you go yours.'

When he came back that night she said everything I told her to say to him, but he just sent her packing. I then told him I was very disappointed and that I wouldn't have him being unkind to her in my house anymore.

'You're not tellin' is who I have to marry, and who not, are ye?'

'Course I'm not..! And don't be so damned cheeky..! I'm just tellin' ye that you're not upsettin' that lass, or her mother for that matter, under my roof.'

But still poor Renee came, and although it got on my nerves her sitting there night after night and me not knowing what more to say, I couldn't make her go away or stop her coming. This went on for about nine or ten weeks and then Joe came in one night and said 'Me and Renee's made it up, Mother,' and they were as thick as thieves after that, and I was glad for both their sakes. Renee had a good job making suits in a Pelaw clothing factory, so she was earning a good bit more than he was, especially as he wasn't always in work; but it didn't seem to bother either of them, she was as easy-going as Joe was, and I knew why she loved him.

22

On the Sunday that war broke out in 1939, the news came on the wireless and everybody rushed outside and there was a lot of shouting in the streets. Joe was getting himself ready for church at the time, and immediately he heard the news he came running down saying he was going to join up.

'What..? Don't be such a fool! There mightn't even be a war yet. They're just makin' threats.'

'It's already started, man!' he says, all excited and laughing.

'You listen to me, wor Joe... If they want ye, they'll sharp enough send for ye. Have no fear of that. You just get on with your own business and wait and see what happens. War's nothin' to cheer about.'

'This one's goin' to be different! We've got planes and bombs and tanks to back us up this time!'

'Who has?' I says to him. 'Who has..? Them or us?'

He thinks for a moment. 'Both, I suppose.'

'Aye... Both..! Ye want to think about that before ye go chargin' off to sign up.'

'Nobody's ganna fight for my mother and sister, but me.'

'Who's askin' ye to fight for we..? We're perfectly all right. Take a look out the door... Is there any Germans comin' down the street..? Gan on! Take a look..! All ye'll see out there is a whole lot of bloody fools shoutin' their heads off... When the Germans start comin', if they come, that's the time to get all hot and bothered... If silly buggers like you go pilin' into the recruiting office, they'll have an army to fight a war with. If yous don't, maybe they'll have another think about it.'

It was like talking to a brick wall. The next day, Monday, without asking Renee or even telling her, he went up to Newcastle to the Army Recruiting Office and tried to get enlisted. They wouldn't have him because he was still on the Merchant Navy's books and they said seamen for the Merchant Navy were going to be just as important. Of course he wouldn't have it, and for three days in succession he pestered them, he said he'd go for nothing if they'd have him. Edmund had volunteered and was going into the Royal Engineers, so that's where Joe decided he wanted to be as well, so he could keep an eye on him, according to Joe. In the finish they took him but said he'd have to wait until they sent for him. He was given four shillings and sixpence signing-on money. 'Blood money', I called it. 'Here y'are, Mother,' he said proudly. 'That's what they're payin' your son to go an' fight for ye. That's how much they think you're worth... Four bob for you and a tanner for our Francie.'

I looked at him and he just stood there. Then he burst out laughing and put his arms around me. 'I'm only kiddin'... You're worth more than all the money in the world.'

One day I read in the paper that his regiment was being called up. He'd been working on repairing one of the bridges across the Tyne for the last three weeks, and he was in bed with a very bad cold.

'Champion!' he says when I told him.

'They'll not take ye in with that cold. Ye'll not pass your medical.'

'Then ye'll have to get is better, Ma. Ye've got to. If I miss it now, they mightn't take is at all. Wor Edmund and the regiment might go without is.'

I think he thought you just went to the barracks, got your uniform and rifle, went off to France, shot all the Germans, and then came back.

He insisted I do all I could to get him well and got himself into a right state about it, so I gave him a mustard bath and sat him up in the big chair with all the blankets I could find, and the oil stove right in front of him, and he sipped India bark with a drop of whiskey, determined to sweat it out before morning time; God forgive me for doing it. He was a very fit feller and the next day he passed A1 and they took him in.

I'd asked him what he was going to do about Renee. They were supposed to be engaged but he hadn't saved a penny, he never saved a thing in his whole life; in the thick of winter he once gave away a lovely heavy overcoat and came in freezing, I don't think he even knew who he'd given it to. I told him Renée would have nothing unless he married her and got some allowance from the Army, otherwise he couldn't expect her to wait for him.

'She can live with me. It'll cost her nothin', and she can be savin' all the time.'

'What about you?' he says.

'I've got all I want here. She's the one who's goin' to need it.'

I'd put a hole in the first half-a-crown he'd ever given me, as I did with all their first wages, that was all I wanted.

'I've got nowt to get married with.'

'I'll give ye the £20 I've given the others to get married. And if you go up to Newcastle, I'm sure Johnny'll give ye £10, same as he gave wor Edmund.'

Johnny was happy to give him the money, just as I was, and when Joe came back from training camp three weeks later on a forty-eight hour pass, he and Renee got married. He went back to camp and hardly any time at all passed before he was home on another forty-eight hour pass, this time because he was being sent overseas.

Edmund spent the last day with his wife Nellie, Joe spent it drinking with his mates...and what a state he was in by night-time. He and Edmund were due to get the half-past ten train from Shields to Newcastle, and then from there to Catterick or wherever it was they were going. Johnny, Renee and Nellie were going to the station to see the lads off, but Johnny told me I wasn't to go. So when Joe came back home from the pub, I told him I was going to say my goodbyes here.

'Ye have to come, Ma,' he says. 'If you don't come to the station, I'm not goin'.' He took off his coat and sat down.

'Get up.'

'Na.'

He wouldn't have talked to me like that if he hadn't been so drunk, army or no army.

'You're only makin' it harder for me, Joe. Don't be so selfish. Renee's waitin' for ye. So's our Johnny and Edmund. Nellie'll be there.'

'I don't care. I want you up. I want you to see me go.'

He wouldn't be pacified and kept on insisting, and time was gettin on and I knew the train wouldn't wait and he'd be in big trouble if he wasn't on it, so in the finish I said all right. I put my hat and coat on, and because I hadn't time to find my shoes, I was still in my slippers when we went out the door and up to Mile End Road. All he had on belonging to the Army, was his khaki greatcoat and his hat, he loved those two things; I don't even know whether he was entitled to wear this peaked cap, the kind the officers wear, that he'd bought for himself; underneath he had his white shirt and civvy clothes on. When he'd joined up he'd given everything he owned away...coat, suit, tie, shirts, shoes, even his socks. All he had left, was what he stood up in. I think he thought that when he came back a big conquering hero, he'd be well off and would be able to get himself all the latest clothes.

All the way to the station he was stopping every couple of yards and stepping in front of me to talk in his daft, drunken way, making me laugh and making me cry at the same time.

'Come on, Ma. We'll look after each other... You can make me meals and do the washin', and I'll kill all the Germans.'

What a carry-on, I thought we were never going to get there. I kept thinking 'If only I can get him to the station, when he sees all the other lads goin', and wor Johnny and Edmund and the lasses, he'll be all right, he'll be happy to go.'

When we got to the station it was packed solid, I've never seen anything like it, I never knew that many people lived in Shields. Some were crying, some were shouting and laughing, and some were saying nothing at all; others were so drunk they could hardly stand. I couldn't imagine how they were going to pack all those soldiers on the train that was just standing there waiting, it seemed to be chock-a-block already. All Joe's mates were there and Joe was tearing the buttons off his army coat and giving them away for souvenirs. It was a sight I'll never forget as long as I live. All of them were just bits of bairns dressed up as soldiers, just like my two were, apart from a few older ones who looked like regular soldiers. Some mothers were seeing off more than me, and for them it must have been worse. Most of the soldier lads were laughing and shouting and kissing and waving and hugging and shaking hands and trying to be brave. And here was our Joe bubbling like a big soft kid.

'I'm not goin' to leave ye, Ma... I'm goin' to stay and look after you instead.'

'No you're not, Joe. You're goin' with wor Edmund and the rest.'

311

'I'm not. I'm stayin' here.' He was hanging on to me with his great big arms around my neck, hugging me to him. I couldn't get him off, and it was breaking my heart.

'Get on that bloody train, ye bugger, ye! You were the one that wanted to go and fight for me, weren't ye? You were the one who said nobody was goin' to fight for your mother but you, didn't ye..? Well get on with it, and don't be such a bloody coward! The sooner ye get the job done, the sooner yous'll all be back again... Go on, away with ye... I'll clout ye if ye don't leave go.' I was slapping his face to bring him to his senses and great big tears were rolling down his cheeks.

'There's no need for that, Ma. I love ye and I don't want to go... What do I want to go to France for? I won't even know what they're talkin' about.'

I was pushing and shoving to try and get him on the train and poor Johnny didn't know what to do with himself, the little wise head just didn't know what to do or say. Then our Edmund says 'Howay, Joe. We're gettin' on now. Let's away.' Edmund was as smart as anything, with all his gear on, a real soldier. Joe was a proper mess.

We had just got him on to the train when Francie came running up, she was working in the bar of the 'Banks o' the Tyne' at Tyne Dock and the boss had let her away early so she could see her brothers off. As soon as she saw him on the train she started yelling 'Joe! Joe..! Ye can't go without givin' is a kiss..! Joe!'

'Oh, Francie,' I said, 'I wish ye hadn't come. We've had a terrible time gettin' him on the train. And now he's seen you, here he's comin' off again.'

Edmund got off with him and they both kissed their sister, and then with their arms over each other's shoulders, the two of them got back on again; by this time the MP's were shouting at the stragglers to get on the train, and blowing whistles all over the place. But when the train pulled out, Joe was shouting and waving and laughing along with all the rest of them.

That was the last I ever saw of Joe. Little did I realise when I'd been shouting at him and calling him names and belting him, that I'd never see his big daft face again.

Two days later we got a telegram from him saying he was having to hide to miss parades because he had no badges, khaki shirts, battledress, boots, gaiters, belt, haversack or anything else that he'd been issued with...he'd left them all at home and every time he was stepping outside his barrack-room he was having to borrow kit from other fellers... and could we send it on to him as soon as possible. We found all of it under his bed in his room, including the proper little side-hat he was supposed to be wearing...they'd taken his peaked cap off him. So Renee and me packed it all up, put it in his kitbag, made a big parcel, and sent it off straight away.

We heard from Edmund that Joe had got himself into trouble over people trying to boss him about. Apparently this sergeant had jumped the queue in the canteen and Joe had told him to get to the back and the sergeant had said something nasty to him, so Joe had sloshed him and ended up in the guardhouse. It was a good job it was wartime and they were in a hurry to get them over to France, or goodness only knows what they'd have done to him for it.

After the two lads had gone, I had this terrible dream about Joe... He was hanging on to the side of this sinking boat and was trying to climb up the side, but every time just as he got a hold on top, he fell back in again and these great big waves were coming over him and smashing down on his face. In the dream I was saying 'Don't worry about them waves, Joe! Just keep your head up, son. Keep tight a hold and ye'll be all right,' the way you'd say to a bairn learning to swim. But when the waves finally cleared away, there was nothing left except bits of the boat sticking up with no Joe hanging on to it, and miles and miles of black sea all around.

I woke up one morning and the keeper ring that the boys had bought for my fiftieth birthday was in three pieces. I told Francie about it and she just said 'Don't worry, Ma. You're probably only rememberin' that dream our Joe used to get...' When he was a little bairn Joe used to have this dream about drowning and clinging on to my hands. All of a sudden, in this dream, I'd let go and he'd sink and go down to Hell. He never talked about it when he grew up, but he always said drowning was the one way he didn't want to die. I must have had this dream of his on my mind, when I had mine.

Joe and Edmund hadn't been away for more than a few weeks before we heard on the wireless that their regiment had gone across to Dunkirk, and it was scarcely a week after that, that the telegram came to the shop. It had the War Office stamp on it and I told Francie to read it out. I saw the tears in her eyes and I said 'Read it, Francie! Quick! What is it..? It's Joe, isn't it? It's about wor Joe. I know somethin' bad's happened to him... It has, hasn't it?'

'Missing. Presumed Killed' is all it said.

'"Missing. Presumed killed"..? That doesn't mean they know for sure though, does it? "Presumed" doesn't mean ye know for certain... How can they know..? Just because they can't find him, they've no call to go round sayin' he's been killed... Not wor Joe... That's the easy way out... It'd be a lot different if it was their bairns they were talkin' about! They wouldn't be so hasty to come to conclusions then!'

I just couldn't believe he was dead. He could just as easy be in a prison camp... He might be wandering around France suffering from loss of memory. Nobody had seen his dead body. Nobody ever has.

After the telegram I worked harder and harder in the shop, cleaning, tidying and sorting out the stock, shifting things around and re-arranging Joe's things, as though that might make a difference; and I scrubbed and scrubbed on my hands and knees to try and rub things away and bring them back to what they once were. I'd never been one for fortune-tellers and people like that, I thought they were just for gullible people; but whenever I heard of one now, I was going to them, and sometimes they raised my hopes and bucked me up a bit and sometimes they made me feel worse.

Johnny and Francie knew Joe was dead but because they wanted to pacify me, they wouldn't say he was definitely dead and they wouldn't say he wasn't either. They didn't know what to say to me, poor bairns. They were just as upset as I was. And so was poor Renee...poor Renee. She was a nice lass but all we could think about was Joe, in our hearts he was still ours.

All of my customers knew and they would keep asking if there was any news, but after a while they all stopped.

Once this foreign seaman came to the door, I think he was Polish by his way of speaking. He says 'Mrs Robinson?'

'Who wants to know?'

He gave this funny name so I was none the wiser.

'It is, and it isn't... Why? What d'ye want?'

'You got son...Johnny Robinson?'

By now Johnny had gone away as well. I'd never worried about

Johnny because I knew they wouldn't dare take him because of his eye. But as soon as the news had come about our Joe, Johnny had gone straight down to the recruiting office and got himself in. He had left Evelyn and his two bairns, Joe and Johnny, neither of them three years old, and joined the Service Corps. How he managed it, I'll never know. Buggers with squints and flat feet were being kept out, so how or why they took him, why they took my son when he only had one eye, God only knows. I should have known better; Johnny would do any mortal thing once he'd made his mind up, and the first I knew was when he came to see me in his uniform the day before he was sent abroad. He was now in Belgium, Edmund was in Greece or North Africa, they were never allowed to tell you very much.

'Yes, I've got a son called Johnny,' I said to this seaman. But I don't know what that's got to do with you. And I'll tell ye this: don't dare tell me anythin's happened to him, or I'll claw your bloody eyes out!'

'He big man? Very strong?'

'He's strong all right, but ye wouldn't call him big.'

When this feller was describing him, I was sure it must have been Joe he was talking about. He seemed an honest man and he wasn't asking for anything.

'This man is fighting man.' He put his fists up to show what he meant.

I could feel my heart going.

'Yes, yes. Go on!'

'He take out of sea. He safe. He ask me come see you and tell.'

I could have dropped dead on the spot. 'That's wor Joe..!! Francie! Francie!' I went yelling up the stairs. 'It's wor Joe! He's alive! Quick!' I was so excited! It was the best news I'd ever had in my life. I was picking things up and putting them down. 'Come on in, son..! Come in..! Come and tell us all about it... Make him a cuppa tea, Francie. And then get yourself over to Renee's. She's the right to be the first to know. Then go to Nellie's. And then we'll have to send up to our Evelyn's... No, I'll tell you what... I'll make him a cuppa tea. You fry him some eggs and a bit of bacon... Now, sonna, tell we all that ye know. I want to know everythin' right from the start. Take your time so ye miss nothin' out.' I was hugging and kissing him as though he was my own, it was as though he had carried part of Joe in with him.

When Francie came in she brought a photo of Joe with her. She walked straight up to the feller and said 'Is this him, mister? Is this the one you're talkin' about?'

'No,' he said straightaway. 'Not him.'

'Who is it then?' I yelled at him at the top of my voice. 'Who are ye talkin' about? If you've come here to - !'

He burst into tears, put his arms right around me and cried like a baby, and I knew he was sincere, I could see he was so upset at raising our hopes for nothing; he was saying all these words in gibberish, but you didn't have to be Polish to see he knew he'd made a terrible mistake. As it turned out, he'd been telling the truth, only he'd been talking about Geordie Robinson's lad, Bob. So I got Francie to take him around to Geordie and Lizzie's to tell them that their lad was safe and that this feller had seen him and spoken to him.

Although I didn't get to know about it for a very long time, not three weeks before this had happened, Francie had been working in a bar and this soldier had come in wearing the Royal Engineers badge; Francie had asked him if he had ever met a bloke called Joe Robinson.

'Spike Robinson, ye mean..? Aye, I knew him, pet. But he went down off Dunkirk. He was on one of the last ships to leave the beaches. The Jerries dropped a bomb on it and all the men who weren't killed, jumped into the water. Another ship that was already packed came by, and they got as many of the shipwrecked ones on board as they could. Not five minutes later, a bomb went down the funnel and the boat broke in two halves and sank in less than a minute. Not a soul was saved, not a single one. They all went down. Terrible it was... Terrible...'

Francie had then burst into tears and the soldier had said 'Was he your boyfriend?'

'He was me brother.'

The poor feller couldn't finish his drink, he didn't know what to say so he went out and didn't come back. Francie never told a word of this to me because she knew it would have crucified me, but that's why she wouldn't have anything to do with the Polish seaman until she'd showed him Joe's picture.

In the October of 1940 Francie met a big handsome sailor called Dave Duncan, and typical of Francie, she'd only known him a few weeks before she wanted to marry him. He was supposed to be an orphan but I didn't trust him, so I made Francie go up to Scotland, which is where he came from, to check up on him and make sure he wasn't married already; he seemed to be genuine enough but I couldn't bear a wedding so shortly after Joe. When Francie came back, she said everything was all right and she wanted to go ahead and marry this Dave.

'If ye want to get married, Francie, I cannot stop ye,' I said. 'You're old enough to know your own mind. But I'll tell you this, there's goin' to be no dancin' and singin' and all that carry-on here.' I'd have no oration in my house, I wouldn't even have the wireless playing any music or comedy shows; anything to do with laughing or people enjoying themselves, and it went straight off, I didn't care who was listening to it.

How anybody could get married, not knowing each other for more than six weeks, was beyond me, but Francie was very headstrong; she could be a proper bloody idiot when she wanted, and was more stubborn than all the rest of them put together. I said in any case she'd better go up to Newcastle and see what Johnny had to say; Johnny was on leave after doing his basic training, and was spending it with Evelyn and the bairns in Heaton where they'd lived since Johnny's job with the Public Assistance had moved him there, he and Evelyn had been married for four years now.

'What is it you want me to do?' Johnny had asked Francie, he thought maybe she needed some help with filling in papers or something.

'I've come to get your permission.'

'If you've got my mother's, you've got mine, Francie. I hope you know what you're doing,' that's all.'

The very next day one of my customers came into the shop and said 'Mind, you're a dark horse, Mrs O'Callaghan. You never told me your lass was gettin' married on Saturday.'

I've never been one for going round shouting my head off about what I was going to do and what I wasn't, some people like to know more about your business than you do yourself; and because Francie worked in bars and always had the lads running after her, the tongues never ceased wagging. But this was news to me and I was taken aback.

'Aren't you the busybody?' I says. 'I don't go tellin' everybody things that don't concern them.' I was a bit offhand with her and she probably didn't deserve it, I was just so vexed that Francie had gone ahead after all and not told me.

When Francie comes in, I said 'Is this true what I hear, that you're gettin' married on Saturday?'

'Yes,' she says, perky as you like.

'So, you've decided not to take my advice, eh..? Well I'll tell ye this, Francie... Yous'll get nowt out of me. There's no parties or celebrations goin' on in this house. And that's final.'

'It doesn't matter, Ma. Johnny's puttin' on a reception for we up in Newcastle.'

I couldn't believe it. 'Johnny..? Wor Johnny?'

'He said we weren't to bother you at all. So we're not.'

I thought 'If Johnny's doin' that, he must have a good reason for it.'

'All right then, Francie. All right. Have done with it, then.'

Half an hour later Dave Duncan came in with a bottle of wine. He walked straight through the shop as though he owned it, and into the back. After I'd got rid of me customers, I went in and there he was sitting at the table, grinning like a Cheshire cat. 'I've beat ye, Ma. She'll soon be mine. And there's nowt ye can do about it.'

I grabbed the bottle up and stood there looking at him, for two pins I'd have smashed his face with it. He was a cocky bugger, what with his good looks and his quiet manner of talking, and because he was so big he'd got used to looking down on people. But the grin fast left his face when he saw what I was about, and he ducked right down. I didn't hit him with it, I hadn't made a move. But he had, and we'd both remember that, he'd know better than to make game of me in future. He mightn't have had any mother or father to care what he did or who he married, but Francie certainly had. I put the bottle down out of the way so he'd have to get up and fetch it if he wanted any more. Not another word was said about him taking Francie from me. From then on Dave Duncan was a different feller and I got to quite like him, he had a good sense of humour. In any case, they weren't married any time at all before he was called up.

318

Walter was now fifteen and working as a telegraph boy for the post office, and he looked just the part with his black uniform and red piping with his little pillbox hat; he had this black bike and rode all over the place on it, taking telegrams that filled people's hearts with joy or broke them; there couldn't have been a single house that didn't get a telegram of one sort or the other.

Francie was still living with me but Renee had gone back to stay with her family, and she was probably better off there. We hardly knew her really, and she'd have been able to comfort her family and they would have been able to comfort her better than we could; and I think her being with us reminded all of us too much of Joe.

When the air-raids started we never went in the shelter, we had one in the yard right enough but I didn't care much for them. If a bomb had dropped on that when you were inside, you were a goner anyway, we'd seen the damage they did all around us. 'Ye can please yourself what ye do,' I said to Francie, 'but if I'm goin' to get it, I'd just as well get it here in me little shop, as cooped up in one of those corrugated tin things out there.' Francie felt the same way, so we stayed together in the house and made cups of tea for ones in the shelters. Some of them would have lost their homes in the raid or just heard they'd lost their husband or their son, some would be praying and some would be crying, but most of them just sang songs or played cards. They were nearly all women and bairns. If the men weren't away fighting, they were in the home guard or doing fire-watching; and if they were very old, most of them wouldn't be bothered to get up out of their beds to go out into the damp and cold. 'I'm comfortable here,' they'd say. 'If God wants me tonight, let him take me while I'm in me own bed.'

The German planes hardly ever left us alone. Night after night they'd come over and drop bombs all over the place. They never managed to hit the shop, but the vibrations would sometimes shake the whole street, and stuff would get knocked off the shelves and get broken on the floor. The next morning we'd do what we could to salvage what we could; you could wash the jam off the peas but there was nothing you could do to get the salt out of the jam; all you could do was rearrange your shelves so stuff wouldn't fall off so easily.

One night Francie, Walter and me were sitting down to a plate of eggs and a slice of gammon, the first we'd had in ages, when there was a hell of a bang and soil and gravel from the railway embankment came straight through the window, covered the whole of the table, and completely buried the plates. We just looked at each other and started laughing; at least me and Walter had eaten some of ours, poor Francie hadn't taken a bite. I wouldn't care but that was the second time we'd lost our fry-up; the first time it happened was a Friday night a couple of months before when we'd been lucky enough to get some sausage and bacon.

'Come on, Ma,' Francie had said. 'Let's close up for the night and pop across to the snug for a glass of stout first. It'll do we the world of good. We'll cheer ourselves up and enjoy the sausage and bacon all the more.' So we'd gone across to the snug bar across the road and were only there about twenty minutes before we came back, all the time we'd been talking about nothing else but the sausage and bacon we were going to have, we couldn't take our minds off it. So we'd hurried home and I'd done the cooking while Francie had set the table.

'Put out everythin' really nice,' I was saying. 'Salt, pepper, vinegar and the best knives and forks. Walter, put your comics away and fill the salt cellar up.'

'Oooh,' the two of them were saying. 'It smells great! I can hardly wait!'

'Bide your time. Ye'll enjoy it all the more for waitin' for it.' But it smelt so delicious, I could hardly keep my own mouth from watering.

At last we got everything ready, and the sausage and bacon was done and I put it out on the plates we'd had warming in the oven, being careful to give everybody the same. Oh, how I was looking forward to this... It was a good clear night with practically a full moon, so it was very quiet as far as the planes were concerned and there should be no interruptions tonight.

'Howay, Ma! Sit yourself down!' Francie was dying to get started but wouldn't dare touch it until I sat down. 'It'll get cold if ye don't hurry up!'

'Be patient, Francie. I'm puttin' the pan in to soak.'

No sooner had I come in, sat down and picked up my knife and fork, when there was a knock on the door.

'Who on earth can that be at this time of night..? Go and see who it is, pet. And get rid of them as quick as ye can. We'll wait for ye.'

When Francie went and opened the door I could hear this man's voice. I listened and listened as hard as I could and then I recognized it. 'Oh my godfathers! It's the priest!' Francie was keeping him talking and saying loud, so I could hear, 'Yes, Father. Yes, Father. Oh no, Father. Yes, Father.'

This was to give me the chance to hide the plates. Now I could hear their voices coming closer and I knew she was bringing him along the passage. Quick as I could I whipped up the plates, put them in the pantry, and shut the door.

The minute he stepped into the kitchen his nose went up and he said 'Can I smell bacon, Mrs O'Callaghan..? And sausages..? Bacon and sausages on a Friday..? I surely hope not.'

'Well, I... We...'

'You should be ashamed of yourself, Mrs O'Callaghan..! And you, Frances..! And you Walter...you're old enough now to know it's a grievous sin to eat red meat on Friday. I hope for all your sakes that you haven't let a single morsel cross your lips yet. I only hope I'm not too late... And I can smell drink taken...'

He sat down and went on and on so much that we all felt thoroughly wicked by the time he had finished; he never came that he didn't stay for three quarters of an hour, and you always felt that much worse than you did before he came in; as far as he was concerned, the War only made Hell that much closer.

As soon as he was out the door, Francie rushed to the pantry and brought out the plates; they looked so horrible with being cold and greasy, and what with that and all that the Father had said, none of us could face them. I just picked them up, chucked the whole lot in the bin in the yard, and we all went up to bed.

Ever since I'd left the Thrift Street lodging house, Johnny Graham would find out where we were and turn up every now and again to see if I wanted anything. He'd always helped with the rottenest of chores at the lodging house and would do anything you asked in exchange for a sandwich and a cup of tea, it wouldn't matter whether it was emptying slop buckets, delousing sheets, scraping out burnt and greasy pans or swilling smelly yards; this was his lot, he used to say, he was fit for nothing else on this earth. And although he was only a little feller with a crooked leg and bad asthma, he'd never been afraid to pile in and try to pull anybody off me if I was having a fight with them.

He was clean enough in himself, and as neat and tidy as his raggy old clothes would let him, but there was always a smell coming off him that I don't think he could help, and, poor bugger, he was so miserable. He was difficult to deal with because he didn't know how to go on with people and he'd take advantage of you if you let him.

I don't think anything pleased him more than when he used to mind the bairns while I was about my work at the lodging house; he was good with them because he was patient and gentle in a rough kind of way, and he would play with them for hours on end. In his 'spare time', as he called it, he'd make toy trains and castles from scraps of wood that he'd put aside from something he'd given to chop up for firewood, pieces he thought would be just the thing for maybe a little boat or a sentry. Later on that day he'd get out his penknife and borrow a hammer, and straighten some bent and rusty nails he'd saved up, and then start making whatever it was he had in mind. He wasn't much of carpenter but he'd spend as much time and care on a toy for the bairns, as any Swiss man making a watch.

Sometimes you wouldn't see him for ages and then he'd turn up when you least expected it, this little feller with his thin curly hair and his lame leg, wheezing from the effort of walking. He once told me that when he'd been only a few days old, his mother, who had a bad heart, had fainted and dropped him on the stone floor and his leg had got twisted up. I don't know whether that was all there was to it or not, and I never saw the leg uncovered, but it must have been in pretty poor shape because it was a good few inches shorter than the other, and he always had to wear a leg iron and a big boot to stop him from being lopsided, you could see him coming a mile away. Early on he'd been left an orphan, and what with his asthma and his bad leg he never stood much of a chance. He said he'd served his time in the shipyards, but you couldn't believe anything he said. Mind, he'd have a go at something no matter what it was, if there was a few coppers in it...plumbing, joinery, making gates or cleaning drains. 'Your light needs mendin', Francie,' he'd say. 'There's a hole behind that chair wants blockin' in.' Or 'Them shoes need cobblin'. I'll see to it. You get on with whatever ye have to do. Just give's two bob to get a few bits and pieces.'

You wouldn't ask him to make furniture or anything, you'd usually only give him something that if he made a mess of it, it wouldn't matter very much. He'd just hand it to you or show you what he'd done and you'd know he'd done his level best, even if it looked a right mess.

To his credit, he had so much confidence in himself you couldn't help admiring him, even if you couldn't help laughing at the same time. He mightn't have learned much from his failures, but he was never put off by them. If somebody had asked him to build a house he'd have gone off to borrow some tools and got on with it.

For all he'd been given so little to start life with, Johnny Graham was proud in his own way and always wanted to work for a living even though times were so hard that even an able-bodied man with a trade very often couldn't get work. Because of this he could be very difficult and got hurt very easily, consequently he was a very lonely man inside and never had any friends apart from us. He wasn't without his cunning though, and if ever he and I'd had a tiff he'd always make it up through the bairns; he'd wheedle his way into the house when I wasn't there and ask them how I was, and then when I came in he'd make on he was on his way out, and had only called to see the bairns, not me. Then when I fetched him back for a cup of tea and maybe a slice of jam and bread, he'd make out he was hard done by and I'd treated him very badly. When I had the fish-and-chip shops he'd sometimes show off by coming in when the shop was full, and say 'Gis some fish and chips there, Francie. Piled up.' Then he'd just walk out, eating them, without even as much as 'thank you'.

He was funny with drink. I'd give him money because I felt feel sorry for him, but I couldn't bear to see him drunk because he couldn't hold it. He'd be falling all over the place and because of his bad leg, nearly always hurt himself; then he'd start shouting and bawling and crying, and he'd go on for hours with his nose running and getting himself into such a mess.

The time little Johnny was in the eye infirmary, Johnny Graham never missed a day going up to see him, and he always took something even if it was just a lemonade top with a bit of string through it. If they wouldn't let him in, he'd wait outside the window with a little packet of black bullets or a toy he'd just made; he wouldn't let me give it to him, if the window wasn't open so he could toss it through, he'd take it all the way back to the lodging house and bring it every day until he got the chance to give it to him himself. I knew they didn't like the look of him at the hospital, and when they wouldn't let him in I'd lift little Johnny up to the window to wave; he'd be as happy as Larry then and he'd be holding up whatever he'd made and pointing to Johnny to let him know who it was for. If ever they did let him into the ward, he'd always have his hand behind his back pretending he hadn't brought anything, and he'd tease little Johnny right to the very end; that was his way of showing his affection.

When young Johnny was twenty-one, we'd had a bit of a party for him and his 'Uncle Johnny Graham' came. He'd waited until all the presents had been handed out, and all the time he was just standing there grinning with his black teeth and his hand hidden behind his back, then he walked over to the table where Johnny was standing, pulled out this little bottle of stout and plonked it in the middle of the table, right on top of all the other presents.

He must have learned the speech off by heart because he says 'Happy birthday, Johnny, from your Uncle Johnny Graham. I hope ye enjoy every drop and that it'll make ye a very happy man.'

The war had been going on for nearly three years when Johnny Graham came to the shop one afternoon, and he was very quiet. I hadn't bothered with him because the shop had been busy, and after a while he said 'I think I'll have to get on home, Francie. I don't feel too good.'

'Right ye are, Johnny,' I said. 'I'll probably see ye the morrer.' And I thought no more about it.

He went to his bed that night and was dead the next morning. The lodging house had been closed a long time and he'd been living in this tiny little room, all neat and tidy with next to nothing in it except the things he'd made...little pictures done with crayons and coconut shells done up like doll's faces that he had up on the walls.

Because he'd died from being gassed, people said he'd done away with himself; but I didn't believe it. His memory had been going and sometimes when you were talking to him it took a while for things to sink in, but in my opinion he wouldn't have done a thing like that. The police went to the house and they had an inquest on him and it was said there was a leaky gas pipe. In the end it was a matter of one guess against another, only God would know what really happened.

I buried him because he didn't have anybody else, and I had an awful job getting him into sacred ground; he hadn't been to church very often, if ever at all, and nobody knew what church he belonged to. I went to the Catholic priest because that was my religion now, and I felt that in any case, if I was paying I should have had the right to choose; but he was quite nasty about it. In the end I managed to get a minister from another church to do it, though not without a bit of a kerfuffle. When we got back from the funeral, we got on talking about Johnny and how funny, how awkward, and how canny a little feller he'd been, and how he probably couldn't have done any more with his life, or been any other way, considering all he set out with.

He'd always loved it when the bairns called him 'Uncle Johnny', and they all did, I saw to that. And they all loved him; you couldn't help it, even though he was a proper little waster at times. I remembered the time we were living at that awful place behind the Robin Hood, and he'd somehow got himself all the way up from Shields one night, and was shouting and bawling and rolling drunk in the street. 'Francie..! Francie..! Me Francie..! Come oot. I want to see ye!' It was just after the trouble with the neighbours and young Johnny had been very embarrassed for my sake. I was sitting in the chair and saying to myself, 'Go away, will ye..? Go away..! Haven't we got enough without you actin' on and bawlin' your silly head off!' Johnny had then gone down and told him off and told him to go away. I think it nearly broke our Johnny's heart having to do it... And young Francie remembered the times years later when he would sometimes meet her from work at dinner-time and take her home and make her a meal...or what he called a meal, he never ever had anything but scraps; he'd be so proud to be taking her back and would be telling everybody they met that she was his niece.

23

Food had become so scarce the Government brought in rationing, and what a curse that turned out to be... Apart from the fiddle-faddle with tiny wee coupons...and you had to account for every single one...Weights and Measures Men were all over you, and even sealed packages of food were taken out and checked. One day I got in big trouble.

My back had been bad for about ten days, and because Francie was working in a bomb factory in Birmingham, I had to take on an assistant, a girl of about thirteen or fourteen she was. One afternoon I said to her, 'I'll have to go and lie down for a while, pet. But first I'm goin' to give ye a little job to do, then ye can have the afternoon off to go to the pictures... What I want ye to do is weigh out the flour in that big sack and put it into these paper bags. Use the scales and measure out a dozen half-stone lots, and a dozen quarters. The rest in pounds. Pour it into the bags and fold the tops over like this. And then put them on the long shelf... Right, let's see ye...'

She seemed to know what she was doing so I said 'That's it, that's the way. Do them all the same way and give's a shout when ye've finished.'

A couple of days later I was serving in the shop when a very posh lady came in, well spoken she was and just as well dressed, and definitely no ordinary customer; I'd never set eyes on her before.

'I'll have one quarter-stone bag of flour, one quarter-pound of sugar and two ounces of tea, if you please,' she says.

'Right you are, madam.' I got what she wanted and put them on the counter. 'Will there be anythin' else?'

'No, thank you. That will be all.'

'Grand. I'll just wrap them up for ye. I'll get some clean brown paper to save your clothes. The flour's only just been put up and there might be some on the outside.

'No, thank you. I shall take it just as it is. How much is that?'

'That's funny,' I thought. But she paid, picked up the bags, and went out. Five minutes later the Weights and Measures Man came in, I knew who he was all right.

'Do you own this shop..? What is your name..?' He knew very well it was my shop and what my name was, he'd been in many a time. 'I want you to weigh these items there right in front of me. On those scales... Now weigh that... Now this... And this... Now weigh all the bags of flour on your shelves.

While I was doing it, I had customers coming in and out and wondering what on earth was going on, and I felt a proper fool, but there was nothing I could do except ask them to come back later.

He then weighed samples of everything in stock with his own scales that he took out of his case and put on the counter... Out of a total of about a hundredweight of flour shared out in bags, there was one and a half pounds short.

'Do you realise you have been selling food underweight, Mrs O'Callaghan..? And that that means you have been overcharging? And it is a very serious offence in wartime?'

'No, I most certainly didn't...I didn't know they were under-weight, I mean... I don't know what to say... It must be an accident. I wouldn't do it intentionally on purpose. Maybe it's my assistant that I've had helpin' with the weighin' out. She's only a girl and she was probably hurryin' to get finished... I'll empty them all back and start again. I'm very sorry. Ye can watch me do it properly if ye like. I'll do every one right now.'

'It's too late. We already have proof that you have sold a member of our staff short measure.'

'Yes, but you saw yourself when I was weighin' it out that it was only a tiny little bit in each bag. It wouldn't amount to a few tiny grains hardly. And the one your lady got was the worst of the lot. A mistake was made, I can see that now. Fetch her back with it and I'll be glad to give her her money back.'

'It's too late, Mrs O'Callaghan. You shall be hearing from us in due course.'

A fortnight later I was summonsed to go to court on two charges...one for having stocked goods in short measure...and one for having sold them. When I got there, they wiped the floor with me. They made a big scene of it, with the Weights and Measures Man and the Weights and Measures Woman speaking in loud posh voices so everybody could hear, saying I'd cheated them. They didn't see fit to mention that I'd offered to make good my mistake but that they would have none of it.

You'd think I was no better than a guttersnipe to hear the way the judge talked. I was standing there listening to his high sounding words, and although I couldn't understand them all, they shook me up badly. To think that anybody could say such things about me and treat me like a common thief... Of course it was wrong for anybody to cheat poor people, and my customers were certainly poor, but for him to suggest that I would, or even could, treat my own kind in this way, made me sick to my stomach. I was shamed, not ashamed. It certainly hadn't been deliberate on my part; God knows it, and he's my real judge.

When I got my chance to say something, I told him that in thirty years of dealing in different kinds of business, nobody had ever made such accusations against me before... But when you're ignorant like me, what difference does it make... Them with their highfalutin' talk that always makes them sound right, and you with your common way of speaking that always makes you sound wrong. I was fined and I came away with my head down. What would my customers say when they came in to the shop? What if they never came back...?

Johnny was home on leave at the time and told me to just carry on as if nothing had happened, that way we'd soon find out what my customers thought about me. So I opened the shop as usual the next day and nothing seemed to be any different and nobody said a word. A couple of days later two policemen I knew came for the fines.

'Were you two there?' I asked them. 'Did ye see it all..? Did ye hear what that judge said?'

'Forget it, Francie. They're all doin' it... All the big shops are... Only they get away with it.'

'But I wasn't..! I wasn't tryin' to get away with anythin'!'

'Don't fash yoursel', lass. There's a war on. There's more things to worry about than that.'

'Loyalty and tact,' was what Johnny said about my customers, just them two words, and he was right. They were poor but good people and I never met better. They weren't in a position to start any wars, yet they were the ones who suffered the most; they lost their homes to bombs, their men folk to bullets and shells, and yet they were always full of concern for their neighbours.

Apart from being had up in court, and even though my customers mightn't have minded, I could never forget, and my little back-street shop never again gave me the pleasure it used to. It was awful having to decide who could have this and who could have that; you only had so much to go round and you felt really sly having to say to people, 'Now don't tell anybody, but I might be able to let ye have so-and-so, if ye come in at such-and-such a time...' The unlucky ones would always find out that they'd missed out, and all sorts of rumours would be flying about a load of bananas come in or a box of fireworks; people keep coming in and asking about them and you'd have to tell them something.

Rations might have been allocated fairly on paper, but not in reality. Some people needed more than their entitlement, and some needed less; and the swapping and selling of coupons that went on was something I had no control of, although I tried my best to do the proper thing. I held one hundred and eighty-two ration books, and all the collecting in, adding this and subtracting that, cutting them out and sending them in to the Food Office, always troubled me. People would carry them around in their purses or pockets for so long, till they got the money to use them, that they'd get all crumpled up and torn and you couldn't read them properly. Pages would get pinched or lost and people would then have to make do with far less than their full share, and sometimes you'd be giving them food from next month, knowing they were going to be in trouble when next month came. Sometimes the coloured little squares with their horrible little numbers hadn't been cut properly and you had to decide whether to give them the full square or half, or none at all. Some people didn't trust themselves with them because they were worth money, and they'd ask me to look after them for them. To me they were the most precious things in the shop and I was terrified in case they'd get pinched or a bomb would drop on the shop and they'd all be burnt, and then all those people would have to go without; so I hollowed out the part of my gas-mask that was supposed to keep the gas out, and put all the different ones' ration coupons in; if there was an air-raid, even if you brought nothing else out with you, you had to have your gas-mask or you could be fined, and nobody would pinch a gas-mask because they were government issue and worth nowt to anybody.

Travellers and delivery men would call and ask me if I could use an extra sack of sugar in exchange for a few tins of fruit or salmon or something which wasn't on ration. Perhaps they would have a few extra pounds of sweets to swap, but they would always ask for the normal price, and I always sold it at the normal price. These people, ordinary men and women, were only trying to help somebody out, they weren't spivs, but it was still against the law. How I went on with things like that, was to put the names of all my regulars in a hat and make a draw each weekend to give the winner the chance to buy the odd extra tin of biscuits or box of chocolates that might have come my way during the week. When whoever it was won, their name was crossed off the list so that in the long run, everybody won. Then I'd start off a new list and do the same again. It was great to see their happy smiling faces when their number came up.

Coupons weren't vouchers, they didn't buy anything, they just allowed you to buy something if you had the money to go with it, and it was heartbreaking to see people having to leave their rations of bread unclaimed just because they couldn't afford to pay for their entitlement. Others would come in begging and pleading for extra bread or dried milk because their bairn was poorly, and I wouldn't be able to give it to them even though three or four loaves might be going stale in the bin...I had to hang on to them in case their rightful owners eventually came for them. No method of rationing is fair because everybody's needs are different and they change from day to day, and it turns people against you because they always think that no matter how great the shortage, you yourself must have plenty of everything.

Even though I'd always been very careful with money and never spent more than I had, all of a sudden I was finding I couldn't pay my debts; and try though I might, I just couldn't discover the reason for it. There was a war on and times were hard, but people still had to eat and I was still in business, and prices were still the same.

Every night as soon as I closed up I'd empty the till, put all the money on the table, count it and put it in a biscuit tin. Then I'd get out all the different bills the various travellers had left when they'd brought their stuff in, and put them in another one...I didn't use the bank or the post office to pay my bills, I paid everything by cash so that at any time I would know exactly how I stood...Then I would count out the correct money for each bill and tie both together with an elastic band, and then put all the different bundles inside my leather attaché case which I kept in the bottom of the pantry in the kitchen, ready for when the travellers called for their money. Any money that was left over, I'd stuff into another gas mask and put that in the case as well. This way all my money was in the same place.

What was happening though, was that a few days after I'd paid the various travellers, one by one they'd come back and say 'I'm sorry, Mrs O'Callaghan, but I seem to be short of a few pounds.' They'd show me what they had in their hand, and they seemed to be right, and so I'd have to make it up to them. I knew they couldn't all be coming the game, so the next time I put up the bundles, I'd take the elastic band off every one and count it again to make sure I hadn't made a mistake. But every time the bundles were right. Then I noticed the profit money in the gas-mask was going down.

I checked and rechecked every night, and then if Francie was home, I'd get her to do it, and then to make absolutely sure I'd make us both do it all over again together, and sometimes we'd be up to one o'clock in the morning doing it. One night Francie lost her temper and said 'Mother, you're makin' me a nervous wreck. I'm sick of it..! Money! Money! Money..! That's all you ever think about... It's comin' between you and your wits..! It's always right when we check it... You know that as well as I do... The business just can't be the gold mine you seem to think it is.'

'Don't you dare to talk to me like that, my girl..! Of course it's right! Haven't I been sayin' so all along..? Somethin's happenin' to it after we check it. Somebody's pinchin' it out of the gas-mask. That's what's happenin'... Do you mean to tell me ye think I love money for its own sake, ye little fool..? D'ye think I like runnin' me fingers through it, or somethin'..? It's money what keeps we alive... Anyway, I'm goin' to set a trap, that's what I'm goin' to do. I'll catch the bugger! And I'll skin him alive!'

When the delivery men brought their stuff, they always went behind the counter to stack it up, and then they'd take away the empties. Uptil now I'd always trusted them to get on with it without standing over them. But from now on it was going to be different, I was going to check everything and everybody that came in and out. And nobody was going to go behind the counter any more; I blocked up the way through with bins so that even friends and relations couldn't get by. Every time after a delivery, I'd go and get the attaché case and open it up and check that all the money was still there. And it was. So either one of them was playing it extra cute, or it was somebody else, somebody I hadn't suspected, maybe one of the customers.

One morning, a nephew of mine came in and tried to squeeze through to go into the back, all the relations were in the habit of coming and going as they pleased, they'd been used to going into the back and making themselves a cup of tea whenever they were passing the shop. He was just about to shift the tins, when I stopped him.

'Don't move anythin',' I said to him. 'Just leave them where they are and stay put where you are.'

'Why? What's the matter, Aunty Francie?'

'Nobody crosses that counter. Not any more.'

'But I just wanted to use the lav. I'm dyin' to go.'

I could hardly stop him from doing that, so I said 'All right. But ye'd better be quick about it.'

He was in and out in less than five minutes and away out of the shop, and I never thought any more about it. But a little while after, I had to go into the back for something, and on my way in I saw two ten bob notes lying on the floor. I rushed straight to the attaché case... Out of every bundle, at least one note had been taken... Now I knew, and I was boiling. Just then one of the 'tecs I knew called in for a packet of Woodbines and says 'What's the matter, Francie? Ye don't look very pleased with yourself.'

'I'm not either! I've just had some money pinched.'

'I know who that'll be. That'll be that nephew of yours. I've just seen him goin' out. I've had my eye on him for a while. He's a right shifty character, that one. I'll go and nab him. I've been dyin' to pick him up.'

He grabbed his cigarettes and turned to go out of the shop in a hurry.

'No, ye won't! Ye'll do nothin' of the sort on my account... You lot can be funny buggers as well, when ye like. You'd give your own mother away if it suited ye... I'm keepin' me tongue between me teeth. If it is him...and I don't know for sure that it is yet...I'll deal with him in my own way.'

'All right, Francie. Suit yourself. But if ye change your mind, ye only need to say the word, and I'll have him behind bars before he knows what hit him.'

Less than an hour afterwards this nephew's wife came in. She wanted to go in the back as well, but I stopped her short.

'Ye've gone far enough,' I says to her as she was getting ready to pull a bin out of the way.

'What d'ye mean?'

'I mean just what I say. No more, no less.'

'What's the matter with ye?' she says, all agitated.

'Nowt's the matter with me!' I says, feeling myself getting madder and madder. 'This isn't some half-way house, that's all. I'm sick of just anybody walkin' in and out of my house as though they belonged.'

'If ye've anythin' to say, why don't ye come out with it?' she says all cheeky like. 'Instead of insultin' people.'

'Right!' I says. I wasn't going to get a better offer than that. 'For a start, I'd like to know where your man gets all the money to buy ye your fancy coats, from? Where he gets it from to buy his big rounds of drinks in the bars? For his gamblin'? And for all the time he spends at the billiard hall..? Have ye ever thought where it comes from...seein' as he's always on the dole?'

'I don't see what it's got to do with you, Aunty Francie!'

'Do ye not, now..? D'ye really not..! Well you get yourself out of my shop and go back and tell that lazy sod of a husband of yours to be back in this shop within the hour. Tell him if he isn't, he'll be behind bars before tea-time.'

'What!'

'I've got no more to say to ye. You just tell him that. He'll know what I mean all right!'

Twenty minutes later he was in the shop with a face as long as a fiddle.

'If I tell the truth, Aunty Francie, will ye promise not to tell the lads..? Please, Aunty Francie. Give me your word on it.'

'I'll promise ye nowt, ye bloody little waster. Nowt but this... If I don't get the whole truth about how you've been pinchin' my money and how much ye've took, and for how long ye've been takin' it, I'll bray ye meself. I'll knock your bloody brains out with me own fist. I don't need my lads to fight my battles for me. I've knocked down a lot bigger and tougher than you.' As I was talking to him, I was shutting the door and turning round the 'Closed' sign. Then I put the sneck on.

'Right! Ye've got five minutes... Get started.'

He was shaking like a leaf. 'I will, Aunty Francie. But please don't tell the lads when they come back.'

He told me he didn't know the exact amount, but that it must have been hundreds, and that he'd been doing it for months and months.

'On my oath, Aunty Francie, I'll pay back every penny, I swear...if only ye don't tell on is.'

'Your oaths don't count for nowt with me, mister. Empty your pockets out!'

He was a grown man and a lot younger than me, but he just stood there and let me feel in his pockets. He hadn't even had the gumption to take out the four tablets of soap he'd pinched.

'What do you want with these, ye dirty little tyke?' I said as I took them out and put them on the counter. 'Don't tell me it's for washin' yoursel'..! Ye'd pinch the shirt of your own mother's back, ye thievin' little swine. Wouldn't ye..! You couldn't pay it back, and ye know it. So don't stand there tellin' lies, ye flamer... After all the hospitality I've give ye...lettin' ye come in whenever ye wanted to, makin' yourself a meal out of the stuff in my pantry and never a penny for it... And ye'd go and do a thing like this to me. This is the way you pay is back... Well, I'll tell ye this... Ye can get to hell out of my shop, and don't ever come back... If I catch ye anywhere near my shop, or my home...I don't care what you're doin'...I'll knock every tooth down your throat. And then I'll let the police have ye, because they want ye as well. They've just been in this mornin'. And don't ever show your sickenin' face to me in the street or anywhere else.'

From that day, if he ever saw me in the street he'd turn back and go the other way.

It had been hard work keeping the shop going all these years, it had had its ups and downs and I'd had good times as well as bad in it, and whether it was a success or otherwise I couldn't blame anybody but myself. After the episode with my nephew the shop went champion right until after the war when the Corporation decided to pull it down along with all the houses round about. I was going on fifty-seven then, my family was all raised and only that little handful, Walter, was still at home. So I thought maybe it was time to take things a bit easier.

Up until the time my husband Johnny died, way back in 1914, my life had been fairly tough and on occasions I'd felt desperate, like the time with the big dog and the time in the lane outside our Alice's, but it had passed in a day or two...maybe I was too young to really know what the word meant. But after Johnny died, and then his father...the only two friends I ever had among the Robinsons...and then at different times during the long years with O'Callaghan, I began to find out. I'm not talking about the grief of losing somebody you love or seeing something awful happen to them. I'm talking about when everything seems to be against you and you cannot see any end to it. At times like that, only hard work and determination got me by. I did it because of my bairns, and how I did it was through keeping the memory of my mother slowly killing herself for us kids, always in the front of my mind. She served as the best example of willing self-sacrifice I've ever known, and it kept me going all through the times I had bairns of my own, knowing I could never let her down and that I could never be called upon to work harder than she did, because nobody could. I made up my mind as a girl of fifteen that I'd do my best never to shame her in her grave; I wouldn't do anything that wasn't honest, and I'd put my bairns above everything and everybody.

I wasn't brought up with customs like first-footing or birthday parties because we couldn't afford it, and it wasn't the usual kind of family because of my father's drinking. My mother never had the time or the energy to go to church and the church was never a great comfort to her, hard work was her God. But she did try to keep Christmas and we always got a stocking, even though it was full of cinders with half an apple or an orange on the top; I never saw a Christmas card until I was fourteen, and even then it wasn't for us, it was in one of the houses I was in service at. The only fun we had was what we made for ourselves, because we never had any toys and there was little time to spare for it; we worked practically as soon as we walked. Yet for all my mother worked herself into an early grave and everybody could see she was doing it, she would no more have liked being called a 'drudge', than I would. She didn't do things because she was made to do them, she did them out of choice; not always with enjoyment, but always gladly.

For the short time I had him, I was happy with Johnny although he was a hard man in his way; he was hard but he was good, and he was every bit as hard on himself, and I couldn't ask for more than that. O'Callaghan was a bad man to me and he hadn't one saving grace as far as I was concerned. All the time I spent with him giving him every chance to mend his ways, was all a waste; they were miserable years, far more so than the war years or the years when I was a girl. It was the bairns that kept my spirits up and made living worthwhile, and it was only when we'd left O'Callaghan and they were grown up, that I was really happy for the first time in my life. There was no strain then, nobody to shove us around...no Mrs Robinson, no Mrs Callaghan, nobody. And during those years there was no real shortage of money. Those few years until the War when I lost our Joe, were a gift from God.

Epilogue

My name is Joe Robinson, 'young Joe' Robinson, you might say, and Francie Nichol, later Francie Robinson and then Francie O'Callaghan, was my grandmother. Francie's life did not end at the end of the Second World War, but her story as she told it to me, did. So I will finish it for her as best I can.

My first memory of Grandma O'Callaghan, as we always called her, was of a jolly rosy-cheeked and robust woman serving behind the counter on the right as you went into her little shop in William Street. It was 1940 and I was two and a half years old. The bell used to jingle- jangle when the door was opened and like magic it always made my grandma appear from somewhere; either she would come down the very steep stairway at the back of the shop, come in from the kitchen beyond the stairs and through the back of the shop, or she would straighten up from bending down behind the counter, always with a smile and a twinkle in her eyes. I had no idea then, and would not have been able to comprehend it, of the life she had had; nor would I know about it until many, many years later. For me, she began then; she began as this very good-humoured, buxom, loving, tough person, very different from my mother who was shy and physically almost frail by comparison.

'Come here and let's have a look at ye,' she would say, coming from around the counter and bending down, but making me toddle over to her.

'Howay then! Come on, me bonny bairn.'

When coaxed and encouraged by her stamping her foot and her lovely girlish laugh, I managed to make it across the floor, she would sweep me up in her powerful arms and hug and kiss me. Almost immediately the shop bell would go as a customer pushed the door open.

'Hello, Mrs O'Callaghan. Is that one of your grandbairns..? Aah, isn't he canny..? It is a he, isn't it?' There wasn't a whole lot of difference between the way mothers dressed their boys and girls or did their hair at my age.

'Why aye! This is wor little Joe, me first grandbairn. Wor Johnny's lad.' And then turning to me, 'Yes, he is. Aren't ye, lover?... Now just you wait there a minute, and as soon as I've seen to this lady, I'll see if I can find somethin' for ye.' I might have been only two and a half but I knew what that meant, and I'd be raising my eyes to scan the sweet jars even before she had set me down. Grandma never kept a customer waiting, no matter how long it was since she had last seen you, and she switched between the role of grandma and shopkeeper as easy as wink.

That shop was the most exciting place in the world to me, the culmination of a journey by tram and bus, by foot and by human carriage, all the way from the big city of Newcastle. Although I didn't realise it then, it was the snuff and tobacco, nutmeg and spice, sweets and fresh bread...few of them packaged and sealed...that produced the wonderful aromatic blend that made it like no other shop, like no other place on earth.

Behind the dark wood counter were the little drawers in which she kept spare money for the till: notes in one, silver in another, and bronze coppers in another. On the counter itself were the constantly used cast-iron scales with their brass pans and weights cluttered nearby. Most important of all, that was where my grandma stood reigning like a working queen over her demesne, sleeves rolled up, big hands smoothing her pinny, a greeting on her lips.

Behind her was the wall with its shelves of sweets, cigarettes, snuff, tea and sugar, all items for which there was the greatest demand. On the opposite side of the shop, in the relative darkness, were the sacks of potatoes and other less exciting things, and from the ceiling hung a gas light and a number of busy fly papers. Straight ahead, beyond the business part of the shop, were the stairs to the bedrooms. Further along was the kitchen with its fireplace and iron oven at the far end, and a very worn armchair on either side of the hearth. On the right of the kitchen was a sideboard with a small cupboard above, and on the left, a small table by the window which looked out on to a small yard. In the yard, and over to the left, was the washhouse where 'Uncle' Johnny Graham would sit on a small cracket, working on two red, very basic, wooden train engines that he was making for me and my younger brother Johnny who was eighteen months old. Uncle Johnny was small, slightly monstrous with his huge and fascinating boots that had iron rods coming out of them that went up inside his trousers, and, probably because he didn't have an easy way with children, rather frightening. His black clothes were stained and a strong, not altogether unpleasant, smell came off him. Further down the yard was the lavatory with its scrubbed white, split wooden seat that could give your bottom a bad nip, its chain with a home-made ring handle, and its cut-up, rust-stained newspapers jammed behind the thick water pipe.

The Second World War was on and the only time my little brother and I would be here would be on a Saturday when my mother and father would come down to visit their relatives, primarily Grandma O'Callaghan in her shop, and Granda and Grandma Smithwhite who lived in Whitehall Street near Tyne Dock. My father would usually catch Granda for a quick gill at the Stanhope on his way home from his plumbing job, but he'd be itching to get down to see his mother.

It was on such a visit to Shields, a visit that never lasted very long, never long enough for a meal because nobody had time for that, that I remember seeing my Uncle Joe. He was on leave before going to Dunkirk and had come into the kitchen in his beloved greatcoat, probably the only thing he liked about the Army. He had been to see his pals and had come to see his brother Johnny, my father, for the last time, though neither of them knew it. On the table he had a bottle of brown ale, and he had poured out a drink for my father and himself into two white cups. They had been talking together and my father had gone out into the shop in answer to his mother's call. Straight-away Uncle Joe grabbed one of the cups and made me take a sip. It was bitter and appalling, yet there was something slightly alluring about it. I wasn't taking fluid through a teat anymore, and was being introduced to all sorts of things like sarsaparilla and sweet milky tea, but had certainly never tasted anything like this. I must have screwed my face up because Uncle Joe had a wonderful grin on his big well boned face. He was totally different from my father...I was still trying to absorb the fact that I had a brother of my own, a creature who wasn't just an extension of myself but a separate entity with likes, dislikes and desires that would frequently conflict with mine... That this big tough unbespectacled fellow who talked rougher and with

339

more hesitation than my father, was just as much my father's brother as 'very little Johnny' was mine, was something I couldn't have comprehended; even 'Uncle' Johnny Graham was more easily assimilated

When Grandma called for Uncle Walter or Uncle Joe, it was very different from the way she called for my father. 'It was, 'Wa-alt-er! Come here, this minute!' or 'Wor Joe! Come here, lad!' With my father it would be more like, 'Johnny... Can ye come here a minute, son?' in a quiet voice, and everybody knew the difference. When Walter heard we were here, he would clash his bike against the wall outside the shop, and before it had slithered down on to the pavement, would be through the shop and into the kitchen to make sure the pile of Dandy comics he kept under the cushion of the armchair, were quite safe. Then he would smile the beguiling O'Callaghan smile where pleasure was always reflected in the eyes.

The episode with the beer was the clearest recollection I have of Uncle Joe, and it might well have been the impact of that one mouthful, rather than his wonderful face, that provided the anchor that makes the whole thing still so vivid in my mind. Shortly after that he was sent to Dunkirk from where he never returned. Shortly after that my father perpetrated the only deceit in his life, in order to pass the eye test and join up to avenge the death of his brother. Naturally I knew nothing of this at the time. All I knew was that before long, he also was in uniform and far, far away.

From then on we saw little of Grandma O'Callaghan. Apart from anything else, my father had made my mother promise that she, Johnny and I, would all be evacuated. Tyneside, with its huge shipbuilding yards and armament factories, was expected to be one of the Luftwaffe's prime targets. Dutifully, my mother locked the council house doors in High Heaton, an unnecessary precaution, and took us to Amble and a few other places on various local evacuation schemes, but for one reason or another, she was dissatisfied with the hospitality. At one house the woman made Johnny and me sleep on a rubber sheet, so sure was she that city kids would regard beds as places to empty their bladders in. Mam wouldn't have it though, and she'd remove the rubbers and replace them with sheets; and then the woman would put them back on again and there would be harsh words from the landlady and tears from my mother. In the end we

340

left. The next place we went to, Johnny and I couldn't eat the food even though the woman tried to force us; my mother's family had been bakers, and as a consequence Johnny and I had this impediment whereby lousily cooked food made us throw up. She wouldn't let Mam cook anything so we moved somewhere else where Mam didn't like the man. In the finish she wrote to Dad and said she couldn't stand it and would rather take her chance with the bombing, as many others were doing. He was in Belgium and we didn't hear from him, so she just brought us back.

In 1944 my mother was pregnant with brother number two, Michael, and because there were complications she had to go into a nursing home in Gilsland near Carlisle. Johnny and I were sent to stay with Grandma Smithwhite in South Shields for several months, and because there was no way we could get to see our mother, we were encouraged to go and see Grandma O'Callaghan; by then I was seven and responsible enough to take my brother on the trolley bus. Every Sunday after dinner we would either get the trolley on Stanhope Road down to the Town Hall at the bottom of Broughton Road, and from there would walk up the hill to Grandma O'Callaghan's at No. 58. The shop would be closed then, and although sweets were strictly rationed, Grandma would always have a bag of liquorice in all its wonderful forms...straps, pennies, string, logs, twists and, best of all, pipes with red balls for the lighted portion for us to take back to Grandma Smithwhite's. I don't know whether our subsequent passion for liquorice was created by Grandma O'Callaghan, or whether, more mundanely, it had simply been a genetic thing; certainly when our father came back after the War he manifested an affection for Pontefract Cakes, what we simply called 'liquorice pennies', that was close to an addiction.

Grandma 'Calla', as we called her behind her back, was very different from Grandma Smithwhite. Grandma Smithwhite looked rather like a Quaker with her waist-length grey hair and her slightly haughty dignity. She was very kind, but strict and no nonsense, and whenever Granda Smithwhite broke wind whilst asleep in his rocking chair after a session at the Stanhope Hotel, she would wake him and say 'Shush, Jack..! The bairns..!' 'Tell them it's that lorry up the street,' he would say without even opening his eyes. Grandma Calla was firm enough as well, but she loved a bit of carry-on and would chase us all over the place with a shovel or a poker, shrieking with laughter.

After one of our Sunday visits, Johnny and I were waiting for the trolley bus back to Grandma Smithwhite's, when we decided we could no longer tolerate the 'rudeness' of the black statuary outside the Town Hall, which featured half-draped semi-nudes; every week we would feel obliged to turn around and stare at them for periods of up to twenty minutes, if we had just missed a bus. So the two of us, one seven years old and the other six, each taking a different 'black lady', climbed up and smacked their 'bare bots' as loud and as hard as we were able, in order to teach them a lesson. Whether it was the first stirrings of public spiritedness, or of some deeper, baser thing, I really don't know to this day, but I do know that during the following week when we were at school, a policeman called at Grandma Smithwhite's in answer to a complaint. Had he gone to Grandma O'Callaghan's, I can only imagine what her response would have been. Eventually the rude ladies were taken away and remained away for quite a spell. By the time they were returned, Grandma O'Callaghan was still there, but Johnny and I had grown up and were long gone.

Both my father and Uncle Edmund returned safely from the War, and my father resumed his previous occupation with the National Assistance Board, and Uncle Edmund and Aunt Nellie set up a greengrocery business in Denmark Street near the centre of Shields. Every Saturday afternoon at four o'clock when my father had finished doing 'his papers', work he had brought home with him from the office, he would get the 'Number Six' which was a single decker bus from Worswick Street, and go to South Shields to see his mother and two brothers; his sister Francie had emigrated to Australia with her husband 'Duncan' and their little boy, David.

My father would stay for tea and Grandma would pull out all the stops to make him the best meal of which she was capable. And once she had served it, she would stand at the kitchen door, pinnied and ready to fetch him anything he wanted, arms folded, watching him eating, with such a contented smile on her face, the way only a proud mother can. And even though he was now used to cooking of the highest standard at home, he would eat every bit and roll his eyes and keep saying 'By, this is grand, Mother.' And she loved it. Mam would say to us, 'You know, your Grandma gives your poor Dad rabbit week after week, and he doesn't really like it.' But it didn't matter. We all knew Grandma thought he liked it, and that had she given it to him every day of his life there would never have been so much as a grimace out of him.

After tea Uncle Edmund would arrive and he and my father would sit at opposite ends of the sofa, and call in Uncle Walter for his weekly court-martial. Uncle Walter was only nineteen or twenty and his trouble was that he liked a good time, and during the week he would inevitably cause my grandmother some distress by the things he got up to. One week he and some of his pals had got drunk, dived off the pier, and one of them had got drowned, and there was a lot about it in the local papers. But he never seemed to learn, hence Saturday was judgement day. He would sit between my father and Uncle Edmund while they cross-examined, lectured and thumped him. Then he would get up, red-faced and close to tears, straighten his gaudy tie, run his fingers through his shock of wavy hair, and off he would go to meet his pals and chalk up a few more debits for the next week. Whenever our whole family went down, it would be on a Sunday rather than a Saturday, and under these circumstances Uncle Walter's case would be adjourned for a week.

When Grandma had to give up the William Street shop, she started charring for different ones; she wasn't of a pensionable age yet and she wasn't inclined to 'just sit on me behind'. There weren't any lodging houses any more but there were enough old widows with big houses and plenty money who appreciated having somebody like Grandma to clean and tidy for them. She didn't earn much, and though several at different times said they were leaving her something in their will, things like that weren't meant to be taken too literally, I suspect they were said mainly to achieve the effect of a bonus.

Ever since Gertie had returned to her mother Lily in Hull, she had kept in contact with her Aunt Francie, visiting when she could, or writing letters. The whole family loved her, but nobody more than cousin Johnny, and had it not been for the fact that they were related, something might well have developed between them; as it was, he was always the letter writer from 'Aunt Francie's side'. Gertie had never been hale and hearty and even during the time she lived with her Aunt Francie and the family in Frederick Street when they had the fish-and-chip shop, she was always getting colds and sore throats and it would take ages for her to throw them off. One day, evidently after the National Health Service came in, she wrote this undated letter:

9 Emily St
Heston Rd
Hull

My Dear Auntie

I hope you are feeling much better.
John said you were not so well but there is one thing I
am pleased to hear and that is you have given up work.
I wonder how long for. I should get your teeth out as
early as you can because they might injure your health.
Mother gets her false teeth this week.
You will think I have been a long time in writing but
I have been very ill. In fact all arrangements were made
for me to go in the hospital. The taxi was ordered and
everything but at the last minute I would not go and then
mother wanted me to go to bed at home and I would not.
I thought Ralf ought to look after me and I am in bed
now and he is bad with the flu. It was dropsea, Auntie,
and it even reached my head. I had a fat face just like a
pig and the pain was sending me silly, but thank God I
am almost better so I will close now with the promise of a
cheerful letter next time.
Best love to all.

It was the last time my grandmother heard from her, and shortly afterwards she died; she had been suffering from 'consumption'. TB was a scourge then and there was still no cure for it.

Every Christmas Day Grandma would come up to Newcastle for dinner and tea, and my brother Johnny and I would kid her on about how much she ate, and she would take it all in good part; in fact there seemed no limit to the amount of kidding she could take. The trouble was with our father; when he was present you had to be very careful what you said, we had more leeway with our mother than with our grandmother.

Not long after the War my father and mother went for a week's holiday to Scarborough, and Grandma O'Callaghan came to look after Johnny, Michael and me. Although Michael was in his cot, for some reason Johnny and I were put in our mother and father's bed with Grandma in the middle. On the first night Johnny and I were lying in bed, and Grandma had got into her nightie and was leaning forward to pull back the covers to get in herself, when her very ample bosom was revealed, and Johnny and I, ex-little-guardians of public morality, burst out laughing. This was the only time I can ever recall Grandma O'Callaghan raising a hand to us, and she raised it and lowered it several times, quickly and hard. The next night, before she said 'Look away, the two of yous! Look away!' we were already turned away, me strictly to the right, Johnny to the left, with eyes screwed up so tightly it was a wonder we didn't do them a permanent injury. From then on we never saw a single bit of her from the time we went to bed at night, till the time we went down for breakfast the following morning.

My father was well thought of at work and every now and then he would be up for promotion. He was very discreet when he talked to our mother, but Johnny and I had very sharp ears; we could be playing with our tanks on the floor and reproducing all the sounds of modern warfare, arguing over what territory on the carpet belonged to whom, and still hear every word that was being said. We gathered that to get on in the Civil Service, sooner or later you had to go and do a spell in the 'Home Counties', a place a long way from home; places like Perth and Yarmouth were also mentioned from time to time. But though he was ambitious within the bounds of decency, Dad never took any of them. I am certain that not wanting to live any farther away from his mother than Newcastle, had something to do with it. I think Mam would have gone more readily; in fact she would have gone anywhere with him, and I am sure that distance from her mother-in-law would have proved no bar at all...Although Grandma wasn't possessive in any way that we kids could detect, but she never made any bones about the fact that Dad was her favourite, and she would brook no more criticism of him than he would of her, and that would definitely include my mother. The O'Callaghans...Edmund, Francie and Walter...accepted their mother's partiality with amazing grace, treating it at worst with good humour, and at best as though it was entirely deserved. But it sometimes put Mam out a bit.

Uncle Joe's wife Renee married again and we lost contact with her, I suppose some thought it was for the best. Uncle Edmund and Aunt Nellie remained in Shields where they expanded their family to two boys and a girl, and expanded their business to include chimney sweeping. I think Uncle Walter got tired of being the whipping boy and joined the Rhodesian Air Force for a while before realising there wasn't much freedom there either, and went to join Francie and Duncan in Australia. Many years later I met up with Walter in Australia. He had settled there and never got married, but lived with a succession of women who had been battered by their husbands or had in some other way fallen foul of life. He still complained about the Saturday-night court martials in Shields which he irreverently called 'nothing more nor less than a "kangaroo court"', and he was a dreamer's revolutionary.

When she was seventy, Grandma went out to Australia to spend a year with Francie, Duncan and Walter, and it was only then, with the degree of documentation that was required, that she discovered her true date of birth. For as long as she could remember she had always thought she was a month older than she really was, and whenever she'd had the wherewithal to celebrate her birthday, she'd always done so on the 18th March instead of the 18th April. It didn't matter very much then, and after getting over the initial surprise she realised it wouldn't have changed her life, and just laughed it off.

When Grandma had gone to Australia, she had let her house for the year she was to be away, to a couple she knew well; but a few months after she left, they were offered another house, took it, and hastily got a replacement to take over their own obligation. When Grandma returned, it was to find that the new tenants had painted the whole place a dreadful red; it didn't look like a home any more, it looked like some kind of opium den. She couldn't even bear to sleep in it until she had completely redecorated it; but like everything else, she took it in her stride and when you went down to see her she would joke about it.

A few years after Grandma returned she was joined by Aunt Francie, because Duncan and Francie had split up.

On the afternoon that Uncle Edmund and his son Edmund had been on a roof top cleaning a chimney, and O'Callaghan's funeral procession had passed by in the street below, they had just turned away and got on with the job. When Walter heard about it, he had shouted 'Hip, hip, hooray!' Grandma didn't go. She knew about it but said she'd washed her hands of him years ago and wasn't going to make a hypocrite of herself now just because he was dead; the priest would be saying he was this and he was that, and there wouldn't have been a mention of what he was really like.

In 1972 my father entered hospital in Newcastle for a gall bladder operation, and I drove down and brought Grandma and Aunt Francie up to see him. Grandma was now eighty-three but looked much younger; her face was full, her complexion ruddy, her hair showing only a few grey hairs, and her voice was strong and full of good cheer.

Confident that Dad would make a good recovery, and having satisfied Grandma's concern that he would be all right, I suggested we go back to my home in Gosforth for some refreshment, perhaps a glass of stout for Grandma, a sherry for Aunt Francie, and some sandwiches.

I had never seen Grandma drink before, and she only took a few mouthfuls, but she really seemed to enjoy the atmosphere. Normally she never got out of her house in Bywell Avenue in Shields where she lived with Francie, because her legs would not support her; even the local priest was doing a kind of Kitchen Mass at her home in Shields to ensure she remained in a state of grace, and to humour him she was going along with it. As she was sitting there, perfectly content with one sandwich and one drink, I suddenly realised that in my thirty-four years I had never had a conversation with her; in the past, all communication with her had been in the form of greetings and banter. What little I had learned about my father and his family, I had learned in my childhood and entirely from my mother who had always been a story-teller in the quiet narrative manner, talking about families as though she were reading chapters from a book. My father had never told me a single thing either about his own life or his family's.

As Grandma sat there and I asked her about my father, simply for the sake of chatting, she began to talk in the most marvellous way, not at all like my mother who never let feeling get in the way of the narrative. As she talked, she laughed, she cried, her voice trailed to a whisper and then rose into a song as she called out the cries of the Tyne fish-lasses before this century opened. I sat there and could hardly believe it. I had heard Maori storytellers and Irish sean-chaíanna with their highly crafted though formalised skills, but never anything like this. Her expression was changing to that of the character she was talking about, her arms were going this way and that, and she was telling us of things I had never heard before because my mother would not have known about them.

After I had taken Grandma and Aunt Francie home and was driving back to Newcastle, I made up my mind to see if writing her life story would be a realistic proposition. I worked in the bacteriology department of the Royal Victoria Infirmary and was doing research connected with my work most evenings of the week, but I felt I just had to give it a try; if I waited until my research was finished, it might well be too late. I suggested it to my wife Judy who, whilst being enthusiastic, pointed out the obvious difficulties including how taxing it might be for Grandma. But the following night, having worked out a rough plan, I went back to Shields and put the idea to my grandmother, and she agreed without any demur.

From then on, several times a week I went down to Shields as soon as I finished work, with a notepad and biro and a cassette tape-recorder I had bought for the purpose. Grandma was always ready and eager to get started by the time I arrived, and never once put our session off or curtailed it. Sometimes we talked at home, sometimes in the car at the beach if it was warm, and at other times we went to the nearby Marsden Inn and sat all evening with a small drink each. The trouble with the Marsden was that within five minutes of my setting the little recorder on the table, or getting out my notepad, even though we had discreetly tucked ourselves away in a corner, Grandma was such a wonderful raconteur that the whole place would fall silent, and I would look around to see everybody looking our way and listening intently to every word she was saying; it didn't matter whether they were courting couples, old men, or groups of workmen supposedly playing dominoes.

Within a year I had written the book in a biographical third person format and started sending it to publishers in the North East, feeling that if anybody was going to be interested in it, it would surely be a local one. It was a slow process of sending and waiting, and Grandma, who had thoroughly enjoyed our sessions and clearly loved to talk about people long gone but still part of her, was now left alone. I was getting on with my scientific research and Judy was sending off the manuscript for another six weeks whenever it came back; and come back it did, though I couldn't understand why.

One night Judy and I went to see 'Joe Lives', a one-man musical featuring John Woodvine, which was based on the life of Joe Wilson, a nineteenth-century Tyneside poet, that had been written by Alex Glasgow, a local writer and folk-singer. We were both very impressed with the whole thing, not least with Glasgow's obvious sympathy for the poor class, and that night when we came back I wrote to Alex Glasgow with a view to having him make a musical out of the biography I had written of my grandmother.

Alex agreed to look at it and a few days after I had sent it to him, telephoned to say he liked it very much but that it deserved to be published as a book, and could he show it to his friend Sid Chaplin, the well-known Tyneside author. Within a week I received a letter from Sid asking if I would like to go to his house and discuss the manuscript which he had now read. I went around that same night to meet a very gentle man in his sixties, apparently in poor health, who was kindness itself. He made some suggestions as to how the manuscript might be improved, and offered to send a few sample chapters to a publisher friend of his in London.

Ten days after that I got a letter from John Bright-Holmes, the chief editor of George Allen & Unwin Ltd, to say he would like to see the rest of the book, and little more than two weeks later he wrote to say he would consider publishing the book if I would re-write it in first person, reduce its length, and work with one of the firm's professional readers who had already seen the manuscript and commented favourably on it.

At first I thought I was perhaps being asked to make some quite considerable compromises; after all, I was aware of 'artistic integrity' and that sort of thing. On second thoughts, I wondered if such things might be as elusive as the Holy Grail in the real world; maybe it was a good story but I hadn't done justice to it. However, if I were to write it in first rather than third person, all the purple prose passages, all the outpourings of an educated mid-twentieth-century man would all have to go, and the vocabulary and descriptions would have to be limited to that of a partially literate nineteenth-century woman. All this was exacting enough, but having to defer to an Oxbridge lady called Chloe Green, who sounded on the telephone exactly what I expected Virginia Woolf would have sounded like, made it look as though I was in for the literary equivalent of a series of cold showers.

The way it worked was that I would send the material to John Bright-Holmes, who would pass it on to Chloe Green, who would make her edits and then return them to John Bright-Holmes, who would consider them, add his own comments, and then send the whole lot on to me. It was all a very civilised business, made so as much as anything by John Bright-Homes's urbanity, and for me, at least, the whole process was edifying.

One day I received the letter from George Allen & Unwin that I had long been waiting for to say that the book had been accepted for publication, and after work that night I went down to tell my grandmother the good news.

After that, things swiftly moved in all directions. The PR lady, Joy

Hill, arranged for serialisation in a Tyneside newspaper, for the Daily Express to do a full page feature, for George House of Tyneside television to do a news item, for Independent Television's George Taylor to do a feature on his sports programme on the boxing interest, for Robert Robinson of BBC 2's Book Programme to give it a spot, and most important of all, for BBC Television to do a serialised dramatisation of 'The Life & Times of Francie Nichol of South Shields'. The Head of Drama at the BBC, Bill Slater, came up to Newcastle and I met him at the Central Station for a drink before going down to Shields to meet my grandmother.

I knew nothing about being an author, and I knew even less about the theatre, about the adaptation of books for television, or how the BBC operated. And my grandmother was relying on me entirely. When I took Bill down to meet my grandmother who was waiting with her face shining, and the kettle on, they instantly took to each other. He was handsome, beautifully spoken and well mannered, and she was affectionate, funny and frank. The sight of the Head of BBC Drama embracing and kissing my grandma in her little council house in Bywell Avenue, South Shields, was something I will never forget.

From then on I ferried all sorts of people down there, including Martin Bell who was working for Robert Robinson, various national and local journalists, photographers and other people whose contribution to the whole process I wasn't always quite sure about.

Then Eric Davidson, the new director of the planned television dramatisation, and Doug Mawson the sound engineer, came up to begin work and every day we would drive down together to my grandmother's. Doug would set his reel-to-reel tape recorder going and Eric, using a proof copy because the book wasn't out yet, would get my grandmother to tell the whole story again, drawing her to expand on what she had told to me. Aunt Francie was always there to attend to Grandma's needs which appeared to be negligible...she never once asked for a break for any reason...and Aunt Francie was the one responsible for silencing dogs, kids, and ice-cream vendors who came down the street and invaded the space on Doug's tape that was being reserved for 'Francie, Reel 2, Take 4'.

All day and every day my grandmother talked and talked, and always on cue, like somebody born to it. At lunch-time Eric, Doug and I would repair to the Marsden to give Grandma and Aunt Francie some time to themselves, and both Eric and Doug, who had always worked independently and had never met before this assignment, said they were amazed at my grandmother's memory, her stamina and her powers of speech. She could be stopped in mid sentence, if the reel finished or if there was some interruption such as the gas meter man at the front door, and pick up exactly where she left off...the place, the time, the event and the emotion. It was then, watching from the sidelines, that I realised what a wonderful theatrical talent she had. There had never been any indication of it throughout all the years I had known her, at least not to mine or any of the other untutored eyes around her, and I knew she had never been to a play in her life and that she hardly ever watched television or read anything. Yet here was this talent as wonderful as her character and as wonderful as her life. She wasn't histrionic or temperamental or anything like that, but she certainly warmed to the attention she was getting.

The world my grandmother lived in prevented her from grasping the significance or insignificance of the people who were coming to her house and making such a fuss of her and managing her at the same time. But she knew from their posh accents that they came from a different, more powerful world than her own, and she respected them. She respected them and she was affectionate to them and they responded to her. From the outset she told anyone who came in to just call her 'Francie', and she called them by their first names, and it was all so easy and ingenuous. I don't know whether Bill Slater had hand-picked Eric and Doug because he thought they would suit my grandmother, or because he thought they would suit me, but whichever it was, both my grandmother and I liked them very much.

One day, towards the end of the recording sessions, Eric said he had just got wind of an Independent Television series called 'When the Boat Comes In', which had already been filmed and scheduled and was causing some consternation in the BBC. With the exception of 'The Likely Lads', a comedy, the Tyneside dialect was relatively untried on a national audience. To date, the Cockney and quasi-Lancashire dialects had been about as far as British television drama had ventured into the culture of the provinces, and TV mandarins in London were dubious about how much Tyneside fare the television-viewing nation would be able to stomach. Shortly afterwards Aubrey Singer, the Head of BBC 2 Television, decided the risk was too great and suspended all further work on the dramatisation of the *Life and Times of Francie Nichol of South Shields*.

Eric, who had been so enthusiastic about the work, telephoned me in despair a few days after he got back to London, to tell me the news and to say he had been given a new Robin Hood series to do instead. I watched it when it eventually came to be televised, it was a variation on the usual tale, it was Robin Hood with the pox; but whether Eric terminated Robin in this way to vent his disgust, I never found out, I never heard from him again.

My grandmother waited and waited for the television series which would celebrate her life and provide some extra comfort from the proceeds, and in the finish I had to explain that she hadn't been deceived or anything, but that nobody would be coming to interview her for a while, it was just in the nature of things. It didn't break her heart, she had suffered worse things than the non-event of a television programme, and was grateful for what fun she had had and for the attention she had been paid by so many people. The book was published that year, 1975, and the newspapers showed great interest and that also pleased her. Now she could have her daughter read to her about their lives.

Two years later I came to live in Ireland and the year after that my father died. Grandma was at the funeral. She was less mobile but still mentally alert, and Aunt Francie told me she had recently threatened to clout a young GP who had come to the house and spoken to her as though she were a child.

But when my father died, the last of her Johnnies, I think she probably felt the world she belonged to had well and truly gone. In 1981 aged ninety-two, she died quietly and without any fuss, just as my father had done. Several years later, Uncle Edmund, who held my father in as much esteem as did their mother, and who couldn't have loved him any less than she did, also died. Were I to some day write an epitaph for these three people, it would simply be that 'Whereas some people are broken by adversity, and many more are coarsened or embittered by it, some are not...some have their characters strengthened by it. And it has nothing at all to do with church or state.'